A BACKLASH RECKONING

62
/400

"A BACKLASH RECKONING" is a work of non-fiction and opinion, on the connections among: a global environmental crisis, politics, economics, and media in the United States.

ISBN: 078-0-692-16457-0

Published by the author through IngramSpark and LightningSource.

A BACKLASH RECKONING

Can A Green New Deal Prevent
A Climate Catastrophe, And Save Civil Society,
In Spite Of The Right?

David Heintz

Dedication and Thanks

This book is dedicated to the heroes of the Environmental Movement,
and friends of Democratic Socialists of America
(may they find their true connections and common ground):
Rachel Carson / James Hansen / Bill McKibben / Wangari Maathi / Bill Nye
Tim DeChristopher / Elizabeth Kolbert / Naomi Klein / Vandana Shiva
Bernie Sanders / Barbara Lee / Alexandria Ocasio-Cortez / Cornel West
and to movements and truth tellers like
350.org / Occupy / Greenpeace / Sea Shepherd / Black Lives Matter
Me Too and Time's Up / We Call BS and Never Again / Earthjustice
The Union of Concerned Scientists / Rainforest Action Network
I Million Women (Australia)
Environmental Defense Fund / Democracy Now / TruthOut / The Intercept
Rev. William Barber's Poor People's Campaign and Call for Moral Revival.
One half of the author's net revenue from this book
will be donated to these and similar projects.

Thanks to my dear Rrosa Seconda, aka Celeste Connor,
my sons Nathan and Corbin, and dear friends,
William, Farley, Steven, Dana, Gil, Ric, Tung, Marc, Dave, Jodie,
Uncle Tim, Tom and Max, Mie, Peg, Betty Jo and the gang at Gray Loft
and to many other friends, former students and colleagues from CCA(c)
who have supported me in this work.

Thanks to Nina Rogozen and Celeste for editing,
Stephen Joseph for the Mt. Diablo foothills photograph on the cover,
Alicia Greenleaf for the interior template design and reminding me to kern,
to Zeeshan at RemoteFace for the final layout and the website,
to Dr. Lewis Engel and to early readers Justin Wykoff and Tina Curiel.

And a special thanks to the likes of Jon Stewart, Stephen Colbert,
and Andy Borowitz, for helping me hang on to a shred of sanity throughout.

Remembering Robert, Nick, Joseph, Sue, and others departed.

CONTENTS

INTRODUCTION

This book was nearly complete, over 450 pages long, on November 8, 2016. I was writing the last argument, about sadness – how our children or theirs will experience regret beyond anything most of us can imagine. Since then, many parts have been edited out, a few new parts added, and most of the rest rewritten. Part One explains why these revisions were necessary.

The book is based on 4 premises that appear here as the first 4 Arguments, in order.

> *Argument 1: The human species faces an unprecedented, self-made, existential threat, a Global Environmental Crisis, in which Climate Change is just one part.*

Global Warming / Climate Change is only one of a dozen parts of a Global Environmental Crisis that is more complex, vastly more dangerous, and expanding faster than most of the world understands or can imagine. And there are a dozen other global crises competing with it for our attention.

> *Argument 2: We are doing next to nothing to avoid the worst possible outcomes. We have barely begun to imagine them.*

In spite of our apparent good efforts, given the very real threat, we are only doing a small fraction of what is necessary, and that, half-heartedly.

> *Argument 3: Bad ideas and faulty thinking are major causes of this Crisis. Mental mistakes can be identified and corrected. Those first steps are essential before any solution will become possible.*

The Crisis is caused by historical mistakes, like our abuse of fossil-fueled industrial power for progress and profit, also by mental lapses like short-sightedness, denial, and our inability to foresee unintended consequences or avoid them. In the bigger picture, our ideas and organizations are not prepared to keep pace with the complexity and speed of the problems we have created. We cannot manage the Crisis until we name, define, and correct the mental mistakes and stop the abuse. We need a revolution in our thinking.

> *Argument 4. When we wrap our heads around this fast-moving and complex set of crises, 2 things will occur: we will start to think differently about them, and a simple, radical but feasible solution will emerge.*

There are patterns in the Global Environmental Crisis that we have yet to recognize. There are patterns in its causes that include politics, economics, information, and psychology. Those patterns in turn are connected to the other crises we think of as separate and comparably severe, like war, racism, poverty and economic injustice, refugees, misinformation, and corruption. The patterns are so complex, and changing so fast, their impacts *SEEM* impossible to manage. This helps to explain why we are doing next to nothing about most of the crises.

We think changing our minds is easy and changing the world is hard, but that is backward. Change enough minds and the world will follow.

We must believe it is possible to connect those issues, like dots in a puzzle, see the broader pattern, and to agree on a big-picture vision. When that mental revolution occurs, the complexity will fade, the speed will become manageable, and a radical but feasible solution will become obvious.

PATTERNS

When we recognize a pattern, we connect our thinking with our perceptions, getting the most from both. It is a fundamental tool in forming our most basic knowledge, and it is essential to noticing emergencies and making decisions to manage them.

The Global Environmental Crisis will soon emerge as the most urgent priority for everyone on the planet, except maybe for those who profit from it, or who profit or gain power by ignoring it. Global nuclear war, much less of a threat before Trump, is the only comparable risk. Given that exception,

The other crises we think we face are subsets of the Eco-Crisis, trivial by contrast, or parts of a larger pattern we have yet to recognize.

The critical question is: When will we awaken to the urgency and start to act on it?

There are many obstacles in our path, in our politics and economics, in our information and decision-making systems. Many are the result of inadequate education and misinformation. Some are caused by rampant corruption. Some mental mistakes are natural, parts of human nature. Others are unique to the Crisis. There is a powerful mindset that refuses to believe that Climate Change threatens our survival. It is based in fear, denial, and identity politics. It is made worse by information overload and distraction. That mindset is one of the first obstacles that we have to overcome. The role of mindsets in these crises gets its own section in Part Two.

Nothing in our experience prepares us for Argument 1, so many of us simply refuse to believe it. It puts us in oppositional camps, defined by pre-existing beliefs and prejudices.

Katherine Hayhoe is an atmospheric scientist and associate professor of political science at Texas Tech University. She is also a devout evangelical Christian. She says we ought not to use the word "denier" to describe those who don't accept the climate science, the proven causes, or dire predictions – it just alienates

3

those we are trying to persuade and shuts down the conversation. Calling them "deniers" makes them seem malicious, or makes us seem elitist, she says, we should call them "dismissers." But too many of us have been misled in a decades-long campaign engineered to keep us dismissive of science and ignorant of this Crisis. Others have been conditioned not to trust experts, the media, or the government, with some justification. Those efforts have been vastly more malicious and elitist than any name-calling. They use fake scientific "skepticism" to cover an epidemic of very real denial, that has now helped to elect a totally incompetent president. I respect and appreciate Ms. Hayhoe's work to reach the "dismissers." But to ignore that history of mis-information and deception makes her position questionable if not naive. Jump to pages 93 and 107-10 for more about denial.

> *"It's much easier to fool people than to convince them that they have been fooled."* attributed to Mark Twain and others

This unprecedented Crisis will force us to look at a half century of history and the larger structures of human societies, if we are to have a chance to address it properly. It is essential that we identify and define the root causes, and to see if a patterns links them to the other non-environmental crises. If the United States is to regain its status as a world leader, it will succeed or fail on whether and how – and how fast – we act to resolve this Crisis.

Scientific facts are demonstrably true and irrefutable, even if later science forces adjustments in them. Most scientific predictions are 90 percent reliable or better. But scientists are honestly skeptical and modest by nature. In a complex and fast moving situation, they know that many predictions cannot be proven until time eliminates some of the variables. And they generally don't like to be alarmists or to talk about odds: the odds that human survival will be threatened, in a generation or a century; or the odds that environmental factors – known, partially known, and unknown – may create threats that the scientists themselves don't want to imagine, or at least to voice in public. Deniers dismiss the bearers of bad news as *alarmists,* even *catastrophists.*

Pessimists and catastrophists are criticized for creating unnecessary panic or despair. But the so-called *skeptics* ignore scientific facts and reliable predictions, to avoid thinking of them as "too scary." Other experts and commentators say the optimists are the ones doing the damage – to our general attitude about risk and possibility – by giving us false hope when ...

We. Really. Face. Unpredictable. Levels. Of Risk.

So, loud and urgent warnings may be better, even if they scare some people. We have to look at the maze of manufactured and exaggerated fears that have let us ignore the real ones for so long.

There is a lot of variation in what scientists consider the likely risks; but they are multiplied by combined impacts and factors of speed and timing that are hard to measure, describe, or predict. For example, increasing heat can combine with food shortages and bad water to make large geographic regions turn uninhabitable or inescapable and deadly, possibly over surprisingly short periods of time.

Alarmists like Bill Nye, Al Gore, Vandana Shiva, Bill McKibben, and I are on one side, trying to mobilize radical action. Corrupt Republicans, cowardly Democrats, and oil executives are on the other, trying to convince us all that the status quo is acceptable, and that, somehow, everything is going to be OK. Other Democrats try to smooth over the differences from the middle, providing no real vision or guidance. Most of us have a mental bias to accept only the news that confirms our beliefs or supports our denial, and to reject the unfamiliar and scary. That is a big barrier to the awakening that has to happen.

The confusion and inaction can be maddening.

The Paris Accords of 2016 are a set of voluntary limits on emissions, agreed to by most of the nations of the world, which Trump is trying to abandon. Some cities, states, and other nations are actively resisting this insanity and holding to the limits. The 2 Bills, Nye and McKibben, have said (paraphrased) those accords would be great ... if they were agreed to in 1995. Other experts say the same thing in different words: that they're great, compared to doing nothing, but, compared to what we need to do, they are a disaster.

So the task for me and my book here is to talk to both sides. We need to give the severe pessimists – the ones who think it's too late and there's nothing we can do to avoid doom – a few good reasons for hope and the possibility of a solution ... if we start now and move fast. We need to rattle the optimists into looking hard at the worst possible cases. And it is only fair to slap the deniers or dismissers, the fake skeptics and fools, and all the lobbyists and legislators who've sold their souls to the carbon industry, with the shocking truth – that most of us have been tricked into not knowing or caring about this existential threat, for 35 years or more.

In a crazy paradox, we now live in a new kind of information environment. It appears to bring us all the news, facts, and opinions we need, from local to global. We assume all the important information is at least available. But our devices have made us addicted to distraction and a fake sense of social membership, that makes the crucial facts and predictions, and their urgency, almost impossible to notice or absorb.

We find ourselves trapped between an unprecedented deluge of data, brought to us on addictive devices, and the combined risks of the Environmental Crisis. We have to try to imagine an unimaginable disaster, 30, 20, or as little as 10 years away, and then to imagine the almost impossible actions that are needed *NOW* to *TRY* to slow the oncoming disaster. If we wait 20 or 30 years to be sure it's happening, we'll find our best efforts are too little and too late.

From the earlier text:

As much as I try to be a rational man, I know that four emotions color all my thoughts. Living on this amazing planet as a conscious being, I am often in a state of wondrous awe. *I have a* passionate desire *to pass to the next generation the living environment and the creative legacy that have sparked the wonder and the awe. But I feel a* sickening dread, *believing that we are on the verge of destroying both our civilization and the ecosystems that support our lives.*

Most shocking is our lack of foresight, our blindness to the consequences of our actions. Unwitting, we steal from our children and unborn generations their most precious human rights – to a livable planet and a viable future. Incredibly, all we need to change direction – the information, ingenuity and resources – are at hand. We only lack the understanding, a vision and the political will.

So I am also angry *at the naked greed, destructive aggression and willful ignorance that depletes and sickens the planet, kills and injures the innocent, continues to deny the damage done and shirks responsibility for it.*

As a teenager in suburban Ohio, in the 1950s, I somehow realized that we could not continue to multiply and consume without facing serious consequences, probably in my lifetime. I don't know how I knew this. Nobody taught me to think this way. I couldn't understand why this was not common knowledge, a public concern. I wish for nothing more than to have been wrong.

In scout troops and church groups we went door-to-door, collecting used coat hangers and newspapers. We counted and bound the hangers and sold them back to dry cleaners. We baled the papers and sold them to paper mills. At age 14, I got a summer job as a surveyor's assistant, and kept it through three summers until I went off to college. During the first summer, we hiked through virgin forest, fighting heat, humidity and mosquitoes to document the topography. The second summer, where the lush forest had been, we marked the positions for streets, sewers and water lines. The third summer, we laid out the last row of houses, driveways and sidewalks. By the summer of 1960, the forest had become a subdivision of 500 identical new homes.

There was a science series on TV in 1958, sponsored by Bell Labs. The show was part of a national effort to raise interest in science among kids like me. I distinctly remember the two hosts, an inquisitive, young reporter-type and a wise old science professor-type. One episode, The Unchained Goddess, *was about the weather, ocean currents, evaporation and rain, desert heat and glaciers, the dynamics of hurricanes and tornadoes, climatology and weather prediction.*

The professor-character said that scientists were concerned about the amount of CO_2 (carbon dioxide) and other pollutants we were spewing into the atmosphere. He said something about millions of tons per year. We saw crowded freeways and smoke belching from factories. He warned that this would cause the atmosphere to trap more of the sun's heat and raise global temperatures. Even a change of two or three degrees might start melting the world's ice packs and cause sea levels to rise unpredictably. Film clips showed huge glaciers breaking off and crashing into the sea. A map showed most of Florida under water. The scientists predicted the possibility, within decades, of a chaotic impact on stable society ... in 1958!

In 2010, PBS aired Robert Stone's film Earth Days, *a history of the environmental movement in the United States. In addition to a clip from that 1958 science show, the film included a series of comments by a string of US presidents. Every one, from John Kennedy to George W Bush, warned of the dangers of pollution, our dependence on foreign oil, other threats to the environment and the changes we would need to make. Each successive speech showed that little or nothing had been done. The near total lack of action, in the face of the risks, is stunning.*

The Daily Show *with Jon Stewart was more trusted than most conventional news programs. The trust was well deserved. Fake News* shows apparently deliver more actual news than the real news. Also in 2010, Stewart's program ran many of the same presidential comments that appeared in* Earth Days. *Theirs were edited for sarcasm and irony, a clever but cynical slam on the lameness of government. Jon of course made W the punch line. While George W Bush put a dramatic and urgent spin on the objectives he set, they were the feeblest of all the presidents, and they were pushed decades into the future. Hilarious. Tragic.*

* Fake news: *There are several terms in this book that have had their meaning changed while it was being written. Jon Stewart used to call his Daily Show "Fake News" because it was satirical humor. It turns out that his viewers were proven to be better informed than those who watched other cable news shows, much better informed than those who watched Fox. Viewers of the Daily Show's spin-off, The Colbert Report, tested in 2014 as better informed on campaign finance than the viewers of all other TV news shows, including PBS.*

During the 2016 campaign, "Fake News" was used in a very different way by Donald Trump; he accuses the news he doesn't like as being fake. It has thrown shade and doubt over the very nature of truth and facts. It adds to the many confusions we face in dealing with our several crises. And it adds to the deep ideological divides in our country..

The words "populist" or "populism," have also taken on new meanings in the age of Trump. Check the Glossary on page 170 facing the start of Part Six.

I did not choose to write this book. I often wished someone else would write it so I don't have to. It has felt like a task thrust upon me by circumstances, observations, and connections that are clear to me but invisible to others. I abandoned it several times, for other issues demanding my attention, from writer's block, from a failure of persistence, from repeatedly doubting my voice and my framing of the arguments. I often gave in to a dark pessimism for weeks at a time, about the possibility of making a difference, with this book or with anything.

Throughout my adult life, I have watched our global population continue to grow, our consumer culture increase in speed, deception and waste produced, our Democracy turn ineffective, our media become muted and blind, our military adventurism become more irrational, our attention spans shrink and our planet grow ever sicker. Now we find ourselves speeding into a perfect storm of unknown risks, driven by the ignorant, indifferent, greedy, and corrupt, paralyzed by distraction, denial, and delay. So no wonder, my concern became alarm. Alarm turned into distress. Distress led to dread, anger, outrage, occasional disillusion, despair, and finally to the words on these pages.

THIS BOOK HAS A BRANCHING / WEAVING STRUCTURE
The 4 premises and first 4 arguments will branch out into about 20 other topics, that will intersect with each other, to form clear and recognizable patterns later in the book. I will often suggest you skip some technical or theoretical stuff if you choose, or

jump to other pages where specific ideas are continued.

There is a lot of basic information and knowledge that everyone ought to know, that covers the science and urgency of Climate Change. You may already know most of it, or only a little. Some information has been slower to reach the public conversation because it's continuously changing, hard to document or explain, with outcomes that are hard to predict. Scientific realities like feedback loops, combined impacts, climate or thermal lag, and the role of methane, for example, may be new. I'll try to make them comprehensible. And we'll face the hard truth that there are a dozen other environmental crises other than Climate Change.

We will look into the thinking, good and bad, smart and stupid, honest and deceptive, that is at the root of the crisis, or is stopping us from dealing with it. Some of you may be used to questioning authority or your own thinking. Those of us who have never *thought about thinking* – what goes on, uninvited, in our own heads for example – will find it challenging to question established assumptions. We'll argue, for example that we're trying to solve problems created through most of the 20th century with thinking that is mired in earlier centuries.

The challenge this book lays out, for me in writing and for you in reading, is to create and understand the pattern made when all the dots are connected, which will in turn make a *Big Picture* less complex and easier to understand. I'm arguing that a broad and inclusive vision – of the Eco-Crisis, politics and power, economics, information, knowledge, and a few other broad topics – have to be understood, separately and together, if we are to escape the worst possible outcomes.

We'll explore the topic of imagination, as a uniquely human kind of thinking, in terms of when and where it was missing, where it failed, and where it's needed: to imagine, on one hand, what those worst cases may be, and, on the other hand, what we'll have to do to avoid them.

The 2 middle Parts, 4 and 5, take a sort of philosophic detour into the topics of information and power, as they relate, on one side, to the thinking that has to change, on the other side, to dynamics at the core of the crisis that we may never have even thought about.

We may be relieved to find that the mental and social, political and economic mistakes that created the Eco-Crisis are the same ones that created or allowed many of the other non-ecological problems *in the world* and that they too may be solved with the same, simple but radical solution.

DUTY TO WARN
I mentioned a few pages back that "I did not choose to write this book." And I can imagine some of the blowback I invite by publishing it: *Delusions of saving the world. Communist plot in disguise. Too radical. Too late to matter. Will kill American prosperity. Envious grudge against the rich and powerful. Tree- hugging alarmist.*

There are laws in many states with names like "Duty to Warn," and "Duty to Protect," that require medical professionals to inform and warn individuals who are in danger of harm, by others who exhibit hazardous behaviors. There are some exceptions for confidentiality. And I'm certainly not a medical professional. But this book has been driven by an obligation I feel I have, to tell what I know and believe, as a warning to you and others about an impending ecological disaster.

Medical guidelines were written during the 1964 presidential campaign (on opinions about the sanity of Barry Goldwater) to prevent any medical professional from offering opinions on the state of anyone they had not met in person. (See more about Goldwater on pages 206 and 208.)

But now a group of psychologists and psychiatrists (who question those guidelines) have formed a group, "Duty to Warn," who are taking up the issue of Donald Trump's sanity and his possible danger to citizens of the US and the world.

So we have no choice but to start, 3 pages ahead, with the how and why of Trump's impact on this book, why it forced this re-write and how it has transformed and distorted the profiles of democracy, of the many crises and problems we share, and, yes, even of human civilization. The Eco-Crisis alone is an existential threat, risking the future of the experiment that is us. It ought to be an undeniable clue that our civilization is also in serious trouble.

By the time you get through this book, if you do, conditions may have gotten severely worse, or they may have provoked a backlash. Either way, those conditions will make my radical solution seem possible, then sensible, then even head-slap obvious and our only choice.

A DISCLAIMER: "FAIR USE"

This book was written, edited, designed, printed, and marketed without a literary agent, an incorporated publisher, research staff, or legal assistance. Most of the quotations and references are used without specific permission or release of rights. The author is a life-long educator, and considers this an educational project. So the claim is made that the Fair Use Doctrine applies.

Everything stated as fact, including statistics and quotations, were thoroughly researched, and most rely on multiple sources; though many facts about the Global Environmental Crisis are changing so rapidly, some facts and stats are likely to be marginally out of date. Otherwise the author stands by the accuracy.

AND BY THE WAY

BTW, By The Way, you *WILL* notice that I Capitalize and *Italicize* and **Bold** some words and phrases, in an un- con- ven- tional manner. In this Introduction, I have capitalized Global Warming, and the Global Environmental Crisis. In the pages ahead, I will often capitalize Democracy and Democratic, when describing a political system, and only use Democrat specifically for the party. There are "small d" democrats, and many "small d" democracies, working or floundering, that do not need my special designation.

This approach is meant to emphasize Central Concepts

and Topics as we come across them, and to highlight *SPECIFIC POINTS* in support of arguments. It may sometimes seem like I am *SHOUTING*. Because I am.

DISCLOSURE
I am not a professional or amateur economist (scientist, political scientist, or climate scientist). I have been a junkie for politics and media (separate and together) most of my adult life. I had to do years of research to compile enough knowledge of economics, climate science, and other fields, to make this book as broad and credible as I could.

PART ONE: THE ACCIDENTAL PRESIDENT JOKE

Or: How Trump's election forced this rewrite.

MULTIPLE CHOICE QUIZ: Is the election of Donald Trump:
A. Surprising evidence of a sudden, accidental breakdown of the 2-party system?
B. The obvious and predictable outcome of a political/economic system that has been coming apart for decades?
C. Going to make America great again?
D. An existential crisis in democracy?
E. A threat to the survival of human civilization?
F. A tasteless joke?

ANSWERS:
A. and B. are both true, making a crazy paradox. It is surprising but it should not be.
C. is false, a sick illusion based on fear and false premises.
D. and E. are both correct, and not paradoxical at all.
F. is both true and false: it's tasteless but it's only a joke in Russia ... and Berkeley.

> *"If we are not careful, we are going to end up where we are headed." English translation of a wise Chinese saying.*

Trump is a lot like the Global Eco-Crisis that includes Global Warming/Climate Change. There have been plenty of clues it is coming for decades. We were generally kept in the dark about the evidence and we were conditioned to reject the signs that we may have seen. We did not believe or could not accept the facts of the growing threat. So we have been doing next to nothing to correct our direction or avoid where we have been headed.

15

Now it has become a monumental and urgent problem that will require enormous radical shifts – in thinking and in power – to avoid the dual disasters of a broken government and a dying Earth.

The election was simply, in my view, a random outcome in a system in the process of self-destruction, and a slapstick rubber chicken in face of the once greatest nation in the world.

Neal Gabler, working at BillMoyers.com, wrote this shortly after the election:

America died on Nov. 8, 2016, not with a bang or a whimper, but at its own hand via electoral suicide. We the people chose a man who has shredded our values, our morals, our compassion, our tolerance, our decency, our sense of common purpose, our very identity — all the things that, however tenuously, made a nation out of a country. Whatever place we now live in is not the same place it was on Nov. 7. No matter how the rest of the world looked at us on Nov. 7, they will now look at us differently. We are likely to be a pariah country. And we are lost for it.

Not *losing*. Not in danger of losing. *LOST.*

On July 3, 2017, Charles M Blow wrote in the New York Times:

Every now and then we are going to have to do this: Step back from the daily onslaughts of insanity emanating from Donald Trump's parasitic presidency and remind ourselves of the obscenity of it all, registering its magnitude in its full, devastating truth.

There is something insidious and corrosive about trying to evaluate the severity of every offense, trying to give each an individual grade on the scale of absurdity. Trump himself is the offense. Everything that springs from him, every person who supports him, every staffer who shields him, every legislator who defends him, is an offense. Every partisan who uses him — against all he or she has ever claimed to champion — to advance a political agenda and, in so doing, places party over country, is an offense.

We must remind ourselves that Trump's very presence in the

White House defiles it and the institution of the presidency. Rather than rising to the honor of the office, Trump has lowered the office with his whiny, fragile, vindictive pettiness.

The presidency has been hijacked.

BUT DON'T BLAME THE VOTERS

Those who supported Trump, to the point of voting for him, may be, in Blow's words, "an offense." But I will cut them a little slack and say the offense was part of the accident, an offense to the system at large, not a personal or intentional offense from them against the rest of us.

I have no shortage of angry feelings about that election. A few are right here; more are scattered throughout the book.

But I don't blame the people who voted for Donald Trump. I agree they may be stupid. Certainly many of them are uneducated. No small number are racists and deserve heaps of blame for that. A few are neo-Nazis or in the KKK – American terrorists; their type have killed more innocent American citizens than all the terrorists we've been conditioned to blame. Trump voters may not have a clue about how government works or what it ought to do for them. They may one day wake up to the fact that they were duped ... or that they have duped themselves. They will soon see that they have also been robbed. And when they do, their anger may be directed at the real problems Trump cannot and will not even try to fix. But it is more important to understand how and why they (and many of the rest of us to lesser degrees) have been duped by the combined failures of American politics, a rigged economy, mis- and dis-information, and the artificial divisions engineered into our social systems – all, over the last 40 years.

And after all, the Trump voters were only 20-25 percent of the population. Half the eligible voters were either prevented from voting or stayed home by choice. The other half split almost evenly between Hillary and Trump. There were certainly other factors that influenced them and others: Trump did create the illusion of caring about working people and wanting to clean up Washington. Hillary, like most Democrats, took them for granted and didn't even manage an illusion of caring. On the other hand, and in spite of her flaws, most of the really bad press about her was false – distortions, rumors, and lies planted by Russian bloggers and Republicans. Comey's odd announcements right before the election may have been one of the deciding factors. But in my view, Hillary and the Democrat Party insiders actually deserve most of the blame. They had the most popular politician in the country in their corner and they stole the nomination he earned.

Let's be clear. The people who voted for Trump did not feel represented by either party, and felt, rightly, that they were not given much of a choice. So on one hand we can't blame the voters. On the other hand, we must not forgive Trump and the gang of criminals and idiots, thieves and traitors in his cabinet and in leadership posts in his administration, for the damage they are doing to the nation, the people of the world, and the health of the Earth.

I continue to argue that the Global Environmental Crisis points to a systemic failure of the US government. It calls the nation's role as a world leader into question. When overlaid with the non-environmental crises we face (like the list in the middle of page 2), and when we *take a step back*, it looks like a systemic crisis in human civilization. Given all those crises in combination, given their varying speeds, their complexity and their combined impacts, think about the children.

See Stephen Hawking's comment on page 68.

Young people in 2017 face a future of unpredictable risks worse than anything people my age could have imagined, just 20 years ago.

If young people think the number and speed of changes we face now are typical, they don't understand what we older folks know. This situation is different from anything in our memory and in human history, as far as we can tell. Every day under

Trump, that systemic failure gets worse, and spreads wider.

Decades of doing next to nothing, having no plan to avoid the risks, and now Trump, doing all the wrong things, have brought us to ...

AN UNDENIABLE PROPOSITION:
IF the Global Environmental Crisis is as dangerous and fast-moving as the science proves it is, and,
IF there are several other emergencies that will continue to compete with it for our attention, and,
IF we recognize their connections with the other socio-political-economic factors that dominate the globalized world,

THEN, 2 things cannot be denied:
1. The presidency of Donald J Trump, no matter how long it goes on, represents the end of *politics-as-usual* in the United States. And, even if it ends tomorrow, it is a nearly a final tipping point* for human civilization and life on Earth. It is up to us to decide what comes after politics-as-usual and which way civilization – totally dependent on a healthy planet – is going to tip.
2. Rapid, radical, and coordinated responses, national and global, to Trump and to the Global Eco-Crisis are now even more essential and urgent. It requires the United States to step up and lead the world again. And, in mid-2018, Trump is making that impossible.

* See A Critical State on page 23.

Argument 5: Unchallenged, Donald Trump will represent the tipping point in the collapse of human civilization.

IMPOSSIBLE YOU SAY?
There are three conditions that we use to predict or anticipate the future: 1) Some things will *certainly* happen. We will all die ... sometime. 2) Others are *impossible*. None of us will fly unaided to the moon. 3) Many in a middle category are *possible* – neither certain nor impossible. Our children may appreciate our legacy,

as they inherit planet Earth. Or not.

We think the lines between those three conditions are fairly sharp and that we know where they are. Everyone has a *possibility mindset;* each of us has our own; our politicians and social circles have their assumptions that we may or may not share. Some are unconscious.

But the impossible often happens and the certain does not. Every minute, somewhere in the world, individuals and communities are swept up in events they did not think possible. Often *because* they didn't think them possible. Fires and floods and droughts are expanding that category. Rapidly.

If Donald Trump's election shook your sense of what's possible, as badly as it shook mine, it may turn out to have an ironic benefit: it will force us to look at this mess in a different light and find a comprehensive solution ... from a new perspective.

If we are lucky, the changes in thinking that we adopt, or that are forced on us, will include an expansion of our sense of perspective and proportion. Possibility, proportion and perspective are three areas where Trump's thinking fails. Others are more basic, even childish. Some border on insanity. But those 3 will be among several points of view from which we approach our own errors in thinking, in Part Three.

> *One of Trump's most ignorant scary comments, when asked about the environment, is, "Don't worry about nature. We'll leave a little of it."*

RECKONING?

Since the sexual harassment and abuse scandals that ballooned after the Harvey Weinstein revelations, the word "Reckoning" has appeared more frequently, as an awakening among the public that may create the overdue backlash against the injustices. That backlash must lead – certainly to more revelations, and – ultimately to adjustments in social norms that will begin to end those vile practices.

More generally, *Reckoning* has 3 accepted meanings:

- A *calculation* that sums up financial accounts, balances the books, or adjusts for mistakes or disagreements, usually about money. *By my reckoning, we are about $100 trillion short.*
- A *judgment* or an adjustment in a judgment about what happened or may happen in a specific event, or what made it happen. *I reckon that the snow will delay the takeoff. All of us will have to reckon with the just complaints of abuse victims.*
- *Retribution,* a settling of a dispute, payback, the correction of a (non-financial) mistake or disagreement, often including a punishment, even a *Comeuppance. A reckoning reveals an ongoing injustice to Native Americans and Blacks, and will lead to corrections.*

The blowback to the sexual abuse scandals uses the 2nd and 3rd meanings, although the careers and incomes of the victims may also be part of a calculation, as in the 1st. Our arguments here use all 3: In priority order, the 3rd (a settlement), the 1st (a balancing of the books), and the 2nd (as a shift in thinking).

BACKLASH?
And I am reminded that *BACKLASH* is an important founding feminist book, by Susan Faludi, 1991. In it and since, she argues that there was and continues to be a significant and destructive backlash against the feminist movement that was there for decades, but grew in the late 1960s, 70s and 80s. In that case the backlash was against basic human rights, and their connections to a variety of liberal projects. The dictionary definition includes the word *violent* before *backward movement.* I use the term in the same way, but moving in the opposite political direction: from a liberal/left position, a backlash against the US Right Wing and its destructive legacy. And I have to believe it can be a non-violent backlash.

It may seem like the backlash goes backward in the sense of away from false progress and excessive consumption. But it can also be a sort of whiplash that will leaves us – yes maybe a little dizzy – living sustainably in the 21st century.

MAGA

New York governor Mario Cuomo put his foot in it, according to commentators Left and Right, when in mid-August 2018, he was poking jabs at Trump over "Make America Great Again," with, "It was never that great." Apparently you have to set that idea up a little more carefully, like with some examples of America's past or recent greatness, which I could do and have done. Just not recently. On the other hand,

Several courageous commentators, or just common sense observers, have responded to Trump's Make America Great Again, with, "Explain to us please, exactly when was it that you think America was great, what made it so, and how you are going to bring that back, or take us to it?" It's important to remember, or to learn, that we can love our country, it's gorgeous features, its acts and periods of greatness, while hating much of the current government and some of the big corporations.

Were we great when we waged a genocide before that word existed? Did bringing millions of slaves here make us great? Were we great in Vietnam? Was Nixon great? Was Reagan half as great as the GOP pretends? Was the Bush/Cheney invasion of Iraq a great idea, or nothing but a gigantic war crime? Were Obama and Hillary's protection of the banks, the insurance companies, and the Military-Industrial Complex* great?

* Full discussion coming up on page 184.

Before we can make America great – again or for the first time in recent memory – we need to understand how much of the rest of the world views the United States. While we express shock or disbelief that Russians could have influenced the 2016 election, most of us don't know that our country "influenced" – or undermined, overthrew, displaced, or stole – around 50 elections, in dozens of countries (some of them 2 or 3 times) over the last half century. Greece, Chile, Iran, Iraq, Guatemala, Honduras, Afghanistan, Philippines, Nicaragua, El Salvador, and several nations in Africa. We classified Nelson Mandela as a terrorist for decades. But then he got elected.

In the late *Age of Information*, it has become terribly difficult to assemble the reliable knowledge that would make the world comprehensible. And at this moment in the history of the US and the world, when we most desperately need responsive governments, with intelligent, forward looking leaders who share a long-term vision, the US has put the reins of power, and the economy, and the nuclear launch codes, and the health of the Earth, and the well-being of our children, in the hands of an accidental president, an ignorant, racist megalomaniac, a childish, self-obsessed, moody and unpredictable idiot with a short attention span and a shorter fuse ... and a gang of toadies who are forced to feed his ego on a daily basis, regardless of the facts.

A CRITICAL STATE AT A TIPPING POINT: Two terms, connected to each other, need a detailed definition. *A Critical State* is defined clearly in Mark Buchanan's book, *Ubiquity, Why Catastrophes Happen,* (2002), as the condition in any system that seems stable and secure, but is actually quite delicate, balanced on the edge of collapse. A quiet mountainside covered in fresh snow just before a vibration in the air triggers an avalanche; a fissure under stress in the earth before it turns into a violent earthquake, causing billions in damage and taking thousands of lives; a couple unusual infections in a healthy population that suddenly turn into an untreatable epidemic, also with a high death count.

Malcolm Gladwell wrote *A Tipping Point: How Little Things Can Make a Big Difference,* (also 2002), to explain social trends and consumer fads that spread quickly through a population, then often fade away just as quickly. But *Tipping Point* also defines the moment when a predictable event can turn a *Critical State* into an unpredictable disaster, especially, for our purposes, in natural systems, local to global. We can know they are coming, that they carry large and unknown risks, but we can seldom predict when they will happen, whether they will be sudden or gradual, or how bad they may get. Please watch for the connections between these 2 terms and *delicate balance,* for example.

GLOSSARY FOR PART TWO: (Some Parts will be preceded by Glossaries that define terms that may be new or unclear, or need additional clarification.)

Adaptation: One of 2 strategies, with Mitigation, that can be applied to Global Warming/ Climate Change, and other Environmental Crises. We can and must Adapt to the impacts that cannot be Mitigated (moderated, slowed, lessened); see Mitigation.

Aquifers: We extract fresh water from 2 types of underground pools: one, Rechargeable, can be drained and slowly refilled with precipitation; or Fossil, ancient and not refillable.

Arable (Land): Land that is suitable for farming: mainly with healthy topsoil.

Carbon Cycle: The natural flow of carbon, as CO_2, from the earth and water, through plants and animals; it was in a stable balance for most of geological history, before humans.

Carbon Sink: Any natural or human-made feature that absorbs and holds CO_2, like trees.

Carrying Capacity: The numbers of us the planet can support at a poverty level, probably far fewer than our present numbers.

Combined Impacts: The Climate and Environmental damages that come from 2 or more individual impacts, usually worsening them.

Ecosystem: A self-contained or isolated system of interdependent organisms, and the land, air, water, and other supports for it. May apply to locales or the entire Earth.

Exponential: A mathematical principle most relevant to the accelerating speed of many human-caused impacts damaging the environment. Fully described starting on page 104.

Extinction Events: Geological events when huge numbers of species were made extinct. There were 5 including the one that wiped out the dinosaurs, about 60 million years ago. Environmental activists say humans represent the 6th extinction event, due to the number of species we have killed off or are threatening.

Feedback Loop: * One of 3 poorly understood features of many environmental impacts, that make them self-reinforcing, with or without additional human effects.

Fracking: A method to extract natural gas or oil from unproductive deposits like shale. Treated water is forced into wells under high pressure to break up shale deposits and release the oil or gas. Often causes human-made earthquakes and poisons ground water.

Greenhouse Gases or GHGs: CO_2, methane, and other gases that damage the atmosphere by holding excess heat. Ozone is considered a GHG, even though its damage, through depletion, allows dangerous levels of radiation to reach the Earth's surface.

Holocene: The current geological Age, defined by human impacts.

Inertia: A delay, in climate impacts and in human responses to them. See pages 57-9.

Meltdown: A catastrophic accident in a nuclear facility, in which the radioactive core heats up, melts, and burns through the containment structures. There have been 4 to this date, as far as we know. Fukushima, 2011, is the most recent and worst on record.

Methane: * A major component in natural gas and the most damaging GHG in terms of atmospheric heating. One of 3 poorly understood impacts.

Mitigation: See Adaptation above. "What we cannot Mitigate we will have to Adapt to."

Momentum: (of Climate Change and other factors). See pages 57-9.

Net-Zero Carbon: A state in which total carbon emissions remain at or near zero.

Paradigm and Paradigm Shift: A mental model and changes in it. See page 96.

Permafrost: The top layers of soil near the poles that hold massive amounts of Methane, as long as they remain frozen ... that are now melting.

Sustainable: A term applied to any human practice that can be used, ongoing into the future, with minimal to zero lasting environmental damage or degradation.

Tar Sands: A source of oil that is naturally mixed with sand, extremely difficult, costly and wasteful (of natural gas and water) and polluting, to extract - thick and hard to transport.

Thermal (or Climate) Lag: * Also one of 3 dangerous and poorly understood aspects of Climate Change, that make it's acceleration hard to understand or manage.

Tundra: The geographic regions that contain permafrost.

24

PART TWO: DUTY TO WARN

"May you live in interesting times," an English translation of the "Chinese Curse," a good wish and an ironic blessing, suggesting disaster.

Ironic. A statement that means the opposite of what the words seem to say. It's like, "Your times may turn out to be dangerously interesting ... so good luck with that."

We are living in the most *interesting* times in 60 million years, since the dinosaurs went extinct and evolution started to favor small mammals, our biological ancestors. And most of us have no frame of reference for what a thousand years is, let alone 60 thousand times that long.

> Argument 6: We may lack the mental perspective to understand how absolutely unique and threatening this time actually is. Or why.

We humans are the most adaptive species we know of. We have created ways to live almost anywhere on the planet. We can live for months in space. We can visit the moon and the bottom of the ocean. We have forced our needs and wants upon the Earth, expecting it to adapt. But it can't. We did not anticipate the consequences of our actions. We now find we have to adapt our species to the demands of Nature, and to the damage we have done, in order to end it and then start to repair it.

We tend to take the stable conditions of our lives – *if they are stable* – for granted. But what we get used to, what we take for granted, can turn into the most shocking conditions when they change, especially when they change unexpectedly and rapidly.

Most of us have assumed that the Earth is too big, the climate and the ecosystem too stable, for us to have an impact. But if we understand the science and what it predicts for us, we will see that the climate and the global ecosystem have evolved through many complex and intertwined variations, and are not stable at all, but are in a state of delicate equilibrium, that we have upset.

Our food and water, our society, and our lawful government rely on other stable conditions that we also take for granted. But guess what? They are also in delicate balances, fragile and vulnerable to upset, even collapse. They require constant attention and adjustment. Which we are failing to do.

There are only 5 other times in the history of the Earth when random changes caused the extinction of large numbers of species. The changes we have made are not random, but their outcomes are. There are more of us, consuming and wasting so much that we are destroying the natural world, mostly outside our awareness. Scientists call this age the *Holocene*, meaning it is defined by human impacts on the Earth. Elizabeth Kolbert calls it *The Sixth Extinction*. It's the title of one of her books.

If you were born after 1975, you have never experienced a single day of average global temperature. The average Earth temperature now rises every day. The increase in global heat that wiped out the dinosaurs took thousands of years to do its damage. The rising temperatures today, and the CO_2 emissions causing them, are a sudden spike by comparison, a couple hundred years. And we are reluctant to consider what the next hundred years of heat may bring.

ESTABLISHING BACKGROUND: SEVEN REVOLUTIONS

We are living through 6 sets of changes that we don't recognize as revolutions, so we have not begun to manage or control them, just as they start to spiral out of control. The first 5 revolutions – in technology and science, in economics, in politics, in information (technologies and in actual information), and in social systems – all play parts in a 6th, a revolutionary decline in the health of the Earth. Their impacts drive us toward an inevitable Reckoning. If we are smart, and lucky, it will come as a 7th revolution, in our Thinking.

SEVEN REVOLUTIONS

Revolution 1. Technology and Science: The Industrial Revolution sparked the most dramatic changes in human civilization up to that time. It began around 1780 in Great Britain and rapidly spread through Europe and America. It continues to spread across the rest of the planet. It spawned an enormous creative burst in transportation and manufacturing. It was accompanied by hundreds of scientific breakthroughs. It started with a shift in popular fuels from wood to coal and oil, then to gasoline, diesel and aviation fuel. It helped to revolutionize agriculture with oil-based fertilizers and pesticides, for short-term gain and for long-term toxic damage.

Industrialization raised the living standards for many, if not most, of the world's inhabitants. It created huge wealth for a few, it depleted vast resources and began the serious degradation of our environment. Just since 1970, humans have released into the atmosphere over 1 trillion tons of carbon, as CO_2 and other GHGs. That is roughly equivalent to the total of human emissions, prior to that time.

But the most basic advantages of technology and science, such as clean water and reliable public health systems, have yet to trickle down to the world's poor. It forces us to re-think our notions of *modernity* and *progress*, maybe even of *civilization* itself. Now we find we need a new industrial revolution, and an accelerated shift to sustainable fuels, if we are to survive the unforeseen consequences of fossil fuels.

Revolution 2. Political Systems: Democracy is based on the principle that an educated, informed and engaged public can choose representatives and policies that will serve the common good – government of, by and for the people, to use the US example. Most of the world aspires to a society guided and protected by democratic principles. Yet very few governments fulfill the promise of true democracy, even those who pretend to be stellar examples. Authoritarian leaders tend to see working democracies, and the open information systems that support them, as threats to their power. We need to understand the connections between true democracy, information and the corrupting power of money.

Revolution 3. Economic: Three powerful indicators define a global economic/financial revolution.

First, there is more monetary wealth in the world than ever. But money has a greater corrupting power over nearly every aspect of public life than it has had since the early 20th century, maybe ever. In the US, it corrupts and paralyzes the political process and kills corporate accountability by design. In many countries it makes bribery a normal part of every transaction.

The second indicator of a global financial revolution is the enormous, global gap in income and wealth. Aided by corruption in many countries, economic injustice pits the *have-nots* against the *haves,* across almost all human societies.

The third indicator forms the foundation for some later arguments. It asks the questions: How did the US economy come to be so rigged? Why did American Capitalism become the model for the global economy? Where did the wealth of the corporations and the super-rich come from, how and when, and where is it hiding?

The answers form the first connections between that wealth and the value – in human well-being and in environmental damage – that has been extracted from the global economy, our lives and our Earth. We must start thinking about alternate economic systems and how they might improve those conditions.

A DIGRESSION ON THE 1% AND THE 99%
To gain a little more perspective, we need to clarify some details of the gaps in income and wealth. First, we need to thank the Occupy Wall Street movement for giving us the "1% and the 99%" meme. But the super-wealthy are really a much smaller percentage of the whole population than 1 percent, fewer than several hundred multi-billionaires, more like 0.0001% of all the

Earth's inhabitants. The actual difference, between the average income of the middle class and that tiny minority, in actual dollars, boggles the mind, especially when it is described graphically. Which is what the *L-Curve* does. You can find it online as a simple diagram and description or as a short animation. It's already 10-plus years out of date, so a current version would be even more extreme

The average middle class income has been around $40,000. Imagine that as a stack of 400 $100 bills about 1 1/2 inches tall, about a half inch thicker than this book. Those who make a million dollars a year have a stack of $100 bills that's 3 feet or 1 meter tall. A giant Sequoia tree, or a 20 story office building, is as tall as a $100 million income. The people included in the tiny fraction of 1%, a couple hundred who make an annual $10 billion (with a B), have a stack as tall as Mount Everest, about 5 miles high. So now imagine the incomes of the richest dozen people in that group, the Bill Gates,' the Warren Buffets, the Jeff Bezos' of the world. Imagine how tall their stacks are. Think big. No, really big. They each made – annually, (10 years ago) – a stack of $100s 30 miles high. It would reach to the edge of the atmosphere.

That's the difference. The length of your big toe, to a 30-mile hike. And that doesn't really tell the whole story. Wonder why? Because the L-Curve is talking about income, not total wealth, which would make the big numbers much, much bigger, by multiples of at least 5. And it uses the average income in the US; the global average is much less than $40,000. per year, and would make the proportional difference like 3 times bigger. So the actual *difference* in global wealth could be 15 times greater than the 1 1/2" to 30 mile spread that is based only on incomes in the US.

If this does not seem relevant yet, I promise you it will be.

Revolution 4. Information: We could say we became an information-based species when we developed shared languages and created writing. The current *Information Age* began with the invention of movable type and the printing press, earlier in

China, later in Europe. But since most of the world adopted the telegraph, telephone, radio, movies, TV, the computer, satellites, the internet, and smart phones, information technologies have been at or near the cutting edge of all innovation.

They transformed regional societies and global culture and changed the contours of civilization. They redefined knowledge and information itself, though we have yet to fully understand how or why. Like capitalism and democracy, information technologies have not met their promise. In some ways they hinder it. Artificial Intelligence, autonomous online bots and real robots, international hacking, the loss of privacy, and the lack of transparency in finance and government are just a few of the expanding negative impacts. The ocean of electronic data does not include instructions for staying afloat in it.

The lack of reliable information and the widespread use of mis- and dis-information by corporations and governments help obscure the Eco-Crisis and prevent us from addressing it. Part of the failure is the result of the complexity and speed of our lives and our world.

But, beyond that, our ideas of what information is and is not, how it changes us or fails to, are deeply confused, both far too broad and incomplete. And we have not begun to understand those complications. Part Four will help fix that.

Revolution 5. Social systems: The global revolution in social systems is the hardest to characterize or document because the changes and impacts are different across a variety of regions and cultures. It is a combination of social breakdown caused by the other revolutions, and the failure of many societies to cure destructive age-old habits, or to even try.

Fundamentalist religions clash with late modernism. Shifts in labor patterns and wealth break down family ties and break up communities. International trade agreements are designed by and for corporate profitability, causing damage in regional agriculture and economies, indigenous peoples' habitat, wildlife and the environment generally.

The varying impacts of electronic devices are causing turmoil and breakdowns in families and larger social systems, even as they provide *connectivity* and some economic benefits. Angst and bullying among kids and teens ... and adults ... is given free rein via smart phone addiction.

The Global Eco-Crisis contributes to civil strife, starvation, drought and regional migration in north and east Africa and the Middle East. The War in Darfur has been called the *first eco-war.* The civil war in Syria was sparked by the Assad regime's failure to deal with the economic ravages of Climate Change. Together with other impacts – the Bush/Cheney invasion of Iraq in particular – we see how carbon-induced Climate Change and non-environmental problems destroy local societies and worsen a wide range of racial, religious, and economic conflicts.

Sexual harassment, a symptom of *Rape Culture,* has been outed in Hollywood and in many other male-dominated industries. A few countries have the issue under control. In many others, it is not recognized as a problem. It may seem less evil only in comparison to the use of rape as a weapon of war. Slavery has more people in servitude now than in the 1700s (though that stat may be muted by our much larger population now). Human trafficking, child marriage, and forced prostitution persist in many cultures; we need to learn from the ones that have stopped those practices. The profits reaped from dangerous legal drugs make that addiction harder than ever to reverse. And in the US, gun violence is worse in families than on the street. There are sinister suggestions that police forces and the military have turned a blind eye, even tolerated codes of silence, among rabid rapists and virulent racists in their ranks. As this goes through a final edit, activists have put 7,000 pairs of shoes in front of the US Capitol, representing the number of children killed in school shootings just since Sandy Hook in 2012. Some cynics said that if the murder of 20 6- and 7-year-olds doesn't bring gun regulations, it tells us the Congress just doesn't care ... because it doesn't dare to cross the NRA.

Our civilization is struggling with managing these first 5 revolutions, alone and in their combined impacts, completely aside from the Global Eco-Crisis.

Revolution 6. The Global Environmental Crisis is the 6th of 7 revolutions. Global Warming / Climate Change is only one of a dozen or more components of this Crisis, to be explained just ahead. This book is devoted to establishing the connections between the Eco-Crisis, the first 5 revolutions and other factors.

These 6 Revolutions ought to make us all question how effectively our nation and our global civilization are working, how well or how poorly they live up to their promise.

Revolution 7. A Revolution in Thinking: The first step in a revolution in thinking, for us – half or more of US citizens and our fellow Earth- inhabitants – is simply to wrap our heads around the actual scale, speed, complexity, and catastrophic risks of the Global Environmental Crisis. A challenging second step will be to understand it in the broader context of the first 5 revolutions, and to observe the connections between the Eco-Crisis – causes and remedies – with the non-environmental crises that fill the headlines: war, racism, terrorism, disease, economic injustice and so on. Each revolution may need to be managed differently ... but not separately from the others. It will take radically different thinking, shared across cultures and among governments, to agree on the changes needed to manage these revolutions in a coordinated manner.

PROFILING GLOBAL WARMING/CLIMATE CHANGE
WHAT WE ALL OUGHT TO KNOW

This is a short overview of Global Warming / Climate Change. It only includes what ought to be common knowledge among a majority of the public. There are good indicators that, just over the past 4-5 years (2013-18) more and more of the US public, and

more governments, are catching on. An overview of the broader Global Eco-Crisis will follow. Then we'll return to Climate
Change with the most recent and important facts – the crucial
factors that most of the public doesn't know about.

Most of us probably understand the basics of GW/CC. Everything in this short summary is established scientific fact:
• First, yes, Climate Change is a natural phenomenon, that has
occurred in history, in periods of excess heat and in Ice Ages,
periods of unusual cold. Scientists can understand and explain
most of the fluctuations in the past, and are in agreement that we
are in a completely unprecedented period of sudden temperature increase, and that it is caused by human emissions.
• John Tyndall discovered in 1859 that excess CO_2 in the air (in
a lab) retained additional heat. We now know it also causes the
warmer air to hold more water vapor, which feeds bigger and
more violent hurricanes. The first measurements of the quantities of CO_2 in the air were done in 1950. Ice core samples taken
since that time measure CO_2 concentrations up to 800,000 years
in the past.
• From those measurements, climate scientists establish the
increase in global temperatures since the start of the Industrial
Revolution, repeatedly verified as a rise of 1° C. or 1.6° F. But
human activity has doubled the concentrations since those measurements were made.
• Methane is the main component in natural gas, and is a
by-product of oil drilling and factory farmed meat. It's atmospheric impacts are much worse than CO_2. Earlier it was
thought to absorb 20 times as much heat as CO_2. It's now
estimated to hold 50 to 70 times as much heat. Methane decomposes in the atmosphere over a relatively short time, like 10 to 20
years. But it decomposes *into* CO_2 which lasts hundreds to thousands of years. Scientists are just developing the technologies to
measure Methane in the air and locate leaks at ground level and
in the ocean.
• We know that the main contributors to atmospheric warming

are vehicle exhaust, leaks from natural gas wells, gasses and particulates from coal mining and from coal and gas-fired power plants. The factory farming of beef and pork require extra-rich foods and hormones to boost growth; but it makes the animals belch and fart great quantities of Methane. The climate impacts are about equally serious as either of the other main sources.

• In recent years, climate scientists have observed that the Arctic is warming faster than the rest of the world; so the melting of Arctic ice has been accelerating faster than predicted by earlier models. The same is true of Antarctica to a lesser extent. And its rate of acceleration increases every year.

• There is a pecking order among fossil fuels; each puts out different kinds and quantities of pollution, in extraction and in burning. Burning wood produces CO_2 and particulates, toxic dust that can cause breathing problems. Burning coal produces CO_2, and emits the worse kinds of toxic particulates including Mercury pollution. Burning gasoline produces CO_2, Carbon Monoxide and (in some states) lead compounds as particulates. Mining and oil wells, coal and oil transport all give off varieties of gas and particulate pollution. Oil pipelines leak, oil tankers crash and spill, trains hauling oil and gas crash and burn. Deep water oil wells explode and spill millions of gallons of oil. Natural gas, of all the fossil fuels, burns the cleanest; but natural gas wells are highly prone to leakage, as are other stages of processing and transport. And just remember that Methane, the main component in natural gas, holds way more atmospheric heat than CO_2.

• Most of us know that GW/CC causes glaciers and polar ice to melt and bodies of water to heat up, which causes sea levels to rise, both from the volume of ice melting and from heat expansion, which will impact coastal zones unevenly but almost everywhere, causing mass migrations.

• There were predictions that GW/CC would cause more numerous and more intense weather events, like droughts, storms and floods, over the times we are living in; those predictions are proving to be generally way too conservative; such events are getting more frequent and more severe every year. They continue to threaten coastal zones and wreak billions of dollars in damage.

- In 2003, 35,000 people died in a European heat wave.
- Shortages of food, medicine, health care and fresh water, as well as forced migrations, accompany these extreme events.
- News in 2016-17: Climate scientists use a variety of computer models to document what is happening and to predict how it will impact the future, 20 to 50 to 200 years out. Enough of them have been documented to show that the ones that predict the worst outcomes – the damages that GW/CC *WILL CAUSE* – have been the most accurate models. In 2016, computers monitoring the increase in Arctic heat identified their own data as an error, because it was so far beyond any existing model. It was not an error.

From the summer into December of 2017, California saw two of the worst wildfire season ever, driven by unprecedented high winds over large regions. 2 or 3 of the worst hurricanes and floods ever, have happened in the last few years, and we saw the separation of the largest sheet of ice, from Antarctica, ever recorded. Of the hottest years on record, at least 8 have occurred in the last 10 years. Up until recently, climate scientists have cautioned us not to blame specific weather events on Climate Change; but over the last 3-4 years they have admitted Climate Change is definitely making them more frequent and more damaging.

The US's responsibility: The US and the UK continue to be the highest emitters of GHGs per person. China has recently come close to the US as the highest total emitter, and will probably pass us soon. But the US is quite clearly responsible for the major share of GHGs emissions since 1800. So, at the very least, we should be leading the world in efforts to cut emissions.

Argument 7: Climate Change alone is an existential threat to humanity and most of the life on Earth.

Argument 8: Climate Change is only one of a dozen or more environmental crises.

BEYOND CLIMATE CHANGE: THE *OTHER* ENVIRONMENTAL CRISES

In the past, GW/CC was thought of as the worst of the many environmental impacts, with the rest in decreasing importance. Recently though, the ranking has changed. Global Warming/ Climate Change is now thought to be comparable to the next 2 on this list, the Health of the Oceans and Bad Agricultural Practices. Just ahead we explain the role of cow farts, and the role of herbicides and pesticides. I call this category *Bad Ag*.

Keep in mind that atmospheric CO_2, and Methane, and a few other GHGs, are a primary cause of all three of the top challenges, and contribute, directly and indirectly to most of the others. So the fact that BadAg and Ocean Health are equally as dangerous as GW/CC, does not lower the importance of emissions; it emphasizes that they are still the biggest problem.

You will notice that each of this dozen can be thought of at least 2 ways: as factors that appear to be separate, with different causes and negative effects; but also as interconnected with one or several of the others. More examples of Combined Impacts are coming up shortly.

1. THE HEALTH OF THE OCEANS: The oceans absorb a lot of the excess atmospheric heat; scientists are working to figure out how much. Scientists know the air only holds a fraction of the total heat absorbed, but they can't determine where the hotter water is. They know GW/CC is gradually changing ocean chemistry, but are not sure about the specifics. In mid-2018 they are observing big changes in the circulation patterns in the Atlantic, and they know that will increase the chances of further climate impacts that could be even more disastrous than the ones we already understand.

Additional CO_2 in the oceans makes them more acidic, which in turn affects sea life in many different ways, from destroying coral reefs – the "rainforests of the oceans" – to threatening feeding and migration patterns.

The practice of over-fishing by industrial fleets, by-catch in particular, causes millions of fish to be killed in the process of catching a thousand. In spite of laws and regulations. It threatens to drive food fish, and many other species, to near extinction. (Extinctions are their own category, ahead.) Different methods could be enforced that would be far less harmful. Simply understand that most of the large edible ocean fish have already been killed off. Most of the tuna being caught today is too young to have reproduced. Let that sink in.

We are beginning to become aware of the quantity of plastic trash in the oceans and its effect on marine life generally. It's important to know about the Dead Zones around the mouths of most of the world's rivers, where nothing can live, because of the quantity of toxic chemicals – 1000s of different types, from fertilizers and pesticides, to hormones and other pharmaceuticals, chemical and oil spills – that human activity dumps into those rivers.

2. BAD AGRICULTURAL PRACTICES:

Soil depletion, erosion and the loss of arable (farm-able) land to development, the excessive use of drugs and hormones, the over-use of toxic herbicide and pesticide poisons, and the unnecessary waste of clean water: these are just some of the Bad Ag Practices that threaten soil and water quality, and food production in the long term.

Factory farming of meat contributes to the larger Eco-Crisis in at least 4 significant ways: 1. Deforestation to grow animal feed pollutes, destroys wild habitat and causes species extinctions. 2. So huge carbon sinks – processes that naturally reabsorb CO_2 – are removed from the natural carbon cycle. 3. Factory farmed cows and pigs are fed super-rich diets to make them grow bigger and faster; so their belches and farts emit much more Methane than grass-fed animals. 4. It also requires the use of massive amounts of antibiotics, both as protection against unhealthy living conditions and to promote faster growth, so the antibiotics, carried away in runoff (piss, poop, and rain), pollute soil, rivers, and groundwater.

These practices increase directly as people in developing nations want to eat more meat. And the economics of farming, in the US and, for example, in India looms as a growing cause of food insecurity. Farmers here, there and elsewhere get caught in cycles of increasing debt, by being forced into using chemicals and GMOs (see just below) by giant corporations. Many thousands of Indian farmers have committed suicide over the last decade, and it's becoming an ugly trend in the US. Farmers are basically trapped between chemical companies, banks, and a brutal market that demands artificially low prices.

Homework for the weekend: What is *monoculture*? What is *Grain and Graze*? How much was spent to defeat California's GMO labeling law? Why has the US started to import organic foods from other countries?

GENETICALLY MODIFIED ORGANISMS: I wasn't sure whether to include GMOs in Bad Agricultural Practices or under Toxic Pollution, ahead. Several of these categories overlap into others. Here is a summary of my evolving arguments.

First, some so-called experts and respected scientists have argued that genetically modifying plants and animals – changing their DNA to give them different characteristics – is no different or more dangerous than what we humans have been doing for centuries through selective breeding. That is false, either a gross misunderstanding or a lie. The cute answer is,

> **Never in the history of life on Earth did a salmon have sex with a tomato to make a baby tomato that is frost tolerant.**

Second, regardless of the claims made for GMOs – more production, better nutrition, less water demand, tolerance for poor soils and so on (many of which are proven false) – we must understand that most GMO crops are engineered to tolerate high doses of toxic herbicides and pesticides, many of which persist in our food and the environment generally.

The not-so-cute question is, *Why are the companies that want to control the world's seeds also the biggest producers of toxic herbicides and pesticides? ... many of them cancer-causing?*

Beyond that, no argument about GMO food is complete, in my view, without answering 5 questions, more or less independently of each other: 1. Are GMO foods safe to eat? (Hint: it depends on ...) 2. Are there measurable amounts of pesticides in or on the food, at levels dangerous to health when eaten? (And are there other dangers?) 3. How damaging is the spread of toxic poisons in the wider environment? 4. How dangerous is the accidental release of GMOs into the environment, and why? (Hint: Atlantic Salmon in west coast fish farms.) 5. And why do the GMO/herbicide/pesticide producers lie about these questions, or make them so hard to answer?

More homework: How many countries, and which ones: require GMOs to be labeled? ... have banned GMOs altogether? ... have rejected millions of dollars' worth of US food exports because they were contaminated with GMOs? Who on the Supreme Court used to work as a Monsanto lobbyist? Why did a jury in California make a judgment of 1/4 of a Billion dollars against Monsanto and in favor of a school grounds keeper? How many similar suits are waiting for court dates? How likely is that judgment to stand several appeals?

Please see the comments about Experts Disagree at the end of Part Two, on page 85.

3. BIODIVERSITY AND EXTINCTIONS: We continue to drive more species to extinction than any other set of forces in the last 60 million years. We know that our ancestors hunted the Mammoth, the Dodo, and the Passenger Pigeon until they were all gone. Many species of land mammals, wild dogs and cats for example, exist now only as stuffed trophies, bones, and images.

Biodiversity is a strong indicator of a healthy ecosystem. It's a key to understanding the complexity of evolution. It represents the interdependence and resilience of natural systems, but also their vulnerability. When we interrupt an ecosystem, by killing off one or two niche plant or animal species, we upset a delicate balance and may, unwittingly, combine multiple impacts to undermine the entire system.

Humans are decimating natural habitats and driving away or killing hundreds of endangered species of wildlife globally, from Orangutans who are dying for palm oil plantations, to elephants who are slaughtered for ivory, to tiny frogs and birds that are dying from toxic chemical pollution, to other species forced to migrate away from human land development. The survival of honey bees, which are essential to at least 1/3 of all the food we eat, is threatened by several human activities. See CCD and *Combined Impacts* ahead.

4. FRESH WATER SHORTAGES: Rapid and severe declines in available fresh water are causing deaths by dehydration and disease in drought zones, and drops in agricultural production and food shortages across the planet. As declines persist, they will limit industrial manufacturing and increase the cost of food and all manufactured goods. The statistics are staggering ... but apparently not enough to make governments take action.

In North America, 2010: fresh water consumed for fossil fuel production – fracking and tar sands extraction in particular – exceeded 66 billion cubic meters, triple the yearly use of all North American residences combined. Russia, summer 2010: drought, caused by an unprecedented heat wave (90° F. near the Arctic Circle) destroyed much of the annual wheat crop and drove food prices up worldwide. China, 2012: Grain harvests in the world's largest producer have been falling for ten years. California, 2012 to mid-2015: The worst drought on record results in major reduction in fruit and vegetable production. The El Nino of 2015-16 brought a normal-to-high quantity of rain and snow; without it, that drought would have become a disaster with international impacts. Chemical pollution poisons vast quantities of fresh water, mostly from fossil fuel by-products, chemical fertilizers, herb- and pesticides. As much as 75 percent of all the fresh water we use in the US is wasted. Add in the impacts of GW/CC-caused droughts, we are on track to see growing numbers of fresh water shortages every year.

Earth, 2018: For one sixth of the world's population, fresh water scarcity is a persistent condition. Those numbers are expected to double by 2025. It's a common assumption among climate scientists, and political economists who understand GW/CC, that most of the wars, rebellions, and refugee crises of the future will be caused by water: too little or too much of it.

LATE UPDATES: Detroit, 2012-the present: Republican administrators have poisoned over a thousand children and adults with lead, and contaminated the entire city's water systems, to save a few thousand dollars. Finally in the summer of 2017, several were being prosecuted. But the problem is far from being fixed. It made other cities test their water, to find lead, arsenic and other toxins present, far in excess of safe standards. August 2015, early warnings appear (from Motherboard/Vice) that an oil pipeline running through the bottom of the Great Lakes may be about to burst, threatening the largest volumes of surface fresh water in the world.

We have to understand the connections between these looming disasters and the economic system that creates them.

We can use fresh water to try to understand how hard it is to think about these big issues and big quantities with a proper sense of proportion and perspective. Imagine the Earth is the size of a basketball, about 9" in diameter. In proportion, the total amount of accessible fresh water on the Earth would be the size

41

of a pea, and shrinking. I researched this 3 different ways, and still have trouble believing it myself.

5 and 6. DESERTIFICATION AND DEFORESTATION: These two factors overlap and often occur in tandem. GW/CC causes deserts to expand (desertification), resulting in the loss of arable land and habitable land for both humans and animals, often leading to forced migrations and increased demand for scarce food and water in neighboring regions. Deforestation is caused by 2 human factors: One, directly, by the clear cutting or intentional burning of forests, usually for new industrial farms (Palm Oil in Indonesia for example); it means the loss of wildlife habitat and the loss of carbon sinks. Two, as a side-effect of GW/CC, many more forests are burning due to the heat and droughts; many are dying from the shifting climate or invasive pests. These two factors represent a *Feedback Loop* (see pages 50-1, 55, 63-4). Each problem tends to worsen its own conditions or cause other problems. Forests are powerful, natural Carbon Sinks, they absorb CO_2 rather than let it accumulate in the air, and they produce oxygen. Most of the oxygen essential to animal life was produced by trees, over millions of years.

LATE UPDATE (deforestation, food, extinctions and CO_2): Many climate scientists agree that the increase in the consumption of factory-farmed meat (bad for its Methane emissions) has become the single largest contributor to species extinction globally, because of the forests being clear-cut to raise beef and pork – even more than what is cleared for Palm Oil plantations and other Bad Ag practices. Find out which products use Palm Oil – it's a lot – and observe the deforestation and habitat loss it has caused.

7. PEAK RESOURCES: Is this good news or bad? For a while we thought we were approaching a global "Peak Oil" – to find that we had extracted more than half of all the known oil in the world. I think that would have been good news. It would have forced us to develop alternatives and adjust our economy to them sooner. But we keep finding more fossil fuel reservoirs and inventing new and more destructive ways of extracting oil and gas, like tar sands, fracking, and deep water drilling. Many experts still believe we have found and extracted half of all the oil on the planet. Some oil investors still think new exploration is a profit engine, while some banks and other investors are getting out of fossil fuels completely. Environmentalists say we have to *leave the rest of it in the ground.*

Otherwise, we are running out of almost everything, from arable land to fresh water to rare earth minerals. It means higher costs for manufactured goods, increased eco-damage from new and extreme mining and extraction methods and more habitat loss for indigenous peoples and animals.

8. TOXIC POLLUTION, INCLUDING NUCLEAR WASTE:

Toxic pollution damages the health of all living things. In humans, it causes or worsens cancers, asthma and other *environmental diseases.* It contributes to dead zones at the mouths of rivers, and contaminates soil, water, and air.

The element *Strontium 90* was the earliest example of radioactive pollution. It did not exist anywhere on the Earth prior to the first nuclear bomb tests in 1945. There was public outrage in the late 1940s when it was detected in cows' milk, followed by its appearance in mothers' milk as well. The outrage subsided because authorities realized that nothing could be done about it. Traces of Strontium 90 are now found in every cell of almost every living thing on Earth ... *as are a number of other toxins, including Mercury* (mostly from burning coal) and others.

Nuclear Waste: There is no workable plan for *disposing* or *storing* hundreds of tons of deadly nuclear waste. We are leaving future generations hundreds of toxic dumps that will remain deadly for ... *longer than humans have existed on the Earth.*

Fukushima Japan, 2011: An earthquake in the Pacific created a Tsunami – tidal wave – that flooded nuclear reactors near the coast. The backup generators needed to cool the reactors were destroyed and 2 or more reactors melted down. Uncontrolled leakage of hundreds tons of radioactive water is ongoing, and – now 7 years later – there is no estimate how long it will take to control it or what the total damage to ocean life may be. The utility company and the Japan government have recently agreed to dump additional thousands of tons of radioactive water into the ocean – there's no place to store it. Fukushima may turn out to be the worst environmental disaster in human history. So far.

Revealed in late 2017, an early meltdown in the US – well before Three Mile Island (US), Chernoble (USSR), and Fukishima (Japan), – was kept secret for more than 60 years.

Homework: How does Mercury get into fish? Why is it bad to eat? What is *PetCoke* and who owns the piles of it along the Detroit River? How many other nuclear meltdowns have there been? Also, how does *Clean Coal* work? (Hint: It doesn't.)

MISSING INFORMATION ON EMISSIONS AND WASTE: We know that vehicle emissions are one of the top three sources of excess CO_2 in the atmosphere. Most of us have never been told that 75 percent of the energy released by the gasoline, burning in our cars' internal combustion engines, is wasted, as heat or through mechanical inefficiency. We also ignore the fact that moving a ton of metal to carry the weight of a person or two is an enormous waste in itself. But we've become used to the convenience and the social image.

LIKE EVERYTHING ON THIS LIST, IT GETS WORSE: In May 2018 a toxic chemical disaster is finally being made public. 3M, DuPont and other chemical giants, have been producing PFOA (aka *C8*) and PFOS since 1949 for use in the production of Teflon and fire retardants. Trump's EPA wanted to keep this secret because it would cause a "public relations disaster," something much worse, to them, than a massive and widespread public health disaster. Several producers have been dumping

44

the chemicals, totally illegally, on land (to enter ground water) and in public waterways, for decades. It is now understood to cause terrible cancers and other diseases in farm animals. And now, the many cancer deaths suffered by firemen and other first responders is tracked directly to exposure to the chemicals in fire retardants.

There's a pattern here. Producers, the government and the EPA, (before and since Trump and his EPA head, Scott Pruitt, have been destroying the agency), with the complicity of the mass media (chemical companies buy a lot of media advertising), do not want us to know that dangerous levels of those chemicals are, like Mercury and Strontium 90, almost everywhere, and in almost every cell of every animal, in the world.

We must begin to try to understand how dependent our economy has become on so many different forms of toxic waste. Back to the list.

9. POPULATION: Extraordinary efforts have managed to reduce poverty and starvation in much of the world. But millions still die from inadequate nutrition, thirst or contaminated water, especially in war zones. Many environmentalists believe we humans have reproduced far in excess of the Earth's *Carrying Capacity*, the number of us the planet can support at a high poverty level. Also, as highly populated countries industrialize, China and India for example, and more people enter the middle class, they radically increase demands on the economy and the ecosystem for the production of food – meat in particular, – consumer products, cars, and energy.

Some measurements show that our population is leveling off and will probably not top 8 billion. Other statistics say our numbers may continue to rise to 11 billion or more by 2100.

We cannot imagine a response to the Global Environmental Crisis that does not included a global effort to reduce our total numbers.

If we cannot find a way to voluntarily limit family size, and if governments cannot manage to incentivize it effectively, the impacts of the Crisis will cut our numbers the hard way. See the Worst Case Scenarios, ahead on pages 67-82.

In their 1968 book, *The Population Bomb,* Paul and Anne Ehrlich warned that unchecked global population would, by the late 1980s, trigger a global disaster, mainly from mass starvation and the side effects of social and political upheavals. The global population has doubled since the Ehrlichs published their book, but a truly global famine has not occurred. But it is not impossible, and we cannot ignore the issue.

Homework: What is or was China's *One Child Policy*? How did that go? What if it had caught on as an international trend?

10. INVASIVE SPECIES, INFESTATIONS: Increased globalized trade has multiplied the number of species invasions. Climate Change makes them harder to limit or manage. Asian Carp in US rivers and lakes are threatening native fish populations. Burmese Pythons, illegally imported in Florida as pets and then released, are killing native animals and pets; efforts to catch and kill them can't keep up with their rate of reproduction. A Pine Beetle infestation, caused by GW/CC, has destroyed millions of acres of pine forests. Other varieties of insect and rodent pests are forced to migrate into new territory. Ecologists in several countries are documenting dramatic drops in insect populations, up to 75 percent of previous populations in Germany, for example. Like everything on this list, this single factor alone is an environmental disaster in the making. Another study says that GW/CC is likely to wipe out species of household and animal pests like fleas and ticks. Think that would be great? Think again. It could starve birds, frogs, lizards and other small animals and devastate diversity and ecosystem balance.

11. THE IMPROPER USE OF PHARMACEUTICALS: Increased outbreaks of MRSA and other antibiotic-resistant diseas-
46

es are spreading, in hospitals in particular. The overuse of antibiotics, for humans and in meat production, is causing the rapid evolution of resistant strains of disease. Medical studies show that over-prescribing antibiotics, to children in particular, and the residues found in all non-organic meat, all contribute to the causes of obesity, diabetes and other diseases. More deaths are caused by *legal* medications, *properly prescribed and administered,* than by all illegal drugs and traffic accidents combined – 100,000 deaths per year. Add in mistaken prescriptions and accidental overdoses and the number nearly doubles. The opioid/heroin epidemic in several states is just the latest example; its victims have more than doubled in the 3 years since the earlier draft of this book was written. Some activists are pointing to one family that profits enormously from the epidemic, as do the Congressmen and Senators who were bribed to deregulate the trade.

12. NEW (AND REALLY OLD) DISEASES: The infestation in South America, Brazil in particular, of the mosquito-borne Zika virus caused hundreds of birth defects and threatened to become widespread. Viruses that have been inactive for 10,000 years, frozen in the Arctic tundra, are being released as the tundra warms. So far they are harmless, but there's no guarantee that they will remain so.

While these factors create minor and localized threats to public health and ecosystems, and while they are not all directly related to human environmental impacts, incidents are increasing in frequency and severity.

In the month this update was written, 5 people died in Puerto Rico from a flesh-eating bacteria in the polluted, post-hurricane Maria waters.

TWO DIGRESSIONS: WAR AND WASTE

WAR: For the moment let's just notice:
• The US spends almost as much on military hardware, material, fuel, and personnel as the rest of the world combined, and the US military is the largest single consumer of fuel in the US (ex-

PART TWO: DUTY TO WARN

cluding the totals for transportation and electricity generation, which are distributed systems, not a singular entity). 15 percent of the US military budget, for one year, could fund clean water systems for everyone on Earth who lacks them. Probably a billion people. Permanent systems. The US is the single largest arms and weapons dealer in the world, including attack aircraft.
• The US military is also the largest single source of environmental damage, just behind China, the UK, and the US.
• US soldiers were exposed to Agent Orange in Vietnam, and to DU, Depleted Uranium in both invasions of Iraq (1988 and 2003). Postwar deaths and sickness among Vietnam veterans exceed the number of combat deaths. In the 2 Iraq invasions combined, combat deaths did not exceed 6,000 (until recently). Deaths from DU contamination are hard to count, but are surely 5 times those from combat. From Wikipedia, on Agent Orange: *By April 1993, the Department of Veterans Affairs had compensated only 486 victims, although it had received disability claims from 39,419 soldiers who had been exposed ... while serving in Vietnam.* DU represents a really sinister connection between nuclear waste and the Military-Industrial Complex (see pages197-8).

Pipeline blockaders were called "Eco- Terrorists" by some commentators. The use of DU and Agent Orange represent the weaponizing of extreme poisons, with zero regard to the human killing and environmental damage, on both sides of the battles. Who's the terrorist? Who manufactured Agent Orange and also sells a popular week killer?

The US's misuse of military power actually weakens our defenses, brings disrespect from many other nations, and serious threats from a few, while it wastes huge quantities of resources and causes widespread pollution.

Two different writers distilled the causes for war down to their simplest, most graphic and gut-wrenching truth. Major General Smedley Butler is profiled on page 192-3, in a different context. You can jump there and come back if you choose. He wrote a book called, *War Is Good Business.*

I would recommend another book on the topic, a graphic work of non-fiction – it's laid out like a comic book – *Addicted to War, Why the US Can't Kick Militarism,* by Joel Andreas (2004, updated 2015). Read more about this addiction on page 308.

> *Their conclusions about what causes war: It's good for business and the banks. It helps the powerful to hold, expand, and abuse more power.*

WASTE: When we throw *disposable* or toxic stuff away, it doesn't go away. There is no *away*. It goes to some other location on the land, or in the water or the air. Almost every ounce of toxic material – out of billions of tons – that passes through our hands, homes, industries, machines, and budgets, if not properly recycled or neutralized, does damage to life and sustainability somewhere on the planet. A little of it gets recycled properly. In Europe, trash is burned for fuel in high-tech, zero-emission facilities. Our careless *disposal* of tons of material only means that we are choking sea life with plastic, emitting Methane that multiplies excessive heat, and poisoning plants, animals and people downstream, downwind, or in poorer countries, with toxins that will gradually migrate closer to home, waiting for our children as they grow up.

These factors are more complex than the basic *what we all ought to know,* back on pages 32-35. Some are less well documented or hard to define, others have an unclear timetable or range of predictions. Some risks are hard to factor into the computer climate models. Some are so scary that news outlets simply don't want to raise the levels of fear. But they need to be raised.

The dozen other environmental components of the Global Eco-Crisis are scary by themselves, given that each has its own causes, speed, and impacts. They are even more terrifying in combination.

COMBINED IMPACTS

In the dozen environmental emergencies on the last few pages (other than Climate Change), we see that each one makes some other impacts worse, or accelerates them. *Combined Impacts* describe a range of relationships that change over time, less predictably and in ways that add to the complexity and the varying speeds of all the crises. Some combined impacts have specific names, other don't. It's important to understand and use the concept, because we will find it applies to many of the political and economic factors that affect *everything inside and outside the Eco-Crisis, and* create accelerating risks.

Feedback Loops: One of the most important, relatively simple things about GW/CC, that many of us don't get, is that the basic dynamic is *self-reinforcing,* regardless of lower emissions. The simplest feedback loop is the *Solar Absorption Effect.* It's easy to understand that snow and ice reflect a lot of solar heat back into space. We know that the added CO_2 that we emit makes the atmosphere (and land and oceans) warmer, which makes ice and snow melt, which exposes dark land and dark water. And it's easy to understand that dark water and land absorb more solar heat than the snow and ice. A lot more heat. Which *feeds back* into the system and adds heat, even without more emissions.

The *methane feedback loop* works like the CO_2. Except, as we know, methane holds way more heat than CO_2, and, *as we may not know,* there are huge quantities of methane trapped in the frozen tundra around both poles, in the Arctic and Antarctic. The Arctic is warming faster so the Arctic tundra has begun to melt, releasing methane hydrates into the air. Some scientists call this the *Methane Time Bomb* or the *Methane Death Spiral.* Methane is one of the 3 crucial factors many of us don't know about.

The total amount of Methane that is frozen below the surface of the ice at both poles, and in the ocean bottom near the poles, if released, *MAY BE* enough to double the atmospheric carbon to 800ppm, which will make the Earth uninhabitable for 90 percent of the animal species on Earth. Or all of them. And it could happen in a relatively short span of time.

> *If there is no way to stop the combined CO_2 and Methane feedback loops, we may already be doomed, no matter what we do.*

Wrap your head around that painful idea, if you can, and try to remember it. There is another combined impact coming up, even less well understood than Feedback Loops, and more dangerous. They could lead to a state of mass denial or despair. Or they may be enough to knock enough of us out of our distraction and indifference and makes us demand radical action. Also keep in mind this book's promise, to present a radical but viable solution that may be our only option ... if we can make it happen fast.

> *It gives much more weight to the question, "Do apocalyptic nightmare warnings help or hurt our efforts?"*

Homework: Google these 2 terms: "big holes in Siberian Arctic" and "Methane Craters." You will find different descriptions, of different examples of one terrifying phenomenon: melting permafrost releasing vast quantities of methane.

One lesson that Nature is trying to teach us is that everything is interconnected with everything else. Combined impacts are the cutting edge of that lesson. Here are some other examples:

LATE UPDATE: The permafrost that is melting in the Arctic, emitting quantities of Methane that may be staggering in volume, is also releasing large quantities of Mercury compounds into the air and oceans. Scientists may even have to redefine what the *perma* in permafrost means. Can you find out why?

CASCADE EFFECTS: In the 1800s, off the California coast, otters, sea urchins, kelp, and other species of sea life had evolved into a perfectly balanced ecosystem. But Native Americans, white settlers, and fishermen hunted the otters to near extinction, because their pelts brought high prices. Then the sea urchins the otters had eaten multiplied and ate up all the kelp, which was life-support for other populations of sea creatures. That turned a thriving ecosystem into a dead zone. This is an example of a *Cascade Effect*. One outcome of human behavior *cascades* into an unforeseen chain of other impacts that get progressively worse.

Search online for the 4 1/2 minute film, *How Wolves Change Rivers*. It is a beautiful example of the resilience of nature when it is left alone, and shows how a negative Cascade Effect can reverse itself over just a few years.

BIOACCUMULATION occurs when a toxic chemical accumulates in fish, animals, and humans as nutrients move up the food chain. Mercury (as methyl mercury, from burning coal) is absorbed by the ocean, and is taken in by the smallest plant and animal life. Small fish eat small quantities of it; larger fish accumulate it directly from the water, but then they get a double dose by eating smaller fish. As they in turn are eaten by still larger fish, the quantities of Mercury per pound of edible fish increase, until, when eaten by humans – pregnant women in particular – the increased levels of Mercury can cause serious health problems, for the mom and the fetus.

COLONY COLLAPSE DISORDER is wiping out bee colonies in localities around the world. Some beekeepers have lost half their bees in one season. Scientists have been struggling to isolate the cause or causes. But if CCD is the result of combined impacts, the causes are harder to isolate and counteract, and that appears to be the problem.

Three factors have become severe in combination: First, a new class of insecticides is sprayed widely on crops to kill insect pests. *Neonicotinoids,* a class of insecticide and a derivative of nicotine, causes nerve damage in the pests. Bees are also insects, so they also pick up the toxin as they gather nectar and pollen.

Second, microwave radiation from cell phone towers appears to mix up the bees' navigation systems, so some may be dying because they can't find their way back to the hive. And third, a type of mite that invades beehives may also be a factor. Though not human-caused, the mites may be getting an advantage because the hives are already weakened by the other 2 factors.

Another recent discovery adds a new element to CCD. The bees are apparently getting addicted to the nicotine derivative, just as humans do to cigarets. So they are taking in more of the pesticide than they might otherwise do, hastening their deaths.

Coal miners used to carry canaries in cages into the mines with them, so the little birds could warn them of dangerous gases in the mines ... by dying. The bees are our *canaries* in a poison-polluted environment.

There are combined impacts in both the causes and effects of CCD. Bees are essential to pollinate as much as a third of all food crops. If CCD cannot be diagnosed and reversed, it could cause widespread bee extinctions, and in turn, crop failures. If crops are already threatened, by GW/CC-caused drought for example, the damage to food production from the loss of bees is multiplied several times over. Some farming regions in the Far East have already resorted to manual pollination to replace the work of bees – farm workers hand-dusting fruit and nut crops, tree by tree, branch by branch, flower by flower – to avoid total crop failures. Does that sound like sustainable agriculture? By banning neonicotinoids and other pesticides, several European countries have seen their bee populations begin to recover, so there is hope for correcting CCD.

FRACKING AND DROUGHT: September 2013: Water shortages across the US Southwest, caused by GW/CC-induced droughts, have combined with the fracking industry's demand for water. In Texas in particular, farmers had to choose: use their reduced allotments of ground water, pumped from shrinking aquifers, to try to save their cattle or crops, or sell that water to the *frackers* who are drilling gas and oil wells across the same areas. On land, free water flows to the lowest elevation. In an un-regulated market, it flows to where the money is. So both kinds of aquifers are being depleted. And many are being poisoned by fracking chemicals.

The Combined Impacts pile up and get more complex. Notice where much of the fracked gas is going. It has glutted the natural gas market, to the point there is not enough demand in the US for the gas produced. In spite of industry promises, the price of natural gas has stayed high, and profits have skyrocket-ed. So the gas extractors are begging for the construction of ex-port terminals, so they can sell the excess gas to India or China. The coal market has a similar problem. As demand for coal de-creases, in the US and Australia for example, it remains steady in China and is rising in India, so coal producers also want export facilities. In Australia, they may destroy more of the endangered Great Barrier (Coral) Reef, to make way for coal exports. Every-one in those markets ignores the fact that the CO_2, Methane, and Mercury all end up in the same global atmosphere. Australia, Canada, India, China, and the US are all seriously confused about the value of mining, importing or exporting, and burning more coal.

The essence of the problem of Combined Impacts rests on our inability to understand that everything in Nature, and in the Global Environmental Crisis is interconnected with humans and everything we have done. We may see Nature as powerful, which it is, and infinitely durable, which it is not. The factor of interdependence is part of what makes Nature so durable and resilient, before our destructive inputs . But the interdependence of all living things also makes Nature much more delicate, more vulnerable to our impacts, than we thought. Like so many other things, it ought to have been obvious.

RETURNING TO THE TOPIC OF CLIMATE CHANGE
There's a lot of stuff we may not have heard about. Some of it is the most important for us to comprehend.

Argument 9: Even those who understand a lot about the Climate Crisis do not understand how serious and urgent it actually is ... or why.

The 350ppm "limit:" Bill McKibben was one of the founders of the organization and website 350.org. 350 stands for 350 parts per million (ppm) of carbon (as CO_2) in the air, the amount that scientists agree *MAY* be "safe" – an amount the atmosphere can tolerate without spiraling into unstoppable feedback loops. The problem is that we were already at that number when McKibben started publicizing it in 2007. In 2014, we exceeded 400 ppm in the Arctic, and in 2016 we passed that limit as a global average. So slowing or stopping our emissions to hold to the 350 ppm limit is no longer possible.

The 2°C "limit" and "Carbon Budgets:" Groups of nations have been meeting for over 20 years to try to deal with Climate Change and its human causes. At different times, different limits, and different ways to reach them, have been proposed, for the maximum allowable increase in global temperatures.

Since the Industrial Revolution, human emissions have caused the global average temperature to rise by 1° C, or about 1.7° F. The most recent agreement in Paris (2015) settled on 2° C or about 3.4° F, as the upper "safe" limit that we – all the people and nations of the world – ought to agree on as the maximum total human caused additional heat that we can allow.

This is related to the concept of a global Carbon Budget, which estimates how much *MORE* coal, natural gas, oil, and gasoline we can burn, and how much additional methane we can release, before we risk passing the 2° C limit. Most climate alarmists, like McKibben, me, and others agree that the Carbon Budget ought to be as near zero as possible, meaning we ought to leave as much of the remaining oil, coal, and natural gas *in the ground*. Even burning what we have already extracted is dangerous. We are going to see, in the next few pages, that the 2° limit set in the Paris Accord is already impossible to meet.

This next item is the 3rd of 3 impacts, with feedback loops and Methane, that are the most dangerous and least understood.

Climate or Thermal Lag (or Inertia), in the atmosphere: Scientists have known for decades that there is a delay between the time CO_2 or Methane are released in quantity into the atmosphere, and the time the maximum heat absorption happens and can be measured. That delay is estimated to be roughly 20 years.

> *Argument 10: Climate or Thermal Lag is the factor that turns Climate Change from a 50-year problem into an immediate existential threat; it makes the 2° C limit and Carbon Budgets ridiculous if not insane.*

Climate alarmists warn us that we could stop our emissions of GHGs totally and globally today, and, without other radical controls, the Earth will continue to heat up for at least 20 years. This is what makes the climate agreements sound good, while they are really doing next to nothing. It could seal our fate, regardless of whether we do a little or a lot. This factor ought to force us to do everything possible as fast as possible, if and when we understand what must be done. Our only chance will be to do everything possible, fast, and trust that the resilience of Nature will give us a break. Check out the Decision Grids ahead.

Thermal Lag or Inertia, in the oceans: Scientists know that the oceans must be absorbing much more heat than the air and land – as much as 80 or 90 percent of the total heat – but they have trouble finding where the stored heat is located. Some is clearly located near the surface, because it is known to fuel hurricanes and make them wider, more powerful and longer lasting. Two things are confusing and therefore create unknown levels of climate risk:

First, we don't know where all the hotter water is, some of it must be deep in the oceans; that is counter-intuitive because heated liquids generally rise. The quantities of recently melted ice, turned to ice-cold water, is complicating the situation.

So, second, this is the crucial point: The oceans will also display Thermal Lag or Inertia, because it takes time to absorb the heat from the CO_2 and other GHGs that dissolve in sea water, so that heat will have the same delayed reaction as in the air. But the lag or delay between the time the GHGs are absorbed and the time the oceans start emitting the excess heat is thought to be much longer than the atmospheric equivalent, from minimums of 20 to 50 years to maximums of 500 to thousands of years. So the delayed impacts of Thermal Inertia in the oceans will be greater than the atmospheric, and will likely occur over much longer time spans, making the distant future even more unpredictably risky, climate-wise than the next few decades.

One TV analyst was trying to describe how hurricane Irma became so strong and so sustained, and how another, smaller hurricane was forming right behind it. He said what we all know, that warmer water at the surface is "fuel" for the hurricane; the warmer the water, the more evaporation, the wider the pattern, the faster the winds, and the more rain to follow. He indicated, in most cases, that the warm water at the surface would be depleted by one hurricane. But in Irma's case, he said the warm water extended deeper into the ocean than "normal," and was there to fuel the next storm. (Although the last 5 hurricanes in the US changed the meaning of *normal*.).

One would think, after Hurricanes Katrina, Sandy, Harvey, Irma, and Maria, that intelligent politicians would take notice and act. Oh ... right.

MOMENTUM AND INERTIA

The terms *Momentum* and *Inertia* take on different meanings depending on context, so they need some clarification: both can be physical (non-climate), physical (climate), and psychological, political, and economic. Physical momentum and inertia refer to the same *principle*: An object or a mechanism at rest will stay at rest until moved by an external force; and an object or mechanism in motion will remain in motion, at the same speed and in the same direction, until slowed or offset by an external force. This is the *principle of Inertia*. *Momentum* is the *measurable force* of the thing in motion, or the force needed to move it, change its direction or stop it. A locomotive and a car, in motion at similar speeds, demonstrate moving inertia. But the locomotive has roughly 1000 times the momentum, as it is 1000 times heavier, and will take 1000 times the force to stop it, compared to the car.

In general usage, *inertia* tends to apply to things at rest, resisting movement, and *momentum,* to things in motion. We have already covered the relatively new principle of Thermal Inertia, different for the atmosphere and the oceans. We need to understand that the contributors to GW/CC (and the other Environmental Crises) all have their own *momentum*. And we have to understand the problem of the *inertia,* the delaying factors, the resistance to change or movement, in our minds and media, and in our political and economic systems.

The Speed and Momentum of the Forces in the Eco-Crisis: It's a challenge to our ability to envision a big picture, a view from a distance, that encompasses most of the dynamics and moving parts in a large system. Try to imagine the combined forces of global, fossil- and nuclear-fueled industry as a single gigantic machine. One that dominates the Earth, guides our economic development and, without our understanding or control, will determine our future, against our reason and our will.

It is driven by several kinds of momentum: the literal momentum of gas and oil moving through pipes and on trains and trucks, from the source to the point of consumption – burning; the momentum of economic growth that demands more consumption, in shorter time spans, producing more profit (while ignoring the side effects of pollution that ought to create debits within that system, or slow it down), and the momentum of private and corporate wealth, ever expanding the gaps in income and wealth between the 1% and the 99%.

Did you notice the mention, over the last few pages, of terms like "unknown levels of future risk?" Keep it in mind.

Inertia and Delays, mental, political, economic, and mediated:
It's alarming to compare the momentum of GW/CC with the
inertia that resists corrective change; the momentum of unsustainable global industry, compared to the mental inertia that delays our ability to see it. In spite of Trump's role in the political
inertia, plus his obsession to stop the environmental movement,
the resistance against that trend is growing.

But the information that would prompt us to think differently or demand change is constrained by our corporate-con-
trolled mass media; it's either ignored, by MSNBC and CNN, or
contradicted by the incessant lying on Fox. The 2 parties are in
a near total gridlock – a paralyzing political inertia – so the US
government can just barely keep itself running, and never
mind the good of the public. Both parties have sold the public
interest for corrupt access to money and power.

INTERIM SUMMARY: DECISION GRIDS
Where We Are And What We Now Know We Need To Do
Greg Craven is a science teacher in Oregon. He has published a
book *(What's The Worst That Could Happen?)* and put a video up
online *(The Most Terrifying Video You'll Ever See)* that summarize
our dilemma clearly and briefly, in 3 or 4 different formats. One
emphasizes known and unknown risks.

On the next page, you'll see a 4 box diagram, based directly on his "decision grid." It intersects the 2 sets of variables: Is
GW/CC man-made and dangerous ... or not? and, What if we do
a lot to fix it ... or nothing?

It's a simple *IF, IF, IF, THEN* proposition:
IF there are known risks, but the worst risks are unknown, and
IF they might be catastrophic, and
IF it's possible to take action now,
THEN the conclusion is an undeniable no-brainer. Immediate
and effective action is the only sane decision.

1a. *IF:* GW/CC is not human-made or is not serious and we spend tons of money to stop it, when we don't need to, *THEN:* We waste a lot of money, maybe wreck the economy, but we're OK.	2a. *IF:* GW/CC is not human-made, or is not serious and we do nothing, *THEN:* We got lucky. Everything's OK.
1b. But *IF:* GW/CC is human-caused and a serious crisis, and we risk wrecking our economy to do everything possible, *THEN::* We avoid the biggest threat in human history. Whew!	2b. Or, *IF:* GW/CC is human-caused and a serious crisis, and we do nothing, *THEN:* Economic, Political, Social, Environmental, and Public Health CATASTROPHE, a worst case scenario.

This is much like our Grandma's warning, "Better safe than sorry," and another way of stating the *Cautionary Principle,* also known as the *Duh Principle*. It guides environmental regulations in much of Europe. There, they must prove a new chemical safe before it can be widely used. In the US, the chemical is approved, with massive lobbying and few tests, and its safety is determined later ... by the preventable damage done.

CONSIDER THE LINKS: INFORMATION-TIME-DECISION
There are at least 3 different contexts in which we need to discuss the relationships between Information, Time, and Decision-making processes. Information gets all of Part Four. Within that part, Freedom is discussed in several different contexts, starting on page 130. Another one is here, talking about the time pressures created by GW/CC, in what we will start calling A *Race Against Time*.

> **At our present pace, by the time enough of us realize an emergency decision is needed, it will be too late to matter.**

I made 4 graphics for a different project, representing 4 examples of the timing of decisions. The one describing our Climate/Environment dilemma is already covered here.

One was about baseball. Hitting a pitched baseball is one of the hardest challenges in sports; 1 hit out of 4 at-bats is a good average. The pitcher tries to trick the batter with the speed and direction of the ball. The batter has less than a second to decide: how fast the ball is coming, whether it's coming straight or curving, and where it's likely to end up as it crosses the plate. He (or she) actually has a fraction of a second to make a decision, based on those perceptions and estimates, whether to swing or not, and where. Imagine you are a rookie batter who has trouble with the curve, facing the best curve ball thrower in the league, and you left your glasses at home. That's like us facing Climate Change.

A second was about the US's decision to enter World War II and the kind of preparation that was needed. You may know that our rather late entry helped to turn the tide. The point was that it took the US a surprisingly short time to convert the entire economy to a war footing, rationing everything that could help the effort, and engineering entirely new systems of products and manufacturing methods. This topic picks up on page 194 in a part about US political history since the end of that war.

The third example was a lesson from high school Driver's Ed. It's called "overdriving your headlights." It still stands as an excellent analogy for the speed and momentum of a machine in motion, the speed and accuracy of information, the attention and reaction time of the person in control, the mechanics of slowing and stopping, the unknown risks of an accident, and so on.

Imagine you are going 60 miles an hour; it will take you 600 feet to stop, even in the best cases. But your headlights only shine 400 feet ahead, and a deer is crossing the road 500 feet ahead; so you won't see the deer in time to brake to avoid hitting it or running off the road to miss it. You are simply driving too fast for how far you can see and what the darkness may be hiding. Each part of that analogy has a parallel in our approach to GW/CC. Can you connect them?

Think about these other analogies:

The Bathtub Analogy: This one comes from the book *Climate Shock* by Gernot Wagner and Martin L. Weitzman. It is particularly relevant to Carbon Budgets and gradually reducing emissions instead of stopping them totally and fast. The authors tell us that some grad students at MIT could not grasp the point until it this analogy was fully explained.

A bathtub, nearly full of water, is an analogy for the Earth's atmosphere; the water is the quantity of CO_2 in it; the edge of the tub is the limit of tolerable CO_2 or the tipping point of passing the 2° C limit. The balance between the faucet flow and the outlet drain (that always kept the tub half full) is like the normal carbon cycle before the Industrial Revolution. For thousands of years, the amount of CO_2 being emitted was always close to the amount being reabsorbed. But now, imagine humans dumping more gallons in the tub. From the natural emissions, plus the human emissions added, the tub is almost full; we can slow the flow of new water we are adding, but it doesn't help; if we add any more, the tub will overflow.

We can't add any more water to the tub or CO_2 to the atmosphere. We have to stop emitting greenhouse gases as fast as possible.

"Stuck in the Tunnel:" I created one more analogy. It illustrates some stuff that the others don't. Most of us know the discomfort and fear that comes with being stuck in commuter gridlock, in a long line of cars moving at walking speed through a narrow tunnel. If it's a hot day, we resist closing the windows, but only for a minute. The longer we are stuck there, the more likely we are to suffocate or choke on carbon monoxide, the deadliest component of the exhaust. People commit suicide by running their gas-powered car in a closed garage ... with the car windows open.

We don't notice the CO_2 impacts for two reasons: Thermal Lag or Inertia, the fact it takes 20 years or more for the CO_2 to create maximum warming; and the fact that the smoke and CO_2 disperse into the air. The CO_2 mixes into the vast atmosphere, which seems unlimited, *AND* it takes time to absorb heat.

So imagine if those two things were different. Think of the atmosphere as the tunnel, and 20 years as one hour.

What would happen if the CO_2 absorbed its total potential of heat in an hour? Now imagine how much worse it would be if the wind and motion of the cars did not disperse the CO_2 into the atmosphere, like in the tunnel. The CO_2 would stay where it was released and create intolerable rises in temperature in a very short time. Every roadway would be like that tunnel, except that the people would die from heat before the exhaust could kill them. Every roadway would become an oven in the shape of a tunnel. A dome of hot air around every fossil-fueled power plant would make it uninhabitable; the heat would shut the plant down or cause it to explode. The cows and pigs and people in every factory farm would be cooked in place. Instant Climate Change Barbecue.

> *Argument 11: Slowing our RATE of emissions is not a solution. It will lead to breaking through the limits we say we've set.*

> *Argument 12: Human civilization has a decade or less to get to Net-Zero CO_2 emissions. We have no choice but to make an effective plan and start doing it.*

CONNECTING DOTS
WHEN we understand how these things are connected:
- CO_2 and methane feedback loops can multiply climate warming factors, even with no additional emissions;
- The CO_2 emitted since the Industrial Revolution has already increased real average global temperatures by 1 full degree C.
- In the last 30 years we have doubled our global population and more than doubled our GHG emissions;
- We continue to do next to nothing to lower emissions;

• We see, therefore, that the CO_2 we have released in the last 30 years will almost certainly create another 1° C. rise and push the world up to or past the "2° C. limit" in another 20 to 30 years, even *with no additional emissions;*

• But that doesn't account for the GHGs we continue to emit;

• And if we continue to emit at our current rate, or even a little less, we will face, in 20 to 30 years, at least an additional 2 or 3 degrees C of temperature rise, for a total of + 5° C or + 8° F.

• Given carbon and methane feedback loops, that is almost certain to push global temperatures *another* 3° C or 5° F higher, which will make most of the Earth uninhabitable. That's what is meant by *Climate Catastrophe.*

THEN

• We will understand the Bathtub Analogy, and that cutting emissions gradually will not slow or stop GW/CC;

• *WE WILL FINALLY GET IT* that we have to cut global carbon emissions to near zero as fast as is humanly possible;

• And *THAT* in turn will be monumentally difficult; we would think that it is *IMPOSSIBLE* ... until we realize it is *ABSOLUTELY NECESSARY TO OUR SURVIVAL.* Period.

• So Greg Craven's "no-brainer" conclusion is like the target this book demands, "Net-Zero" CO_2/carbon in a decade. It means rapidly cutting our emissions to a tiny fraction – 2 to 5 percent – of what they are now, and implementing enough carbon sinks, like new forests, and other techniques for sucking carbon out of the air, to make up for that 2 to 5 percent. And then we have to deal with the dozen other environmental crises.

Remember what the 2 Bills, Nye and McKibben, and others were quoted as saying back on page 6. Reread it if you need to. A more recent comment gives a different, even more cynical perspective. It is as if the nations in the climate accords agreed on what must be done to slow or stop the warming, and how fast, and then they decided to do little or nothing, slower.

Jump to page 137 for a different view of the importance of timing and lag, inertia, or delay.

In the Paris Accord, 190 nations agreed on what they must do quickly to avoid a catastrophe, and then decided to do half that much, slowly.

A RACE AGAINST TIME

It would be a good shift in our thinking to see the Eco-Crisis, and Climate Change in particular, as the top priorities in a Race Against Time. Contributors to the Crisis – like our population, consumption, and waste – are moving at different speeds in different regions. Most are accelerating, so they keep getting harder to measure. That speed is a stark contrast to the slow motion creep of the political processes that our failing to manage it. The current delays in our Information – Decision – Implementation processes reveal them to be completely inadequate to the challenges of the Crisis.

Which fears are rational or irrational? What facts are certainly true and which deserve honest skepticism? What is denial really and what role does it play in national policy? We've been made vulnerable to false fears, and oblivious to the very real threats lying directly in our path. We will have to consciously shift our intelligence to a higher level to manage the complexity and speed of the Crisis ... in time; in other words, before it's too late to matter. These questions and issues are not going to go away any time soon. But we can decide them for ourselves and be prepared to argue them. They fill many of the pages to come.

At the historical moment when we most need a responsive political system, ours is misguided, incompetent, corrupt, and getting worse every day, thanks to Donald Trump.

Mary Robinson is a former president of Ireland and the UN Special Envoy on Climate Change. I've switched the order of these phrases, attributed to her:

"We are the first generation to understand how serious Climate Change is ... and the last generation to be able to do something about it."

SUDDEN HISTORY IN SLOW MOTION

We are in the middle of one of the most rapid transitions in the life of the planet, and the single fastest global upheaval in human history. It could only be equaled by a nuclear war, a meteor impact, or a cluster of volcanic eruptions that cover the globe with poisonous smoke, ash, and debris. In the context of geologic time, our impact on the global ecosystem has been as quick as a camera flash. Relative to evolutionary time, it happened in the blink of an eye. It is a sudden meta-historical event that looks to us like extreme slow motion, or no visible motion at all. Unless we can imagine what the scientists are telling us.

TIME AND TIMING will continue to be absolutely central to Global Warming/Climate Change and the other aspects of the Global Eco-Crisis. We are in a race against time: the speed – or slowness – of our decisions and actions, competing against the speed and severity of the Crisis, which continue to accelerate while we have barely begun to notice. As life-long environmental activist Hunter Lovins says at the end of the film *Earth Days*, "We have wasted thirty years." And that was in 2008.

> *How in Hell is the United States going to catch up with the Climate Crisis and begin to deal with it effectively ... in time to matter?*

August, 2018, just before publication, I heard of another feedback loop that is worth a mention. In countries like India and China, millions are migrating from the country to the city in pursuit of a middle class life. In the age of GW/CC, what are their 2 most basic needs, and 2 of the most damaging to the climate? Refrigerators and air conditioning. Both technologies have to emit the heat they remove into the atmosphere, adding to total heating. But the chemicals that make the machines work are more damaging than methane, and leak as much, both during manufacture and when they break down. We think those technologies can be fixed ... in 20 years ... meaning too late to matter.

A FAILURE OF IMAGINATION

Condoleezza Rice served as Secretary of State in the George W Bush administration. She had to face the 9-11 Commission in 2004 to explain why the Bush security team had not anticipated or prevented the disastrous attacks on the World Trade Center. The essence of her answer was, "No one could have imagined that people would use airplanes as weapons." ... in spite of briefings and other findings that predicted exactly such attacks, in the weeks before they occurred. That gap in intelligence, policy, interpretation, or competence has been summed up as a "failure of imagination."

Tens of millions of people, mostly innocent civilians, paid for that failure in money, injuries, respect, loss of their homes, and death.

The questions must be asked. Are there other dangers, looming on other horizons now, that we have not observed because we can't imagine them? What are their possible costs? Can we imagine what we have to do to *try to* avoid them?

This question neither starts nor ends with Condi, Bush, or Iraq. American military adventurism and the Environmental Crisis both go back decades. We can find clear connections between them and other issues in failed political policies.

It's worth repeating, each of us has a mindset about what events are certain, possible, or impossible, and we are fairly sure we know where the edges are between them. But every minute, somewhere in the world, shocking events occur that individuals and communities did not think possible. Often *because* they didn't think them possible.

Someone posted an image online from a recent march on environmental issues. A young woman carried a large sign that said,

At the start of every disaster movie there's a scientist being ignored.

IMAGINING THE BEST AND WORST CASE SCENARIOS
Popular media has given us hundreds of fictions about how *interesting* our times might become. *1984, Children of Men,* and *Fury Road* are 3 of my favorites. We know such stories are invented, imagined, and produced as if real. Dramas ask us to suspend our disbelief and join in the fiction. When the disasters are predicted as plausible, even urgent, they are much less entertaining.

> *Argument 13: If we cannot – or will not – imagine the worst-case scenarios, we cannot prepare for or prevent them. We may help to make them inevitable.*

> *Argument 14: If we can't or won't imagine the best possible cases, we will never try to make them happen. We may help to make them impossible.*

Dr. Frank Fenner was an eminent Australian scientist. He was born in 1914 and died in 2010. His medical and environmental work was historic. He was most alarmed by human population growth and resource depletion. Fenner predicted that the human race will become extinct, likely within a hundred years, and that half of the other species will die off with us. He also said that this outcome is inevitable, sooner or later, and that "whatever we do now is too late." Was he overly pessimistic or objective? Was he exaggerating the risk just to wake us up?

Stephen Hawking, the theoretical physicist (he died in March of 2018), recently warned that we are near a final tipping point. He said "Trump's action could push the Earth over the brink, to become like Venus, with a temperature of 250 degrees, and raining sulphuric acid." Other scientists said that is ridiculous. But they did not say it is *not* possible.

Similar warnings have been stated and restated by present day experts and alarmists like Derrick Jensen, James Hansen, and Vandana Shiva, but they rarely appear in the mass media. Network executives and producers think those ideas are too

scary to repeat, or *unimaginable* ... to them. They sure aren't the
ideas sponsors want to pay for.

Which is more shocking: the actual possibility of extinction,
or the fact that idea is missing from the public conversation?
Can we ask the question that Republicans and climate deniers
cannot utter or imagine having to answer?

WHAT IF he or she or they are right?

Any prediction is speculative, somewhat subjective, and totally
unprovable until the future scrubs away the variables. Some
dire predictions of thirty and fifty years ago have not happened.
The *Population Bomb* has not occurred .... yet. Nuclear war has
not happened ... yet. But Rachel Carson was right; entire ecosystems have been wiped out and poisons have spread across the
planet. And most of the early predictions of climate impacts – of
sea level rise in 20 years, or the numbers forced to migrate in
fifty years, or the 4° C temperature peak in 80 years – could all be
low by 50 to 80 percent, both in severity and timing.

In December 2017 new statistics from a large number of
climate scientists prove what we have expected: the computer
models that predict the worst outcomes are ... guess what? ...
consistently the most accurate.

The reality may be far worse than predicted and occur far sooner.

The earlier, long version of this part had 9 Scenarios, a couple
silly ones that are still here, several versions of bad and worst
cases that are now merged, with one historical example thrown
in for contrast, also still here. It ran to 22 pages, in a smaller font.
This version has just 5 scenarios, the first with 2 parts, and one
short digression.

BEST AND WORST CASE SCENARIOS:

Scenarios 1a and 1b: Blasphemous and Ironic

Either the Deniers are Right, or it's the Rapture:
"Everything's going to be OK, maybe even Heavenly."

One expert said that the two most extreme predictions were the least likely: "It's the end of the world." and "Everything's going to be OK." But, he added, *It could be the end of the world as we know it, and everything is definitely NOT going to be OK.*

Scenario 1a: Is it possible that we are experiencing the *End of Days?* Christianity, Judaism, and Islam all have their versions of how human existence on the Earth will end. God will destroy His Creation or allow us to do it ourselves. So, in the US, any day now, all the born-again Christians will transport directly to Heaven. The rest of us will perish here or suffer eternity in Hell. Or both. There may be surprises in Heaven. Or not. Christians will be shocked if God is also Allah and a huge wave of devout Muslims arrive at the same time.

Only slightly more plausible, imagine,

Scenario 1b: The deniers are right and the climate scientists are wrong. Global Warming is the product of unknown but natural forces and will self-correct over time. Or, it will turn out to be equally beneficial as destructive: more rain on the deserts, more farming in the Arctic. Nature will prove to be way more resilient than we imagined. Ocean life and ecosystems will recover with just a little more regulation and TLC. Coastal cities will learn to live with canals instead of streets and will look like a modern Venice, Italy. Imagine gondoliers on Wall Street. The few bad impacts of GW/CC will be offset by geo-engineering. The elitist alarmists will retreat to their ivory towers and eat crow. The human race will survive, multiply, and contribute to a global growth economy that proves, against all odds, to have no limit.

WHAT ARE THE ODDS (AND WHO SAYS)? The chances of these scenarios occurring are 0.1 percent and 0.2 percent respectively ... according to your author, based on the dozens of sources used to compile these sets of variables.

Scenario 2: Catastrophe Faster Than We Could Imagine
The Worst For Us May Be Best For The Earth.

We can imagine the worst-case scenarios from several perspectives. The worst for human survival might be the best for the ecosystem. The impacts might happen sooner and combine to make things worse, much faster than even I imagined, until now. Methane vents and constant hurricanes, wars over food and water, public emergencies beyond rescue, ecological disasters beyond repair. So many humans die over twenty or thirty years, and cause carbon emissions fall so fast that the Crisis begins to "self-correct." It might give the global ecosystem and the people that are left – a billion or fewer globally, our population around 1800 – a better shot at survival.

Humans manage to shut down all the nuclear reactors and cap all the leaking wells, in an effort to save the other species. But the ecosystem remains severely sickened. Huge chunks of civilization will be lost. Violent conflicts become the new normal everywhere. The end of humans remains a possibility into the unforeseeable future.

WHAT ARE THE ODDS? Possibly as high as 25 percent, although the late human corrections will be highly unlikely, and won't prevent total extinction. Let's add some variables and assume it won't get that bad, at least not that fast.

Scenario 3: Bad But Survivable ... For A While
The path we are on – doing little or nothing – and a dose of bad luck: Human extinction looms as a real possibility. Now it has a name. It's called FENNER-VHEMT.

In the United States, Republicans and corporate Democrats manage to keep the corrupt 2-party system alive. Some cities and states have chosen to abide by the Paris Accord, and many of Trump's environmental deregulations are either overturned in the courts or take years to have an effect. A great deal depends on which party takes power next, but it's mostly about how quickly or slowly the Climate Crisis and other eco-disasters start to have economic impacts.

Internationally, pressure mounts on the US to cut back on its emissions, still the greatest per capita on Earth, with the UK very close to that rate. China continues to lead in innovation, expanding solar, wind, and electric vehicles, but stands little chance of lowering its net or per capita emissions, given its rising middle class. Russia is actually encouraging couples to have more children, in spite of sanctions weakening its oil economy, widespread corruption, and popular protests against the Putin oligarchy.

The growing threats of the Global Environmental Crisis are gradually acknowledged among most advanced western nations, the US, most of Europe and Scandinavia, Japan and South Korea, and large parts of South America. The ongoing devastation in the Amazon comes under some government limits. A few countries like Brazil and Peru ban deforestation and new mining and drilling projects. Bolivia has already established the rights of the environment and continues to lead the way, ideologically at least, even as some forms of mining continue there.

China has already cut back on coal-fired energy plants, but has not eliminated them. Their devastating city smog has made many in and out of government understand the Crisis first-hand. India, on the other hand, continues to use coal to supply energy to their still growing population. Australia continues to fight with itself over coal exports and the preservation of the great barrier reef, which continues to suffer from rising ocean temperatures, acidification, and human abuse.

2020 to 2030

The dynamics of new heat and fresh water melt in the oceans begins to change global circulation patterns. Many species of sea creatures face continuing threats; overfishing continues to deplete the populations of food fish. A few species are able to adapt.

Solar and wind technologies continue to get more efficient and less costly everywhere. China and several European and Scandinavian countries have said they will phase out gas and diesel transportation, and replace it all with electric vehicles, within 10 to 20 years. They have already stopped subsidizing all forms of fossil-fueled technology and put their support into sustainables. Their use of high speed (solar- and wind-powered) rail continues to outpace the US's feeble attempts by decades.

In the Eurozone and a few other countries, gasoline is taxed to $10. a gallon and higher, but consumption only slows. Solar and wind are subsidized ... but only up to the level of oil and gas subsidies, which stay in place. The US continues to lag behind in those efforts. The oil-profit-and-consumption economy remains the ideal. Bankers and giant corporations continue to dominate both parties.

In many countries, from the hybrid Capitalist/Communist states of Russia and China, to the US and across much of South America, and still even in France, Germany and the UK, the needs and wishes of the people, for a cleaner, more sustainable environment clash with big corporations and the ideology of a growth economy. Corruption continues to dog the US government, much as it does in Russia and China. Some countries like Brazil, Argentina, and Mexico, having gone through decades of corruption and fake reforms, finally start to get a grip on it and are running much cleaner and more efficient governments, much more attuned to the public good.

As we know, most of Europe and Scandinavia has had tight restrictions on toxic waste and requirements for public health, which continue. They have used the Cautionary (or Pre-Cautionary) Principle in industry and public services for decades.

73

The US continues to resist regulations, more under Republicans, slightly less under the corporate Democrats, and air and water in the US continue to get more polluted.

At the UN, proposals are made for international buy-in on conservation, preservation, environmental protection and renewal, and proposals to honor "climate debt," like carbon taxes and bigger monetary penalties for pollution damage. But there are no hard mandates or penalties for non-participation. The Security Council veto remains the barrier to sensible change.

Everywhere in the world, Climate Change creates harsher and more numerous weather disasters, in what looks like an exponential growth curve (jump ahead to page 104 for more on exponential). Numbers of climate-related deaths are now counted as a distinct public health category. It continues to be hard to distinguish between those killed in environmentally worsened wars, and those killed by direct environmental impacts. In 2020, the first time an accurate count is attempted, the number of global deaths from tornadoes, hurricanes, droughts, floods, and heat-waves tops 5 million, matching the number of global refugees, for whom there is less and less help. Those rates never go down. Our total population stalls at 8 billion. When hurricanes level islands like Barbuda (totally abandoned after Irma) and low-lying coastal cities, there is no longer talk of adapting or rebuilding. The only issue is where the climate survivors and refugees will live and how existing populations will cope with them. Many nations with existing budget problems begin to fear that their economies will collapse. There are no international plans to stabilize them when that happens.

In spite of a major movement toward more natural high-yield farming, and new meat substitutes, the rising demand for meat in India, China, and southeast Asia prompts more deforestation and factory meat farms, destroying valuable carbon sinks and boosting methane emissions. New technologies for farming in the deserts are subsidized and scaled up. Other geo-engineering projects cost billions, take years, and do nothing. Some existing projects in reforestation are expanded. But

74

emissions only begin to level off and then gradually decline.
Global atmospheric carbon tops 500 ppm. The 2° C. global
"limit" is reached in 2025, 25 years sooner than predicted. A few
countries imagine radical actions. Very few implement them.

Just as scientists deploy new technologies to locate and
measure "methane vents," they cannot believe the evidence of
the rate of increase in atmospheric methane.

By 2025, the countries whose economies were already
collapsing in 2015 – Syria, Pakistan, North Korea and several in
Africa and south Asia – become total disasters. The Crisis makes
corruption everywhere worse, not better.

A few efforts are made to limit the development or trade in
weapons, from AK-47s to nuclear warheads and poison gasses,
but the production and distribution from the US, Israel, Russia,
and Iran defeat those efforts.

2030 to 2040
Throughout the world, droughts, contamination and the depletion of ground water reduces available fresh water to 10 percent
of what it is today. Several countries banned fracking in the
20-teens, and have saved more of their aquifers. In the US and
many other countries, the price of safe, fresh water rises to $10. a
gallon, then $20. ... when and where it's available.

The attempts to protect endangered rhinos, elephants,
mountain gorillas, and bonobos, giraffes, lions, and cheetahs all
fail. The Sixth Extinction, now understood to be human-caused,
looks like it will kill off half of all wild species. Or more. We
hope that the few survivors remaining in zoos can be part of protected breeding programs. But then several zoos are destroyed
by floods and fires, or shut down by heat-waves and droughts.

Lower crop yields and grain shortages impact entire regions. GMO crops fail to produce in areas plagued by floods
and drought. Pesticide residues continue to contaminate crops
for decades. Agricultural zones begin to fail. Food is severely rationed everywhere except in North America and Europe.
Under the worst possible pressures, nations struggle to become

self-sufficient. Domesticated bees – essential to a third of our food supply – go virtually extinct in most of the world. Infestations of insect pests and rats add to the chaos. Violent conflicts over gold and diamonds morph into battles over water and food. They are isolated at first, but soon they seem to be happening everywhere. Global trade becomes chaotic.

Some countries have had near-zero-carbon economies since the mid-2000s – Sweden, Germany, Finland, Iceland. They find it easy to squeeze the remaining waste and excess from their models of commerce and consumption. Isn't it odd that the countries that started to adapt to GW/CC earlier are in the global north? Global Warming is expected to improve their agricultural output for 50 years; but beyond that, all bets are off.

Sea level rise varies widely by region, for reasons not understood. The previous global average of 1 inch doubles to 2 and then 4 inches. Some areas measure as much as 12 inches of rise. The ongoing migration of millions away from the coasts is no longer news. Some cities sink billions into flood protection and abatement, others abandon tens of billions worth of new construction. Wall Street floods 2 or 3 times a year. But there are no gondolas. Every large non-coastal city in the US has to create refugee camps for the Americans forced to migrate away from the water.

The large industrialized countries acknowledge the severity of the crisis and vow to accelerate their mitigation and adaptation programs. But they can't agree on who should lead, where to start, what limits should be placed on carbon. Most of all, they can't find the funding. They ward off the devastation longer than other countries, but only by a decade or so. Without buy-in from a majority, their actions are futile.

Billionaires have been buying up land and water, closer to the poles, wherever they can. The Bush family secretly bought up all the water reserves in southern Argentina, in the early 2000s. (Look it up.) Private enclaves with airports for private planes, stored food and fuel, weapons and private armies, are kept mostly secret. Custom bunkers become the new residential status symbol.

At this point we can imagine two sets of possibilities, in two very different contexts:

In the US, if Trump's time is limited to 4 years or less, and liberals and progressives take power, the US may lead in a radical plan to adjust the US economy to environmental and human rights priorities. But how radical? And how quickly?

Or, if conservatives and the GOP's election rigging and fear-based propaganda stay in control, then the US is stuck with a huge portion of the blame for the ongoing decline in global health and well-being.

By 2035, millions of businesses are abandoned. Financial markets start to collapse. Nobody anticipated the impacts on a dozen international "choke points" – mostly international ports and airline hubs, – so a variety of labor, energy and climate disasters close them. International travel is reduced to a fraction. Commodities markets start to collapse, adding to food shortages and famine. Even in the US and Europe, the electrical grid starts to have regular breakdowns, leaving thousands without power for weeks. Across half the planet, electronic communication becomes spotty, then disappears for months at a time. Most of the nations of the world – democracies and dictatorships, industrialized or not – realize that massive, emergency action must be taken. But civil society has already started to break down. The international organizations and local governments that would do the work start to disintegrate.

The entire South American and Southeast Asian equatorial zones – what *were once* the Eden of biodiversity – turn into desert wastelands. Death by starvation, dehydration and disease takes tens of millions of lives, globally. Countries adjoining the devastation zones – Turkey, Lebanon, Israel, Iran, Saudi Arabia, South Korea – already flooded with millions of refugees, and dealing with their own shortages, close their borders and thousands of refugees starve to death. Other countries fail to fend off the invaders and are overrun. Thousands of their citizens flee or die

PART TWO: DUTY TO WARN

in the ongoing fights for food and water. The surge of refugees from north Africa and Syria in 2015, '16, and '17 were only a preview.

2040 to 2050
Accelerated melting of polar ice pushes sea levels to rise another foot and more. Glaciers and sea ice are gone. Only Greenland and Antarctica still have quantities of pack ice.

Away from the coasts, refugee camps and overcrowding double the regional demands for food, water and medical care, and then double them again and again. New and old diseases, starvation and contaminated water kills hundreds of thousands every few months. International aid organizations struggle to keep pace with the devastation but soon have to abandon most of their efforts; they turn to protecting the citizens at home.

Most governments become ineffective. Devastating fires are left to burn themselves out for lack of fire-fighters and water. Technological collapse causes carbon emissions to drop to 1850 levels, in spite of the fires, but it's too late to matter.

The World Health Organization's predictions for 2050, of 250,000 additional annual deaths from climate impacts, like most other scary climate predictions, prove to be off – too low – by a factor of 30. By 2045, climate impacts take 3/4 of a billion lives. New diseases and bacterial infections, with antibiotic resistance, are the unpredicted new causes. The familiar causes, starvation and lack of water, do not diminish. They get worse every year.

Nuclear meltdowns increase in frequency and severity, devastating hundreds of square miles at a time. Tens of thousands of men, women and children are showered with radiation but don't know it. It kills a few quickly. Many more die in prolonged agony.

2050 to 2075
In 2050, Atmospheric CO_2 has topped 600 ppm and GW/CC has entered an unstoppable, spiraling feedback loop. Some regions nearer to the poles are better able to mitigate and adapt, and

appear to stabilize. Others near the equator, many that were severely over-populated, are written off as lost causes. Regional populations devolve into cutthroat tribalism. By 2070, the global death toll passes four billion. Proper disposal of the dead is a huge public health problem, but then it becomes too much even to attempt.

Niagara Falls no longer exists. Ocean rise has filled the Niagara Gorge, droughts have dried up the upper Niagara River.

2075 to 2100
Many of the former temperate regions – like the American Midwest – become uninhabitable. Rainforests, the lungs of all land-based life, are rapidly dying off. The CO_2 they would have absorbed stays in the atmosphere, pushing temperatures higher. Most of the coral reefs die. Regions that relied on fish as a protein source are left to scrounge for plant-based food that gets ever more scarce. Most ocean life is dead or dying. Octopuses and jellyfish are among the few sea creatures who survive the heat and acidity. On land, the surviving species are migrating in unpredictable patterns. The remaining humans travel toward the poles, some with tools and technology. Some with weapons. Some with caravans of supplies. Many with nothing but the clothes on their backs.

What's left of a public conversation turns deeply pessimistic. In the regions where infrastructure and a class of technocrats survive, they try to defuse the technological time bombs, neutralize the nuclear reactors, seal the leaking wells and isolate as much toxic waste as possible. In others it is all left to chaos and random chance.

More than half of the other species on the planet – food crops that relied on pollinators, livestock, trees, grain, and fish – go effectively extinct. And there's no end in sight.

Most of human civilization will likely be lost. Art, music, and literature, scientific discovery and invention, the variations of human culture, history, and acquired knowledge: all will decay into

79

artifacts for some future intelligence to discover and wonder, "What went wrong?" Our remaining descendants realize they face a catastrophic future – those who tried to live modestly, and the uncaring who consumed without limit, innocent and guilty alike. Do we devote our last desperate efforts to save ourselves? ... to save as much of humanity and civilization as possible? Do we leave explanations for future archaeologists? Do we prolong the agony or end it?

By 2080, another 2 billion have died – most of our grand-children and great-grandchildren. The few humans that survive have grave doubts about their chances for a future.

> *It puts a different spin on Bob Dylan's line "... the worst fear that can ever be hurled, the fear to bring children into the world."* (Masters of War)

The final chapter in the *culture wars* unfolds. An obscure move-ment founded in 1970 becomes a chosen destiny, the Voluntary Human Extinction MovemenT. VHEMT (not science fiction, a real movement). A few, then many try to convince the rest. The choice is to bring children into a world they have little chance of surviving, or to stop making babies. Some see it as a moral imperative. (A significant number of environmentally aware women around the world chose this path decades ago.) For oth-ers, hope still resists the stark reality; they pray they can prepare their children to preserve the species and the few remaining fragments of civilization.

If you had that choice to make, in such a damaged world, what would you choose?

Beyond 2100

By the turn of the next century, all of the scary predictions from 2020 have proven too timid. The severity and timing of the on-going threats cannot be calculated.

The feedback loops that created Global Warming do not stop. The side effects and combined impacts persist. They continue to bake the planet. Faster or slower. Emergency services are a thing of the past. Law and order is a rare regional advantage. The super wealthy who hid out in underground bunkers and walled enclaves, thinking they would be protected from the chaos, are overrun by hordes of scavengers who slaughter and eat them. In other places, battles over food and water kill thousands at a time. By 2120, the last remnants of stability turn to chaos, the remaining humans are trapped in small oases that somehow escape the Climate Catastrophe. But they have no way of knowing whether they are alone or whether others survive, somewhere on the planet. Global temperatures have begun to stabilize, but most of the Earth will no longer support life. The survivors have long forgotten all but the remnants of civilization. They cannot imagine that they represent the last of a once inventive and thriving species.

Or, in a longer, slower storyline, the conditions worsen more slowly; many small, isolated communities survive, but only for another hundred years. Dr. Fenner was probably right but his timing was off. A small fraction of the human race survives through 2250, but no one remembers that years have numbers.

WHAT ARE THE ODDS?
Given the path we are on, doing little or nothing – about 50/50. With a dose of bad luck, 75 percent or higher. This range of possibilities is the most likely. At best, the loss of most of civilization and the death of all but a half a billion of us. At worst, we actually go extinct or we face the threat of it for another century or longer.

Our Mindsets about what is and is not possible are shaped by experience and memory, but also depend on our imagination, or lack of it.

As bad as this scenario is, let's not delude ourselves. Over the last four hundred years, and especially in the last few generations, we have witnessed and tried to forget the most ghastly human behaviors: the poisoning of most of what is vital to our lives, preventable starvation and disease, torture and genocide, child prostitution, slavery and human trafficking, wanton massacres, avoidable catastrophes by the dozens, several holocausts and other unspeakable crimes. What do you think will happen when the food runs out? There is no reason to believe that groups of humans, on the brink of extinction, will hesitate to crush each other by any means possible.

DIGRESSION: **A Scenario From History**
A century of cooling rather than warming

In Geoffrey Parker's book, *Global Crisis, War, Climate Change & Catastrophe in the Seventeenth Century,* he explains that in the 1600s there was a *Mini Ice* Age that affected most of the planet. Few historians have tried to make the connections between its direct impacts – severe poverty, famines, and disease – and the social strife and political revolutions that occurred during that time. But Prof. Parker has done that. While the (global average) temperature *decrease* that created the Mini Ice Age was less than 2 degrees Celsius, less than 4 degrees F, it resulted in the death of *one third* of the human population – about 600 million people – over 70 years, mostly from starvation, disease, and battles for food. If an *increase* of that same number of degrees, + 4° F or + 2° C, would have the same impact on global population today, we would be looking at *two to three billion deaths* over a comparable period, less than a century.

And remember, we are probably locked into that temperature increase, coming in 20-plus years.

Assuming comparable impacts, there's one big difference: the Mini Ice Age was caused by natural factors, and other natural factors corrected it. After about 75 years, the Earth returned to its historic average temperature. In 2018, Global Warming/ Climate Change offers no such escape. Scientists do not imagine a temperature decline, even with our best efforts, for hundreds of years, and in the worst case, thousands.

> *The worst case scenarios are not only possible, they become more likely every day we refuse to imagine them.*

We have no way of knowing whether human extinction, and the death of most other species, are more or less likely, sooner or later. But we have to face the possibility.

From our vantage point now, or in the minds of the last ten million humans, it gets harder and harder to imagine how much may be lost or how much else will be doomed. If humans finally do die out, the Earth will revert to geologic and evolutionary time. *Progress* will once again be measured in tiny increments over thousands of years. But no one will be here to take the measure or remember the difference. In 10,000 years, levels of man-made radiation will start to subside. Mutations will adapt. Trees will grow and spread and evolve. The dense clouds of CO_2 and methane will dissipate, the balance of oxygen will return. Sea life will rebound. Cockroaches and some other insects, a few reptiles and rats and other small mammals, isolated in a few oxygen-rich forests, may manage to come through it all. Many will evolve into new species. Some will develop complex societies, even show the first signs of higher intelligence, maybe in ten million years.

Scenario 4: The Only Best Case:
A Global Mind-Shift leads to a Global Power-Shift

Our best chance of survival will probably be our only chance, even if we do everything possible as fast as possible. To have a shot at a theoretical Best Case, we need to get to Net-Zero Carbon in a decade, and to manage the economic consequences as best we can. The only force capable of making that happen will be an international merger of movements that starts in the United States, like the one that shortened the Vietnam war, or the one that started around the first Earth Day in 1970, but with an even broader and more committed base. It will provoke and expand a national, then global Mind-Shift, a Paradigm Shift as unprecedented as the conditions of the Eco-Crisis, that will lead to political and economic Power-Shifts in the US. That may be enough to put a global Power-Shift into motion.

The kids who are walking out of school and marching today, March 14, 2018, in honor of those killed a month earlier at Stoneman Douglas high school in Florida, are the same generation who are most at the mercy of Climate Change. They will realize, that in fighting the NRA and a corrupted Congress, they face the same larger forces that deny the Climate Crisis. And they will continue to lead. They will seize the economic power, informational power, democratic power, and the intangible power of being right, because the older generation's legacy leaves them no other option. They will exercise their power with their labor and their spending, in the streets and the schools, with civil disobedience, in demonstrations, boycotts and general strikes, in the media, with ballot initiatives and in reclaimed political parties or new ones.

International powers must be re-organized on the principles of a healthy ecosystem and a fair, sustainable economy.

AFTERTHOUGHT
I have found, in my reading and writing, and in my own head, words like Crisis, Unprecedented, Emergency, Catastrophe, Disaster, and others, have started to lose their meaning. It's caused by several things that can be identified and a few that can't: the complex and high-speed nature of our Consumer/Information culture, combined with mounting numbers of real Disasters in the world, and several shortcomings in our Thinking, the main topic in Part Three. Some of our thinking is distorted by these unique times – it is a basic inability to construct and use a mental sense of Proportion and Perspective, relative to reality. By com-

parison, the Global Environmental Crisis dwarfs "most of the other crises *we think we face.*" You'll have to decide whether you and your peers can fully grasp that assertion.

Part Three, next, asks, *So, Why Don't We Get It?* It explores the topic of human stupidity in a time of global Crisis. Part Four looks specifically at Information, as a critical force that has failed us in predicting or managing this mess. Beyond that, it will present a new way of looking at Information as a 4-part force of Change. Part Five will look at Power as an Organizing Principle, in our energy usage, our politics and economics, in our minds, emotions, and decisions. Parts Six, Seven, and Eight will connect as many dots as possible – including the last 2 big ones – to create a Big Picture vision that will take us to the Reckoning that I promised.

But we need to close Part Two with this footnote:

EXPERTS DISAGREE, even the most prominent, often bitterly, *not on Climate Change at all*, but on these 2 topics: nuclear generated electrical power, as a bridge from our current state to a post-carbon economy; and GMOs as a cure-all for food production.

Some nuclear proponents cite entirely new types of generator design that are much safer than current reactors, produce less toxic residue, or none, or that can actually consume nuclear waste as fuel. Most are years from proven workability, and further from being scaled up enough to have an impact. Some critics say we should not try to fix bad technology with new and untested technology, at least until we clean up the side effects of the bad. See the *4th Law* on page 146.

On GMOs, to repeat, some prominent scientists say GMOs are no different than selective breeding (which I and others say is totally wrong, remember the comments on pages 38-9) and must be used, without mentioning the number and quantities of toxic pest- and herbicides that the GMOs are designed to withstand, that are marketed with them and must be used together.

GLOSSARY FOR PART THREE

Blind Spot: An area of the retina, inside the eye, where no light can be processed. Also as a visual metaphor for flaws or gaps in thinking. See pages 99-103.

Big Blind Spot: Your author's term for a general inability, across many social populations, to comprehend extremes of distance, quantity, time, speed, and importance, made worse by the complexity and speed of contemporary culture generally.

Cognitive: Having to do with cognition, thinking, knowledge, mental processing, with categories: Cognitive -

    Bias: A mental prejudice that favors one's prior beliefs. Seeing or thinking about things in a preferential or negative light.

    Dissonance: The mental discomfort that comes when one's views of one's self or the world are shown to disagree with reality.

    Breakthrough: A shift in thinking or consciousness, a change of mind.

Denial: A powerful, usually unconscious form of cognitive bias especially associated with Climate Change, as a refusal to believe: it exists, is human-made, is dangerous, or an urgent emergency. Defined here as "a fear of knowledge that will force one to change his/her beliefs or behavior."

Exceptionalism, -ist: A belief or attitude (or one that holds it) that one, or one's country or class is exceptional, with unique attributes and privileges, often held to be exempt from rules or norms.

Exformation: A term coined by author Tor Norretranders, to describe the complex array of sensory inputs that infants must absorb, and appear not to notice, that are the foundations for all knowledge and thinking, mentioned on page 91, fully discussed in the context of Information, in Part Four. Also see related ideas from Bateson, on pages, 133-8, and McLuhan, starting on page 140.

Existential: Something affecting the existence of one, many, or all, as in Existential Threat, a threat to all of humanity and much of the other life on the Earth. (Also refers to a school of 20th century philosophy.)

False Certainty: A form of Cognitive Bias in which a person believes firmly that something false is true.

Great Dumbing Down: An alleged campaign, by conservatives generally, to deprive many Americans from enough broad education, and critical thinking skills specifically, to be able to be aware and responsible citizens.

Levels of Thinking: From the Albert Einstein quote on page 87, used to discuss the mental processing of Metaphor, Analogy, Irony, Ambiguity, Empathy, and pertaining to flexible thinking.

Mindset: An established set of attitudes or beliefs, about a topic, group of topics, or broad array of topics. We speak of possibility mindsets, an exceptionalist mindset, and others.

Tribalism: Generally the state of being in and identifying with a tribe, which might be based on ethnicity, gender, ideology, etc.

Also as the **New Tribalism:** The state of political division in the US, in which people tend to identify with or against a broad range of - apparently unified - political attitudes, for or against abortion, taxes, gays, tradition, minority rights, etc. See the Millennial Divide, pages 116-121.

World View: Like a mindset, a mental picture of how the world works, in one person's thinking or as shared by a like-minded group.

PART THREE: THINKING
So Why Don't We Get It?

Did the analogies for Climate Change help you to think differently about it? *The Bathtub Analogy*? *Stuck in the tunnel*? Did the *Chinese Curse* register in your mind as ironic? When climate scientists say, "This time WE are the asteroid," do you make the connection?

> **Albert Einstein warned us in the 1950s, "Our significant problems cannot be solved at the same level of thinking with which we created them."**

OK, we have significant problems. We created them. We can apparently solve them. But not with the same *level of thinking* that we used to create them. Einstein was probably not talking about our environmental problems. But if he were here today, he would certainly be among the most vocal *Concerned Scientists*.

LEVEL OF THINKING, IS THAT A METAPHOR?
Metaphors and analogies, irony and sarcasm, all require the ability to move between or combine multiple levels of thinking – or to think 2 ways about 1 thing. If you take a metaphor literally, at only one level, it will seem absurd or meaningless. The mind has to connect an odd idea or image to something in the real world to *get it*. We use *get it* to mean different things in different contexts. To *get a joke* means basically to laugh, to understand intuitively or logically what is funny about it; it's usually something unexpected. To *get* a metaphor or analogy, irony or sarcasm, means to grasp an idea or a contrast in a non-literal way.

Paradox and ambiguity make similar mental demands; a paradox suggests that two opposing descriptions of reality can both be true; in ambiguity, that two conflicting interpretations may both be correct.

We will find, when we look, that *getting* these mental shifts is the sign of a flexible mind. Using 2 or more levels of thinking is a mental skill. The ability to hold 2 opposing ideas in the mind, without stress, is supposed to be a sign of adaptive intelligence. Some have this skill naturally. Some learn it. Some never do.

When we say, *So Why Don't We Get It?* we are using *get it* in a third way, meaning, simply, to understand something for the first time, in this case, the scale and urgency of the Environmental Crisis. An *Aha Moment* that changes a mind.

Einstein also said, "Only two things are infinite, the universe and human stupidity, and I'm not sure about the universe."

Let's hope he was trying to be funny, or exaggerating for effect. *Stupid* is a harsh word. We wouldn't call someone stupid to their face unless we were trying to provoke a fight. But insults and brawls are trivial in comparison to the fight we face, breaking through the blind spots and denial that keep us from dealing with the risks that Climate Change poses to our civilization.

John Cleese, the former Monty Python character, tells us in an online video, that "You need to be a little bit smart to know you are stupid." And he cites Fox News viewers as cases in point, examples of the opposite, not smart enough to know they are stupid ... or that they have been made stupid by Fox. If we can't admit that there are serious gaps in our thinking, we can never hope to mend them with different, more intelligent ideas and clearer ways of thinking.

Argument 15: If you can't admit that we can be spectacularly stupid, as individuals and in groups, you may not be smart enough for the rest of this book.

SMART OR STUPID: SMART *AND* STUPID
Here we will try to understand our intelligence and contrast it

with our failures of thinking, from historic and mental roots to brilliant inventions and deadly mistakes at the global scale.

Scientists are rarely disappointed by their mistakes and failures; they see them as guides to better understanding and more successful science. They are stimulated to find new things that they don't understand. Yet they are appalled at how much we know about Climate Change, as a civilization, compared to how little we are doing about it.

Humans can be incredibly smart, individually and working in teams. Our achievements are many and spectacular: science and medicine, literature and art, strategic thinking and teamwork, brilliant inventions from the sewing machine to the space station, discovery of the echoes of the Big Bang and the structure of DNA. Our intelligence is expressed in a billion combinations of innate aptitudes and learned skills, in methods, systems and processes that multiply the powers of individual minds.

The Scientific Method and Democracy are two of the most – maybe *THE* most – powerful of these systems. One expresses our most creative trait – curiosity – and gives it a pragmatic set of rules. The other extends our most noble mental power – ethical free will – to the wider community, through the spread of information and the vote.

In one of humanity's great paradoxes, we can be both extremely smart and numbingly stupid, even in the same exact endeavors. We invent technologies that transform our world and our lives, yet we fail to imagine, predict, or recognize their unintended consequences, until they overwhelm us. As they are now doing.

In this system that we call a civilization, using laws and governments and an arsenal of powers, we haven't been able to avoid pointless wars, alleviate poverty and hunger, spread the use of medical knowledge, or stop each other from being victimized by our own irrational fears, biases, prejudices, and willful ignorance.

HUMAN INTELLIGENCE AT ITS ROOTS

As infants, between the moment of birth and the age of 2, our brains grew to have the powers to walk, remember, recognize, think, and speak, with very little conscious instruction, assisted only by the attention and fascination of typical parents. It would be thought of as a miracle, except for the fact that we all did it and rely on it for the rest of our lives, without understanding what we did or how. At the same time we were learning those most basic human skills, we were forming the foundation of all the knowledge we would gain and use throughout our lives.

How did you or any of us create that foundation of knowledge without knowing what we were doing? Don't you wonder? What's the trick to the mental gymnastics, the data management, the gradual progression of a tiny person from helpless to aware?

Imagine what it's like to be so new in the world ... and so totally helpless. We can only try to imagine that state, until we are parents, because it happened before we developed conscious, symbolic memory. The problem for the infant of course is that it isn't *like* anything they have ever seen, heard, or felt. Their universe is a roiling chaos of bodily sensations. Their only guides are fear and hunger, the need for caring and an innate curiosity. Most parents retain some sense of the child's raw fear, curiosity, and wonder. Other parents take it for granted, or forget it ... or never notice it.

Each fleeting sensory impulse, each bit of incoherent data, is like a piece in a gigantic puzzle, a dot to be connected. But the infant has no clue that there is a puzzle, no idea that one moment's sensation can be separated from the flow or connected to anything. In the experience of young infants, those hundreds of tiny fragments multiply into the thousands of millions, yet each makes only a fleeting impression. Each glimpse of color or light. Each touch of skin or clothing. The scent of the mother's embrace. The comfort of her breast and milk. The texture of the father's hands. Each discomfort in the diapers. Each sound, coming from different unintelligible locations in space.

Time for us as babies and time for us as adults are two completely different kinds of time. Time for a baby is incomprehensible. Ideas about time and space are years away. The present moment is the only time. And a day is like an eternity. Every successive second is constantly unique, intense and confusing, oscillating between giddy, awkward, and scary, as amorphous as light and the feelings in one's own flesh, all mixed together.

From our first days, there are no guidelines, no map, no clock, no dictionary. Each of us makes our own, intuitively yet methodically, out of chaos.

PATTERN RECOGNITION
In his 1999 book, *The User Illusion,* Tor Norretranders points out that the flood of sensory information we experience, barely notice, and then seem to forget, stimulates a process of pattern recognition that we use to form our first inkling of a mind, and a basis for all other knowledge. It is a sketch of a world view, the first draft of a self-image. He thinks the data dismissed deserves a name. He calls it *Exformation.* We'll expand on this and related topics in Part Four.

He explains that over time, we begin to recognize the dots that repeat and to remember the patterns in which they occur. Each new connection gives us another atom of power in our formative world. Each hint of recognition stimulates our innate curiosity for more. Sorting and rearranging those millions of bits of sensory data – *without trying or knowing we are doing it* – leads to recognizing and remembering patterns that become the basis for all knowledge and all further mental operations.

Stephen Colbert, of course, took this idea to the absurd extreme, "I see patterns where none really exist !!"

Pattern recognition is more than our innate method for comprehending the world, or for forming the basis for the rest of our knowledge. It is essential to most of our conscious, intelligent decisions, as well as our unconscious intuition. We can frame the Global Environmental Crisis in terms of patterns that we fail to recognize.

There is a problem with the fact that we don't remember or understand how that process worked. We don't wonder *how* we know that the person who walked behind the tree is still there, she didn't vanish. We don't remember *how* we learned that a seashell or a leaf was once part of something living. We *just know it*. We take that background understanding, and billions of bits of other basic knowledge, for granted. There are dangers in taking *anything* for granted. The fact that we take a stable climate for granted is an example of our collective stupidity, our lack of perspective, or our inability to recognize a pattern.

Here we are going to look deeper into our stupidity, as individuals and in groups. It may help us take our intelligence less for granted, or be better able to avoid some of the stupidity that persists in our minds and our civilization.

AN INVENTORY OF THE STUPID *in 5 sections*

Section 1. COMMON MENTAL MISTAKES AND BAD THINKING HABITS can be innate or learned, personal or socio/cultural, conscious or unconscious.

I was relieved the first time I heard, "brain fade," as an excuse for saying or doing something stupid. It's like saying "Duh," as in, "I know that, or knew better, or should have." It's a relief. It's liberating to know others experience it. I recognize it in myself. It has a name.

Think about the differences between those 2, and 3 other expressions: *Oops, Uh Oh,* and *D'Oh. Oops* usually comes right before *Uh Oh.* We see we have just made a mistake, and then see how bad the outcome may be. Homer Simpson's *D'Oh!* combines "Oops!" and "Uh Oh," with a little self-realization thrown in. It was entered into the Oxford Dictionary in 2001. From

Wikipedia: "'D'oh!' is typically used when Homer injures himself, *realizes that he has done something stupid,* or when something
bad has happened or *is about to happen to him."* (my italics)

• **Self-deception.** We all rationalize and tell little white lies, we
procrastinate and think wishfully. It's the unconscious choice
of pride and fear over honesty, humility and curious learning.
We have a stubborn tendency to overlook or deny our mistakes,
even the obvious ones. There is evidence that we all lie to ourselves, from time to time or habitually, a little or a lot. Trump
does this to a pathological extreme.

• **Cognitive Bias** has many forms. We want something to be
true, because we need it to be so or because we don't want to
be wrong. So we see, hear, accept and absorb the information
that lines up with our wish, and ignore what doesn't. **Cognitive
Dissonance** is the uncomfortable feeling that comes when your
ideas and beliefs are in obvious conflict with reality; most forms
of cognitive bias are our mental attempts to avoid or escape cognitive dissonance. **Wishful thinking** is one example, sometimes
called **Confirmation Bias.** It's similar to **False Certainty,** the
hardened belief in something known to be false, and includes ...

• **Refusing to admit or correct mistakes.** Beyond personal
self-deception, it is vastly more dangerous when adopted by
political parties and built into governing systems. If we think we
are exceptional – somehow not subject to the rules – it can make
us unable to correct for the past in the present, or plan to correct
it in the future – the most important condition for solving the
Eco-Crisis. See *Exceptionalism* starting on page 98. The flip side
of confirmation bias is ...

• **Denial** is a complex and powerful force in our mental approach to the Global Environmental Crisis. Recall Ms. Hayhoe's
argument from pages 3 and 4. Denial is one distinct form of a
Cultural or *Mental Blind Spot.* We elaborate on both ahead.

• **Ignorance, the lack of education or information.** A self-reinforcing social and cultural well of stupidity. In an enlightened, free society, the love of learning and knowledge ought to be a universal value, the bedrock of Democracy, and a defense against the ignorance of others. The US public has been subjected to 50-plus years of an *anti-intellectual* trend, engineered by conservatives and capitalists to undermine democracy. Ask yourself honestly, in 2018, if it has succeeded.

• **A shortage of logical and critical thinking.** We may lack a set of specific thinking skills that are essential to understanding and evaluating information, especially new or alarming information. Conservative politicians and school boards resist the teaching of critical thinking. They are afraid it will make their kids turn liberal, or question religion, social conventions, or authority. Why are Republicans so afraid of it?

• **Narrow-mindedness, mental stubbornness, inflexibility, a resistance to new ideas,** includes rigid thinking, resistance to change, attachment to obsolete ideas, and old prejudices that cannot be questioned, like racism in particular. *Silo-thinking* or *silo*-based information or management systems describe isolated groups who work in specialized fields and have great difficulty communicating with people operating in other *silos*.

• **An inability to grasp complexity and abstract ideas.** Complexity may require us to form mental representations of complex systems, processes, and interactive forces in flux. It makes our world ever harder to comprehend, especially the Eco-Crisis. Abstract ideas are typically about relationships, processes, and dynamics, like Feedback Loops, that help us understand how they shape real events. We may reduce the complexity of the Eco-Crisis by connecting dots and forming big picture visions in which larger patterns can be seen. If we can do that exercise, with patience, it will also help us to overcome ...

• **Inattention and distraction,** failing to concentrate and focus the mind. It became a social and cognitive problem with the TV. The smart phone makes it a near disaster. The cause, beyond the device itself, can be called the *Data Glut,* or *Information Overload.* It has conditioned us all, those under 30 or 40 most of all, to have shorter attention spans, and *to think* we have unlimited access to all relevant knowledge. But that knowledge mostly comes without the context to understand or use it, or even to remember it. And it makes complexity into an incomprehensible maze.

• **Selective memory.** A form of cognitive bias, an after-effect of confirmation bias, a specific mix of mental blind spot and denial, and a predictor of a refusal to admit mistakes. Society and our shared history ought to correct for this, but conservative school boards and state lawmakers, and much of mass media generally, want to omit the uncomfortable truths, like slavery and the genocide of Native Americans.

• **A lack of foresight.** An all-too-common human trait, exaggerated and made more critical in an era of high-speed change, technological power and missing information. The more complex and fast-moving our energy-consuming world goes, the harder it is to anticipate the unintended consequences. It is tragic to see, now in retrospect, what we needed to do 20 or 40 years ago.

> *"Sometimes I wonder whether the world is being run by smart people who are putting us on, or by imbeciles who really mean it."* Mark Twain

• **A lack of perspective or sense of proportion.** An inability to understand extremes of scale and speed, to connect dots in order to imagine a wide view or a historical perspective – I call this the *Big Blind Spot,* defined on pages 102-3 ahead.

A DIGRESSION: ADAPTATION

We are apparently the most adaptable of all species. We have
conditioned ourselves to live at sea level and at extreme al-
titudes, in the humid heat of the tropics and in the Arctic, to
survive solo in the wilderness (some of us now, at one time, all of
us) and in densely populated ghettos. A few of us have lived in
space and walked on the moon.

We have forced so many components of Nature to adapt to
us: crops, domesticated animals, irrigation, all kinds of buildings
to shield us and create artificial environments. Our thinking
may be highly adaptable, or our least adaptable part. We face a
moment in our history when we need to adapt our thinking to
the extreme adaptations we have forced onto Nature, or we will
find we can't adapt to the consequences.

Section 2. ANOTHER LEVEL: Like thinking, our stupidity, and
its opposite, mental awakening, can operate on several levels.

• **The flip side: Different Thinking and Imagination.** The
essence of different thinking is flexibility – the ability to shift
between levels, to adjust to complexity and mental challenges,
to think creatively, having the ability to imagine and rearrange
ideas in the mind. It is to be comfortable with more comprehensive and dynamic thought processes, often called *systems, process,
relational,* or *holistic thinking.* Scientists and artists, poets and
musicians, engineers and architects, psychologists and philoso-
phers, and others: all are lucky to get the formal training – and
the informal, disciplined practice – to sharpen their intuition
and imagination to the level they can be trusted and relied on to
produce genuinely new and expansive ideas.

• **Paradigm Shift:** *Paradigm* simply means a mental model or a
theory that explains something. Thomas S Kuhn (1922-1996), a
science historian, published *The Structure of Scientific Revolutions*
in 1962. In it he coined the term *Paradigm Shift* to describe a
pattern he observed in scientists' knowledge and sudden shifts

in their thinking. Stable and accepted paradigms are challenged by new and puzzling evidence. Scientists argue with each other. They question their faith in the old model and stubbornly resist abandoning it.

But do not take this to mean "The science in inconclusive," on GW/CC for example. The scientists only disagree on how bad it may get, how soon, how scary to make it seem, and about *how* we will do what must be done.

In Kuhn's Paradigm Shift model, the scientists struggle to find the new idea that will explain the new phenomena and overthrow their established beliefs. At a certain point, often suddenly, they realize that one of the wackier theories is actually the *obviously* correct one, and, like a row of dominos falling, the others change their minds too. They slap their collective forehead, "It's so simple." "Why didn't we see it sooner?" They sigh with momentary relief, and the process starts all over.

If our Paradigm Shift on the Eco-Crisis doesn't come soon, the sigh will be one of despair. And there will be no starting over.

• **Cognitive Threshold and Leap:** Rebecca D Costa uses the term *Cognitive Threshold* in her book, *The Watchman's Rattle, Thinking Our Way Out Of Extinction* (2012), for a mental hurdle that we have to overcome. I imagine her *cognitive threshold* as two alternate images. One, a formidable barrier – a wall of mental inertia. The other, a gateway to a different level of thinking and a more aware state of mind, which can have different names, like *Step Change, Cognitive Leap,* or in a large population, a *Global Shift in Consciousness.* Like Einstein's *level of thinking* idea, *thinking our way out of extinction* implies much more than it says.

Argument 16: When every new crisis demands different thinking, obsolete thinking is the crisis.

Now it's time to explore 3 broader categories of Cognitive Bias in greater depth, some mentioned earlier.

Section 3. COMPLEX STUPIDITY: MINDSETS, BLIND SPOTS, AND DENIAL, TO NEGATIVE PANIC AND MORE

In 1961, when John Kennedy challenged NASA to send men to the moon and bring them back safely within a decade, "... not because it is easy but because it is hard," the engineers who would have to make it happen did not think it was possible.

The idea of a Possibility Mindset was introduced on page 20 and expanded on page 67.

In just over eight years, the moon shot was an accomplished fact. That unprecedented technological triumph, like our efforts in helping to end World War II, bolstered a feeling among Americans that we are truly exceptional. In those cases, that feeling is justified. In other cases, not so much.

EXCEPTIONALISM AS MINDSET

Exceptionalism *is the perception that a country, society, institution, movement, or time period is "exceptional" (i.e., unusual or extraordinary) in some way and thus does not need to conform to normal rules or general principles.* (Wikipedia) It is often part of a nationalistic ideology, a belief that one's country is different from all other nations, in spite of the fact that most other nations make similar claims. It is most evident among conservative, political, and corporate elites, including the glaring assumption that social norms and business ethics (for example) don't apply to them. The empty promise to Make America Great Again is a grotesque example of American Exceptionalism at its worst. The author, Donald Trump, has driven respect for the United States, around the world, down to an unprecedented low.

These times, on the other hand, are exceptional to the point of being completely without precedent, mostly caused by our exceptional abuses of industrial, political, and economic power.

From our militaristic mis-adventures in Vietnam and Iraq, to our levels of consumption and waste, the exceptional mindset is central to our privileged lifestyles, to our assumed right to "subdue the Earth," to be the "cops of world," and to our rigid resistance to lead in addressing Climate Change.

98

It's the rationale – if we can call it that – that Conservatives and Christian fundamentalists use to try to control the information that our schools and colleges are allowed to deliver, about evolution, birth control, sex education, respect for each others' rights, and climate science for example. Also taboo are the country's history of genocide against the indigenous people we call *Indians,* and the horrific practice of slavery, still evident in institutional racism, segregation, and the pathetic state of race relations that we can't seem to escape. That information is deemed dangerous because it exposes the stain on our illusion of historic *greatness.* Too often we deny the worst mistakes in our past, and ignore the real, self-made threats on our immediate horizon, directly in our path.

Mindsets are persistent. Even after a catastrophe like 9-11 shatters our possibility mindset, we can easily fall back into the belief that we understand the divide between the possible and the impossible, between real and fake threats, between friends, enemies, and former friends that we made into enemies.

The United States cannot claim any kind of exceptional status – in economic justice, environmental responsibility, or global leadership – unless and until we admit the injustice and brutality that dot our history, and accept that our Exceptionalist Mindset is obsolete and destructive.

BLIND SPOTS:
VISUAL METAPHORS FOR MENTAL STATES
We use visual metaphors for mental states or processes. Some are just verbal tricks without a real connection between the visual and the mental. But other similarities are real and often startling. Some of these metaphors, properly understood, provide insights into our mental states.

Do you *see* what I mean? Is *seeing believing?* We say some people have mental *tunnel vision,* meaning they *see* or understand only a small area of their *mental field.* Can someone's thinking be *myopic,* mentally *near-sighted?* ... unable to imagine a distant place or time? What is the mental equivalent for *peripheral vision* – the ability to notice motion at the far left or right edges of our field of vision? A *big picture*? When waking to a mental mistake, have you experienced *20/20 hindsight*?

Blind Spot is a visual metaphor for a mostly unconscious gap in perception or awareness, and for our tendency to fill in what we don't see or know with assumptions. It's an extreme form of confirmation bias, in reverse. We may find ourselves literally unable to see something so unfamiliar or threatening that our unconscious mind blocks it out before it can appear in consciousness.

Blind Spots are about missing information. They can be literal obstacles in our visual field, real gaps in our mental attention or awareness, metaphorical gaps in our perception, or social biases and taboos that keep certain topics *out of sight*. But Blind Spots are different from ignorance, a complete lack of knowledge. They conceal information that exists, often "right under our noses," while keeping us from both knowing what it is and *that it exists*. When we need information to make critical decisions, Blind Spots can hide three crucial things: the *FACT THAT* there is a critical decisions that must be made, the *actual information* that we need to make the decision, and the *FACT THAT* the information exists.

> **It is impossible to "see" a blind spot. Blind spots do not only hide information, they conceal the fact that information is missing.**

Blind Spots can be visual, cultural, or mental/cognitive. We learned in Driver's Education to check our mirrors and look directly around the back corners of our cars when we drive.

There are literal blind spots in our eyes, small areas on our retinas that cannot process light. The retina is the screen inside the eye that send patterns of light to the brain, to turn them into images. Those spots are literally blank. They are in different places on the right and left retinas, so each blind spot is "covered" by the other eye. We cannot "see" them (or notice that they exist) without doing a specific exercise. It requires covering one eye and carefully controlling the visual focus of the other eye. You can google the "blind spot exercise" and with patience make a startling – personal and scientific – observation and discovery.

It's extra hard to notice and understand, because even when you see it, you'll find it hard to believe what you are seeing – a mental blind spot in observing a visual blind spot. When you do notice it, you may realize that you are watching your brain reacting to and adjusting for a visual anomaly. It's called "filling in." In the visual blind spot, *something* in our visual-to-mental relay fills in the gap in the image. With both eyes open, each fills in what is missing in the other eye. With only one eye open (this is the amazing part) that *something* literally inserts a sample of the surrounding image into the blind spot. The most fascinating thing about this effect is that it is an automatic psycho-perceptual-physiological response that operates completely outside of awareness. It is an unconscious, mental / visual cut-and-paste, a self-made illusion that hides a gap in our visual system.

Visual Blind Spots have a very real equivalent in our thinking. There are two separate and important, but common factors in actual, visual blind spots and in metaphorical, mental and cultural blind spots.

One is the *obstacle to the information*. In the eye, it's that small area on the retina that cannot process light. In the car, it's the edge of the rear-view mirror, or the post or panel supporting the roof. In our minds, it is an emotional, social, religious, or political block that prevents us from recognizing a piece of information because it is outside our expectations, our comfort zone or a possibility mindset. In our culture, it can be one factor or several in combination: the self-censoring of the news, as influenced by sponsors and corporate managers; taboos (stated or unconscious) against discussing uncomfortable topics, like slavery; or the sheer density of data overload that makes it hard to pick the important, true detail out of the background of spectacle and noise. The parallels between mental and cultural blinds spots come into sharper focus (metaphor intended).

There is also a mental and cultural process for *filling in*. If real knowledge about Climate Change is constantly obfuscated or denied, or is simply incomplete, our perception of the weather as normal *fills in* the gap and lulls us into the belief that the climate is stable and will probably remain so; add to that the work of the fake climate skeptics and willfully ignorant deniers, and the gap in our knowledge is fully *covered* or *filled in* – with false belief, or even worse, false certainty.

THE BIG BLIND SPOT: A LACK OF PERSPECTIVE:
An early image of the Earth from space became immediately iconic. It was called "the Big Blue Marble." The patterns of water and land, clouds and ice, look like a glass marble. The layer of atmosphere is so thin it's barely visible.

When we first saw that image, we thought it would give us all a different sense of perspective – of our size relative to the Earth, of the relative distances in space, maybe even of the beauty and fragility of the planet. That insight only stuck for a few of us. By now, we've all seen so many variations we take them for granted. Any sense of wonder and awe wore off rather quickly.

That image of the Earth from space lets us think we experience the same perspective and sense of wonder as the astronauts who actually saw it. But that is an illusion. It both trivializes their insights and inflates our sense of our understanding. And it is why that image could not change us the way seeing it first-hand changed them. We assume we understand extremes of size and speed but we really don't.

I call this general *lack of a sense of perspective and proportion*, the *Big Blind Spot*.

Edgar Mitchell is an Apollo astronaut, and the 6th human being to walk on the moon. He didn't take that iconic photograph, but he often refers to it when he speaks of his experience in space,
102

"You develop an instant global consciousness, a people orienta-
tion, an intense dissatisfaction with the state of the world, and
a compulsion to do something about it. From out there on the
moon, international politics look so petty. You want to ...

> *... grab a politician by the scruff of the neck and drag
> him a quarter of a million miles out and say, 'Look at
> that, you son of a bitch.'"*

We rely on language, numbers, images, memory, and media to
give us *the impression* that we understand much or most of the
information that comes from beyond our personal horizon, or
that we *could* understand it if we paid attention or cared.

Our experience and memories give us a direct *handle* on
the observable world. History tells us about events and issues
beyond our direct knowledge. We can confirm some of it by
comparing it with our fundamental, pattern-based knowledge,
even if we're not sure *how* we acquired it. We accept some
knowledge because the authorities appear to agree on it. We reject
some because it makes us question what we *think* we already
know. But we don't really have any direct, experiential frame of
reference for the view from the moon, or what the Forefathers
were thinking, or who wrote the Bible, or sixty million years, or
a trillionth of a second, the amount of carbon in the air, or where
our poop goes after it's flushed.

BUT WE THINK THAT WE DO. We assume that we know, or believe that we could comprehend those complicated explanations,
those pictures of star clusters or sub-atomic particles, those long
strings of numbers, before or after the dot. Much of that knowledge is an illusion, even when it is true. A paradox. We have to
be a little bit smarter to recognize the gaps in our knowledge.
The Global Environmental Crisis is both: a huge emergency
that has developed slowly over generations, and an imminent
catastrophe demanding radical change in a decade. It is beyond
anything in our history or personal experience. It is totally

unique and nearly impossible to imagine, especially in its scale and accelerating speed. The reasons we don't comprehend it are many, as we are learning now. But no other misunderstanding could ever be as dangerous. See Section 4 on page 113.

EXPONENTIAL
Dr. Albert A. Bartlett (1923-2013), a former physics professor at the University of Colorado, is featured in a series of online videos titled, *The most important video you'll ever see* (parts 1-8). As Dr. Bartlett explains in Part 1 of his videos, we see lots of examples of *Hockey Stick Curves* that describe *compound or exponential growth systems,* the speeds at which they can expand and the implications. Even when we think we understand the lines on the graph, we have trouble getting a real idea of the extremes of accelerating speed and scale.

> **"The greatest shortcoming of the human race is our inability to understand the exponential function."**
> Dr. Albert A. Bartlett

James Gustave Speth's, *The Bridge at the End of the World* (2008), is one of a few books that deal with the relationships between Capitalism, its impact on the environment, and a path to sustainability. In his opening pages there are 16 hockey stick graphs, all illustrating patterns of increase between the years 1750 and 2000. The graphs include the most telling examples for the Eco-Crisis: human population, CO_2 in the atmosphere, numbers of extinctions, numbers of rivers dammed, numbers of great floods, real GDP, water consumption, fertilizer usage, number of motor vehicles, and 7 more. The point is that they all look like a hockey stick, and represent a suddenly increasing and accelerating *rate of growth.* That is *Exponential.*

This is a summary of Dr. Bartlett's explanation. When something increases by the same *amount* every day, or year, it's called a *linear* increase, a straight line on a graph. For example, if I have

$100, and my wealth increases by $1 per day, my total will follow a steady pattern: $100 today, $101 tomorrow, $102 the next day and so on. Over a hundred days, an increase from $100 to $200.

So we tend to think that something that increases by the same *PERCENTAGE* every day would do the same thing. That is where the misunderstanding starts, but not where it ends. It's why many of us don't understand the difference between simple and compound interest. Do young people today even get introduced to the idea? Do they even know how interest is calculated?

If some quantity like human population, or CO_2 in the atmosphere, increases at a low but steady *percentage RATE* (not net quantity), it will double in size within a predictable time ... unless and until some exterior force stops the accelerating growth.

The point of Exponential is that each new doubling will happen in a shorter period of time, curving up instead of going in a straight line.

And then, if the percentage rate starts to increase, say from 2 percent to 5 percent to 10 percent, the doubling will accelerate even more rapidly. *THAT* is what has been happening with our numbers, our carbon output, and global temperatures. Like the growth of cancer cells and avalanches, the accelerating percentage rate is the factor that sends the rising curve rapidly off the chart. Most important is the context in which all these hockey stick graphs occur – *an Earth that remains a constant, finite size.*

THE *HOCKEY STICK* GRAPH: Gus Speth starts his 16 Hockey Stick curves at 1750, just before the start of the Industrial Revolution, when fossil-fueled industry started to accelerate our population growth, and the rise in global temperatures. Starting on the next page, I start my example at year 0, the beginning of the Christian Era, to illustrate the slow growth of our numbers over the 18 centuries before industrialization, and the increase in the angle of the curve around 1400.

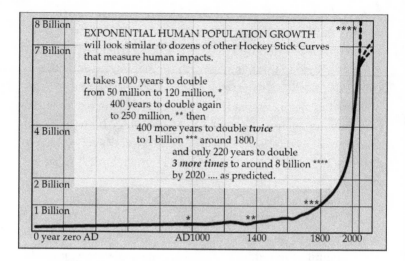

EXPONENTIAL IN PRACTICAL TERMS

Since we began to practice primitive agriculture around 10,000 BCE, our population has doubled 11 times, from about three million, to six M, 12 M, 24 M, then to approximately 50 million around year zero AD, the birth of Jesus. Those first four doublings took 10,000 years to complete – imagine that date 20" off the left side of my graph, in a nearly flat line. They were the product of basic agriculture and the benefits of simple social organizations. The next four doublings, starting at year zero, took only 1,800 years, from 50 million to 120 M, 220 M, 450 M and to one billion around the start of the Industrial Revolution. (That growth was in spite of tens of millions of deaths from the Black Plague in the 1300s and the Mini-Ice Age in the 1600s.)

Without industrialized agriculture – using oil-powered tractors and transport, oil-based fertilizers, and oil-derived pesticides and herbicides – our population could not have grown much beyond one billion globally, around 1800. You can see how we became so addicted to oil.

We doubled our numbers once after 1800, to 2 Billion around 1900, and again, to 4 Billion around 2000. We are on track to double our numbers again, to eight billion by 2020. The last three doublings will only take 220 years. Beyond eight

106

billion, it's unlikely to double again, because the *percentage rate* of human population growth is starting to decrease.

PERSPECTIVE: The Global Environmental Crisis is of a scale and complexity we cannot imagine, expanding and accelerating at speeds we cannot measure, with a force of momentum that seems beyond our power to imagine, let alone slow or stop, even when we know we must. We face monumental delays that we have not started to address. The Crisis propels us into a future of catastrophic risk that we have not yet begun to imagine or estimate. If we still have trouble understanding the implications, it's a clear example of the Big Blind Spot.

COMPARING EXTREMES: The Big Blind Spot is not only about a problem thinking about extremes of size, speed, and risk. It's also about how hard it is to *compare* extremes: what Climate Change is costing us now, compared to how much it will cost our kids, if we continue doing next to nothing: higher costs now, much less in the long term; lower spending now, economic disaster in 20 to 30 years.

"CRISIS? WHAT CRISIS?"
AN EXPANDED LOOK AT DENIAL
Katherine Hayhoe wants us to stop using *denier, denialism,* and *denial* generally. I want to define it clearly, so we may recognize it in ourselves and in the words of the high profile deniers. We need to look deeper into Denial, not avoid it, and to understand how we use it to escape – *to pretend we escape* – painful truths.

For our purposes, *Denial* is a psychological defense mechanism that blocks from consciousness something that is unacceptable, or refuses to admit that something is possible or true, because it sparks uncomfortable emotions. Like other forms of cognitive bias, Denial is more powerful to the degree that it is unconscious. (The unconscious comes up again in Part Five, as *the Power of the Unconscious.*) The scary thought will be blocked before it even penetrates our awareness. I might be in Denial and falsely certain that I am not, until new information makes me admit the truth that I blocked, and in turn, to admit the Denial itself.

> *Argument 17: The psychological defense mechanism we call Denial is simply the Fear of Knowledge that will force us to change our thinking or our behavior.*

By framing Denial as the fear of knowledge, we bring into high relief the potential power of unconscious fear to skew our beliefs and our mental reality. This topic will continue to grow in importance. The unconscious comes up again in Parts Four and Five, in the contexts of Information and Power.

Barack Obama got my vote the first time around when he said, "Denial is not an acceptable response to global warming." He is the first politician I ever heard use terms like *Denial* or *Mindset*, as in, "We need to change the mindset that took us to war."

When candidate Obama made that comment about Denial, it prompted National Public Radio (NPR) to bring in the shrinks. They tried to help us understand Denial and the emotions behind or beneath it. It was an unexpected mental exercise on daytime radio, but I think they did a crappy job. Their discussion was less than comprehensive, and at times misleading.

The psychologists defined and discussed Denial, but they didn't mention how it works in the *cultural unconscious,* even though they implied that it does. (Unlike his mentor, Sigmund Freud, Carl Jung believed that a "collective unconscious" might be even more powerful than the personal.) The radio shrinks had no comment on how deeply Denial may run in the culture, or how to counteract it. They said rather confidently that all Denial falls into three simple categories. *(The following words in italics are theirs.* My comments follow.)

One: CONSCIOUS, WILLFUL OR *"STRATEGIC" DENIAL is a pretense of disbelief. The denier offers contradictory evidence knowing it is false, pretending not to believe accepted facts or inconvenient truths, to persuade others to ignore or reject them.*

This is not really psychological Denial at all. Whether we call it *strategic* or *tactical*, it is simply conscious lying disguised as Denial or genuine disbelief. The *strategic denier* creates public lies that protect the genuine Denial of others, or offers up *tactical* deceptions to confuse the issue. This approach helps to build a *Denialist Mindset* in an unsuspecting public.

Two: (the experts continued) *"FEAR-BASED" DENIAL is expressed when the crisis is depicted in a manner that is literally too scary to imagine or take seriously.* This is the essence of the problem, "how scary to make it seem," first raised on page 5. It ought to amaze and anger us how far professional deniers will go to ignore or discount – lie about – the facts.

In one case, wishful thinking refuses to believe the crisis is real, blindly hoping it won't happen. In another, false certainty convinces us it is not possible.

Three: *"THREATS TO THE WORLDVIEW" DENIAL occurs when one's belief system is threatened by new information. Typically, the denier cannot recognize the evidence or admit the possibility of the bad news, because doing so would shatter their basic assumptions, the background knowledge on which they base their sense of reality.*

This could also be called *Threat to the Mindset Denial.* Many of us have a *natural* resistance to admitting the Eco-Crisis. (It's part of a special category; see page 113.) We grew up in a world where two things were *unthinkable:* public ignorance of such critical information, and the information itself. We couldn't imagine that our parents could conceal such a reality, intentionally or unconsciously. But we had no clue about *their* possible states of Denial, or the conscious and unconscious conspiracies to keep them and us in the dark.

The second and third examples are both too narrow and overly inclusive; there are many subsets, a couple other categories, and more corrections needed.

First, almost all psychological Denial is Fear-Based, reflecting four mental sides of the Crisis: fear of the actual Crisis itself, fear of information about the Crisis, fear that our disbelief is wrong, and fear of how it will force us to change, if it is true.

Any of these overlapping kinds of Denial can be imposed on an individual by a peer group or a cultural or religious community. Denial and other forms of cognitive bias are reflected between the individual and the culture, reinforced rather than revealed, because the cultural Denial and the exchange are unconscious.

We could call it *Peer Group* or *Groupthink Denial*. It comes into play in the classic Paradigm Shift situation. In a group that shares a complex worldview, whether based on hard-won research or dogmatic doctrine, contradictory information is rejected by peer consensus, even when individuals believe it. The peer group's commitment to *what we all know* dominates, until the new evidence becomes overwhelming.

Marshall McLuhan made a prescient observation about public Denial, sometime in the 1960s. To paraphrase,

> *"Only puny secrets need protection." The big ones ... "are protected by public incredulity."... the public's disbelief.*

Upton Sinclair said it more directly,

> *"It is difficult to get a man to understand something when his salary depends upon his not understanding it."*

META-DENIAL: A *higher level* of Denial helps us cover the other forms if they start to crack. We deny that we are in Denial. It helps us to ignore or reinforce our own Denial, to strengthen our

110

false beliefs or accept the Denial of our peer group or chosen *authorities*. Meta-Denial includes a denial of the unconscious, of cognitive bias, and of any reason to question our established beliefs, our *reasoning* or our *rational choices*. Layers of Denial, like new lies to cover old ones, can pile up until their collapse creates a real psychological crisis. Are you listening Donald?

Denial is related to a general fear of change. Our fascination and desire for the new is always tempered by our fear of the unpredictable and unknown. That type of fear is more common among the old and Conservatives. Curiosity and an openness to change are more common among Liberals and the young.

Denial is the armor the unconscious puts up to defend its secrets, its inner workings, the desires and fears that go too deep, to protect the *knowledge* that cannot be questioned. It's connected to the resistance to admit one's own mistakes. The only way to overcome Denial is to have a skeptical and open mind, and to be aware that Denial – as a powerful form of self-deception – is real.

A DIGRESSION: PEER POWER: In Ken Burns' PBS documentary *The Civil War,* historian Shelby Foote described General Pickett's tragic defeat at Gettysburg. The commanding general and most of the troops knew it was going to be virtually suicidal, a futile, deadly sacrifice. But in Foote's words, "It would have taken too much courage to say so, to question the General. ... easier to march to a certain death. ... No one has that much courage."

So Peer Group Denial may be one of the most powerful types. If your peer group denies global warming or evolution, it will be almost impossible for you to question their beliefs, or to speculate on alternative views. To be rejected by your peer group as misinformed or deluded, a trouble-maker or alarmist, would feel worse than suppressing your real beliefs.

Consider General Pickett's state of mind in the context of a professor's studies.

NEGATIVE PANIC

Ed Galea teaches and conducts research at the University of Greenwich in England. He studies human behavior in extreme situations. In a NOVA science documentary on PBS, he describes a type of behavior some ships' captains and airline pilots experience in moments of sudden and unpredictable danger. Two examples are the sinking of the Titanic and the Concordia cruise ship that ran aground off the coast of Italy in January 2012. It's easy to imagine it applying to auto accidents, nuclear meltdowns, climate legislation, and other situations.

Galea cites a condition described technically as "behavioral inaction." In such situations, the person with the responsibility to take charge, to make emergency decisions and save lives, often just "freezes." The terror of the moment simply makes them incapable of taking charge or issuing commands. Galea also used the term "negative panic."

The Concordia captain, Francesco Schettino, was showing off to his friends and family, watching from the shore, and ran aground. He abandoned ship and gave no instructions. 32 people drowned, mostly teenagers.

Observers who survived the sinking of Titanic claimed that the captain, Edward Smith, was apparently so shocked, learning the ship would sink, that he could not give coherent orders, probably causing hundreds of unnecessary deaths. He was among the 1500 that drowned or froze to death in the icy waters.

Some such crises have had better outcomes. In January 2009, the experienced, cool-headed airline pilot Sully Sullenberger overcame a total engine failure and a nearly inevitable crash, in the tightest possible time frame, and landed his plane on the Hudson River. No deaths. One broken leg.

Our leaders may have fallen into that desperate state of negative panic. And if they have, it would be natural for us to mirror it, unconsciously and unaware. In the path of a sudden, unique and accelerating emergency, it is possible that our *captains* or *pilots* have *frozen*, and find themselves incapable of decisive action.

112

For those of us who think we see the crisis looming, and believe we need radical action, that possibility is the scariest of all.

Section 4. THE ECO-CRISIS BRING ITS OWN UNIQUE FORMS OF DENIAL

Is it "natural" to deny Climate Change? The scale, speed and complexity of the Crisis are compounded by information over-load and the many distractions it brings. Beyond the mentions on pages 109 and 119, here are some examples of the unique complications that Climate Change brings to the issue of Denial:

• The worst kind of problem is one that asks for a change of mind now, and some sacrifices tomorrow, to avoid uncertain losses in a fuzzy and distant future, even as the symptoms wors-en every month. The Eco-Crisis is very different from the real and fake fears that are so familiar in the present: poverty and terrorists, jobs and the economy, racial bias and social rejection, feelings of dis-empowerment ... and now, again, nuclear war.

• The personal identity issues of the Eco-Crisis are minimal. Self-images among the general public tend to be much more tied up with ideological prejudices and peer-group stereotypes, im-pressions of social status, short term pleasures and benefits; they either discourage us from becoming eco-activists or threaten to deprive us of the pleasures of consumption.

• We have been conditioned to fear that we will have to give up some of the perks of a *prosperous lifestyle*, even as our incomes have been frozen, the costs of basics increase, and the impacts of the Crisis start to cost us directly and pose more immediate threats. So we resist the understanding; we don't allow our-selves to imagine that by clinging to comfort and convenience, by accepting an economy of war and waste, we heighten the risk of crashing civil society altogether.

• GW/CC, like the broader Eco-Crisis, does not have a clear identity, it's extremely amorphous in our minds (though this book has tried to make it clear, and the public is slowly coming around). There appears to be no *obvious, simple* causes (though I have tried to identify them), or a comprehensive solution (though this book proposes one). Each of us still has a tendency – call it *Confirmation Bias* – to understand the Crisis in the least-threatening terms, as long as we can. We can easily forget or fail to notice the speed of ecological decline, when the rest of the world (or our peer group) goes on running at an apparently normal pace.

These examples are from an article in NewScientist Opinion (online), from August, 2014. Several experts support this idea of overwhelming, Climate-specific Denial. The quotations are literal and verbatim.
• Daniel Kahneman (Nobel laureate, 2002, for his studies on the psychological biases that distort logical thinking): "I am deeply pessimistic ... on climate change."
• Nicholas Stern of the Stern Review describes the mounting costs of Global Warming as a "perfect market failure."
• Philosopher Stephen Gardiner says it is a "perfect moral storm."
• Daniel Gilbert of Harvard University: "A psychologist could barely dream up a better scenario for paralysis." Is he speaking about mental and emotional paralysis? An inability literally to absorb the information – a paralysis of Denial? Or a political paralysis? I'm not sure which he meant. I think all are correct.

This topic is critically important, and comes up again in several other contexts. Gus Speth is quoted speaking about "what we scientists can't do" on page 247.

Section 5. DID THE GREAT DUMBING DOWN PRODUCE THE CULTURAL DIVIDE?
Leftist intellectual Richard Hofstadter (Pulitzer prize-winning author of *Anti-Intellectualism in American Life,* 1963), outlined the social, economic and political forces that have marginalized, even ridiculed and condemned higher intelligence, as expressed in the public conversation in the United States ... for well over 60 years. Here are a few current examples of the trend in the US:
114

- The State of Texas Board of Education's policy, as voiced by governor Rick "Oops" Perry and the GOP platform: "We oppose the teaching of Higher Order Thinking Skills." November 2015, while they are considering allowing concealed-carry guns on campuses, they want to prohibit students and professors from fact-checking the books they use in class.
- Several other states have tried (though some have failed) to rewrite American History textbooks to de-emphasize the killing and forced migration of millions of native peoples, and to redefine slaves as "workers," generally to cloud the immorality of the issues. They'd also like to delete liberal successes like women's rights, labor rights, and minority rights.
- The 2nd US Circuit Court of Appeals upheld a lower court's ruling that a Connecticut city could refuse to hire applicants to the police force who scored *too high on intelligence tests.* Can't have cops thinking too much about their broader impacts.

    (I think the Justice Department needs to check every local and state police force for secret members of the KKK and other white suprematist organizations. The murder of unarmed black men by racist cops, who then avoid prosecution, must stop.)
- Professor (of International Affairs and Comparative Literature at Penn State) Sophia A McClennen pointed out that Stephen Colbert is (was, when on the Colbert Report) a far better source of rational political opinion than Rush Limbaugh. Limbaugh responded with an attack that proved Prof. McClennen's point.
- Conservatives and Republicans have taken an earlier prejudice, against learning generally, to a new low. More than half of the GOP Congressional delegation thinks that "higher education really doesn't have any positive social value."

    Too many of us have accepted the climate deniers' fake argument that, "That's just your opinion." Too many of them simply lie about the facts until the lie is accepted. A similar logical fallacy, used almost exclusively on the right, is "My opinion is just as good as your facts." Or, as Issac Asimov put it, "My ignorance is just as good as your knowledge."

THE MILLENNIAL DIVIDE:
Empathy, Irony and the Culture Wars

THE DIVIDE: A bitter political divide has been growing wider and deeper in the US since the 1960s. The G.W. Bush and Obama presidential terms, for different reasons and by different means, pushed it to a peak. The logical end point, someone like Donald Trump, is merely a symptom of the trend. But it's more than political. It reveals a deeper mental fissure that we have to observe and define, if our government and our civil society are to survive. It forces us to consider the nature of the *New Tribalism*.

ISN'T IT IRONIC? Within the last decade or so, dozens of studies have been done by respected psychologists, sociologists and neuro-scientists, to explore the emotions, impulses and thought patterns that lie beneath the divide. In one study, psychologists found that people in a randomly-assembled group will "self-select" into different groups, based on their appreciation of irony. Some people understand and enjoy irony, others don't. Extending that study revealed a strong correlation between that split and another one, empathy. Some people readily feel empathy. Others, not so much.

One surprising finding was that those who appreciate irony, fans of Stephen Colbert for example (as the pretend conservative personality he played until mid-2015), are much more likely to be empathetic. Those less likely to empathize, with homeless veterans for example, are also less likely to *get* ironic humor. The study also found that those who don't appreciate irony, and are less empathetic, are more likely to be Republicans or Conservatives; those who enjoy irony and are more empathetic, to be Democrats, Liberals or Independents. We're going to look more deeply into these sets of preferences.

Irony and empathy, like metaphor and analogy, require at least two levels of thinking, the willingness or ability to think two ways about one thing. An empathetic person tries to imagine and relate to how another person thinks or feels. To *get* an ironic comment one has to understand the literal statement, and that it actually means the opposite.

Steven Colbert's genius was his spontaneous ability to say (as a fake conservative) the exact opposite of what he actually believed (as Steven).

LIBERAL AND CONSERVATIVE BRAINS: Of the analysts, writers and bloggers I follow on this topic, Chris Mooney seems to be the broadest in scope, the most accessible and fair. He avoids rhetorical extremes and political conclusions. He admits his bias, but studiously avoids adding to the hostile back-and-forth. You'll notice I have no such qualms.

Mooney highlights more than ten studies that document and describe correlations among the characteristics and tendencies of *Liberal Brains,* and those of *Conservative Brains.* New studies reinforce this pattern every few weeks.

The most titillating headline, or the most offensive, depending on which side of the divide you fall, appeared in one online summary of such a study. It taunted, "Are Republicans Just Stupid?" A recent study claims to prove that racists are generally of lower intelligence, more rigid thinkers and less well informed than the average. Big surprise (irony).

Republicans in Congress want to defund the field of political psychology, like education generally, and apparently for the same reason: education simply produces more Liberals.

Politically, you can see this as the last battle in the demise of the 2-party system. It is also the logical outcome of 2 parallel campaigns: a 50-year-long, engineered Dumbing Down of the American public – more evident among those who have migrated to the right; and the gradual enslavement of both parties to corporate funding, and inevitably to political corruption.

Our analysis picks up after the next two pages of examples.

117

THE CONSERVATIVE "BENT"

Conservatives tend to share these attitudes. People in this group have been shown to be *LESS likely:*
• to use or understand irony or metaphor, less likely to be "flexible thinkers," more rigid in their held beliefs, less likely to read.
• to be sympathetic or empathetic for people with difficulties,
• to consider ideas that challenge their mindset,
• to be aware of mindsets, to acknowledge that they exist or that they hold one.
• to have a sense of humor, or to appreciate the humor of others.
• to be, or to want to be creative or imaginative, less interested in or appreciative of art and music, less open to new or unusual experiences.
• to believe in or be concerned about global warming.

And *MORE likely:*
• to be intolerant of other points of view and of cultural differences (like race and ethnicity), poorly educated, resistant to evidence of unconscious forces, even when they clearly demonstrate them.
• to blame minorities for their problems – poverty for example.
• to be skeptical of studies like these, regardless of whether they feel complimented or criticized by them.
• to favor a "strong national defense" and the death penalty, less interested in the rights of criminals or their victims, more likely to think that rape victims invited the attacks.
• to hold traditional values like: authority, loyalty, patriotism and established belief systems like more fundamentalist religions, the literal truth of the Bible,
• to believe in the "wisdom of the market," and that wealth and class status have been "earned" and/or are "deserved."
• to be skeptical of science, especially when it counters their religious beliefs or economic ideology.
• to be more reactive to suggestions of threats, more vulnerable to fearful stimuli, more likely to watch Fox News.
• *And much MORE likely* to be registered Republicans.

118

THE LIBERAL "BIAS"

"Liberal Brains," demonstrate the following patterns.
They are **MORE likely:**
• to be empathetic, more likely to want to help the disadvantaged or want government to do so.
• to use and understand irony, more likely to appreciate and use a sense of humor.
• to be more flexible thinkers.
• to be respectful of qualities like insight and imagination, more open to new experiences.
• to honor non-religious ethics, and to be more open to secular philosophies (as a contrast to revering "loyalty" or "religious tradition" for example).
• to understand their own emotions and the emotions of others, (this is also a quality observably stronger among women than men, including Republican women).
• to be more tolerant of the views of others.
• to be more highly educated, more likely to read for pleasure.
• to appreciate literature, art and music.
• to appreciate knowledge and new factual information, like authentic evidence in science, economics and culture.
• to believe that differences in wealth and class are unjust and the result of a "rigged system."
• to question their own thinking and be open to new ideas, even ones that challenge their core beliefs or religion.
• more tolerant of ambiguity and even paradox, much more appreciative of curiosity and creativity, in themselves and in others.
• more interested in the issues raised by such studies as these I am covering here.
• more likely to question or condemn the use of force in any form.
• much more concerned about the health of the environment and our attitudes toward it.
• *They are notably **LESS likely** to be stimulated or influenced by* threatening or fearful images or stories.
• *And much **MORE likely** to be Democrats or Independents.*

I think these studies are more than amusing observations that happen to coincide with party affiliations. The Divide is a current snapshot of a conflict that has defined the US, and much of its role in the world, for most of the 20th century, especially since the 1960s, and extremely so here in the 21st century. One of the clearest indicators of the difference is the issue of Fear, which I link directly with a loss, or a perceived loss of Power. Yale scientists claim to have found a way to turn Conservatives Liberal: make them feel *not frightened*. In tests that start with subtle messages that make people feel safe, and then ask for judgments about social issues, the Conservatives are more likely to express Liberal values.

For an interesting twist on this, jump to *Are You Scared?* on page 167.

If you knew you could make a choice, would you choose one or the other of the states of mind that define the opposite camps? It brings up a core question: Can a person decide to change their mind?

> *"If you can't change your mind, are you sure you have one?" – Bumper sticker seen in Berkeley, California*

Even as a majority of the US public now accepts the basic facts of the Climate Crisis, the Trump administration continues its obsession with undoing everything *Obama*, especially his modest efforts to protect the environment. These facts exhibit deep flaws in our shared intelligence, in our communications, our basic economics, and our political systems.

> *Argument 18: The political divide in the US can be boiled down to a choice between an obsolete and destructive mindset and an open-eyed view to a livable and humane future.*

Since the fall of 2017, and earlier, there is a growing number of public figures who question Trump's "suitability for office." It's a nice way of saying that his basic competence, his intelligence, even his sanity, are in serious doubt. The Mueller and Congressional investigations continue into a maze of Trump administration misconduct at what feels like a snail's pace, while Trump continues his campaign to create chaos, consciously and unconsciously, from the Oval Office to the UN and most of the world. The American public is dealing with 2 sides of an unprecedented emergency. First, it is true and terrifying that the US and the world faces the greatest set of crises in human history. Second, the systems of information, democracy, checks and balances, justice and law – especially in the US – are completely inept to deal with them.

Observe the implication, in the Divide, that more education tends to coincide with Liberal/Progressive/Democrat ideals and attitudes. The question is whether that is a coincidence. The works on Anti-Intellectualism in America, and cynical commentary on the Great Dumbing Down, seem to agree. Whether you agree or not, observe the pattern of Conservative commentary and tactics, to reduce the political influence of colleges and universities, *BECAUSE* they tend to produce Liberals, or to persuade those with other attitudes toward Liberalism. As we go on we will find more and more GOP/Conservative speakers condemn higher education as, for example, subversive, intentionally deceptive and propagandistic, because of this trend. As we study the divide, its causes and consequences, they seem not to be a coincidence.

    Smarter, well-educated and better-informed people, who tend to be more empathetic, with more flexible minds, are more likely to have Liberal/Progressive political views. Period. DUH.

A BEST CASE SCENARIO, CONTINUED

Progressive Democrats, Independents, Berniecrats, and even a few former Republicans who have had enough will reverse the political pendulum swing. Black Lives Matter and the Enough is Enough gun regulation revolution, the Me Too women's movement against sexual harassment, and many others will come to understand that they are all fighting the same enemy, a culture, a politics, an information system, and an economy dominated by ignorance, fake religiosity, and toxic masculinity – the same system that must be overthrown for radical environmental remedies to be imagined and implemented. And the GOP/Right Wing/Trumpian madness will come to an end.

This book may or may not have an impact. But a "radical revolution in political and economic power" is as inevitable as an Environmental Reckoning. The only remaining question is,

How fast can it happen?

A lot of women and teenagers are interested in politics for the first time. They and people like me – old men deeply frustrated about endless corruption and abuse of power in high places – will join in connecting the dots between Climate Change, gun violence, toxic masculinity, and an economy based on war and waste, carbon and corruption, deception and debt, extraction and exploitation, profit and pollution, war and waste.

They will recognize that pattern as a fear-based union of: racism and fear of ethnic difference, economic and legal injustice, militarism, environmental destruction, police brutality, suppressed and deleted information, and a paralyzed Congress.

We can be guided, toward despair or willful enlightenment, by this view of knowledge and Blind Spots,

> *"The general population doesn't know what's happening, and it doesn't even know that it doesn't know."* Noam Chomsky

I said up front that I feel *awe, desire,* and *fear,* for us and our world, and *anger,* at the greedy, aggressive, and ignorant men that are making our world uninhabitable. I temper my anger with delight, by imagining those men separated from their power.

Two writers have come by very different paths to a conclusion that is relevant, that Empathy in particular does not have to be crushed by selfishness, fear, anger, or ignorance ... that we can deal with them by choosing to thinking differently.

David Foster Wallace put a graduation speech he made in 2005 into a small book, *This is Water,* published in 2009. He starts with a joke about young fish who don't realize they are immersed in water, makes it into a metaphor for unrecognized patterns of thinking, and uses it to scold himself out of a momentary lack of empathy and into a change of mind.

Featured on the PBS News Hour, Lauren Groff writes and speaks of her failure to control her anger, only to realize later, that Empathy, when chosen consciously, is an *Act of Radical Imagination.*

Can I mute my anger, muster empathy, or even tolerance for the liars and thieves? Can I think or speak of them with civility? Certainly not. I have to save my empathy for myself, our children and their future world. But can we willfully imagine ourselves into a different state of mind? ... in which we demand a different world? Absolutely. It's not only possible, it's essential to our survival.

In Part Four, starting 2 pages ahead, and Five, on 155, we will take 2 necessary detours that will bring us back to these arguments with a broader perspective and expanded definitions, of the role of Information, in a couple new forms; and the role of Power as an organizing principle, in much of our personal, social, economic, and political lives, in our minds and in our mistakes.

GLOSSARY FOR PART FOUR

Data Glut, also **Information Overload:** The condition in contemporary culture in which information media gives us much more data and information than we can easily handle, absorb or understand, mentally or emotionally, (with Missing Information being a chronic side-effect.)

Information: We will use the conventional definition, and then examine why it is confusing, both too broad and too narrow, in the process of making a new expanded definition. We will return to the conventional use, with a different understanding.

Latency: A term used by online gamers to describe a critical delay in the electronic transmission of moves, that can impact winning or losing.

Materialist, or -ism: One or another of these terms comes up in several different contexts, that do not include industrial materials or resources. President Jimmy Carter and Martin Luther King Jr. spoke of materialism as a shortcoming or sin in the US's materialist culture: mainly in the form of excessive consumption and waste, irrational and destructive desires, and so on. Several theories and philosophies that led into Marxist and Socialist thinking were based on a materialist view of society; a definition that is only a tangent in this book. But that is relevant to our critique of Capitalism, especially in its Outlaw form: too many Americans have generally become convinced that a satisfying life can be defined in terms of materialist consumption - that the good life can be purchased, with enough cash. And worse, that a modest life of minimal consumption is inherently worse, less satisfying and fulfilling. Marshall McLuhan, ahead in Part Four, gives us the means to better understand how so many of us came to that destructive under-valuation of our lives.

McLuhan, Marshall, and

Media: Marshall McLuhan uses a special meaning for Medium or Media, as anything human-made that is thought of as a tool, a nearly all-inclusive term: all technologies and forms of communication and cultural expression. For McLuhan, all such things **mediate** or alter the connections between humans and the world in different ways; almost all appear to be helpful or advantageous inventions. But, he cautions, the gains they create come with unintended consequences and a cost that is usually not evident until after we have become habituated to their use. Hence, "The Medium is the Message." See the section starting on page 140. We will use some of McLuhan's most important ideas (and those of other thinkers) as we redefine the word *Information.*

Missing Information: see Data Glut's opposite side-effect, above.

Negation, or **Reversal:** In McLuhan's 4th Law of Media, the effect of a medium reaching the end of its useful or helpful function. See page 146.

Subtle Information: A term coined by your author, for Marshall McLuhan's idea that The Medium is the Message.

PART FOUR: INFORMATION
In 4 Types

This quote was hanging in my high school home room. It's a variation on a statement by Bernard Baruch, based on an idea from Thomas Jefferson:

> *In a democracy everyone has a right to their opinion. But no one has the right to be wrong about the facts on which their opinion is based.*

It's related to the notion that in the Age of Information, ignorance is a choice. Anti-intellectualism lets its followers pretend that they have the right to be wrong about the facts that form their opinions ... or formed their parents' opinions. It suggests, in fact, that it's OK to be willfully ignorant, even proud to be "less well educated" – the group that Trump loved so much.

We developed the mental capacity think to improve our chances for survival. It gave us the powers to remember, decide, and plan, mostly on the more basic levels of thinking. The case can and must be made that Information is one of the most critical parts of the failed thinking and the broken system that has brought us to this existential Crisis. A proper understanding and use of Information is essential to good decision-making in minds that exercise Free Will and participate in Democracies, especially for timely decisions in emergencies.

In the Inventory of the Stupid, a lack of education and the inability to process new Information are related. Our education often falls short, in that it generally doesn't cover the dynamics of Information, and the critical thinking skills needed to use it.

This topic may seem a little philosophical, abstract, or technical at times, but it is essential to understanding the complex maze of changes brought on by the Global Eco-Crisis.

FREE SPEECH

There's a good reason why the First Amendment is first (in the US Constitution, it guarantees freedom of speech, religion, assembly to protest, and the press). Thomas Jefferson, it's primary author, said (paraphrased),

> *If I had to decide between a country with a free press and no government, or one with a government but no free press, I'd choose the former.*

It's ironic if not insane that Conservatives get really squeamish when they have to defend the rights of liberals, progressives, or independent journalists. The "Hard Right" screams and wails about personal Liberty, but appears to not have a clue about the demands that true freedom and liberty make on the individual to be engaged, informed, and unbiased.

There is a vital and dynamic link between Information and freedom, one that Right Wingers have forgotten or chosen to deny. For the rest of us, it is blurred by the density of the digital data field and our confusions about what Information really is. We'll come back to this theme in a couple pages.

Just as there are different levels in our Thinking – for metaphor and irony for example – there are different levels and types of Information that influence our thoughts, plans, comprehension, perspective, and decisions, individually and as a species.

We look more closely here at the social, political, mediated, and perceptual forms of direct and indirect Information, the methods and means we use to communicate with each other, to make ourselves *In-Formed,* and to help us become engaged and aware citizens. While they don't correspond to levels of thinking, there are 4 fundamental classifications or types of Information – each makes different demands on us to be understood, and there are a couple, out of 4, that most of us have not recognized or thought about. They will prompt us to both limit and expand the way we conventionally think about Information, Time and Change.

Argument 19: Paradoxically, our conventional definition of Information is correct and incorrect: too broad, too narrow, inadequate, outdated, and incomplete.

At the most fundamental level, prior to any adjustment to the conventional definition, our public Information systems have been failing us, for most of the last half century. A Free Press, protected by the First Amendment, was meant to be a check on the possible failures of government. Sometimes called the *Fourth Estate*, it is needed to act almost like a 4th branch of the Democracy, without being part of the political system.

The purpose of the Free Press, originally limited to newspapers and other forms of print journalism, has now expanded to include TV and radio news and opinion, the internet and social media. Newspapers have been guilty at times of exaggerating or ignoring the truth, and often telling gross lies. But the nature of the medium, and competition among sources, made it easier to sift out the actual Fake News. The new forms make that vastly more difficult, mainly because people can choose the Information channels (radio, TV, internet, and streaming) that confirm their biases, feed their fears, or dodge the uncomfortable truths.

There are at leasst 8 problems with the current state of Information media, in its expanded role as an *Electronic Free Press*.

1. As mentioned above, it's harder than ever to identify and reject Fake News, especially now that it has 2 new meanings (beyond anti-factual news pretending to be truthful): the news some authority doesn't like, because it's true, and comic and satirical parodies of actual news, like the Daily Show (which is often and actually more honest and informative than the network news).

2. Corporate media news relies on advertising revenues, so it is swayed by the biased self-interest of the sponsors. This is even true of PBS, NPR, and other public-funded networks, because (though they deny it) they are indebted to corporate "partners," in the oil industry and others. IMHO, the Pacifica radio and TV networks, are the most consistently reliable.

3. News reporters rely on sources from within the govern-

ment, for interviews, commentary, verification, or denial. So they are reluctant to alienate their sources by reporting the hard truths about the actual *Swamp,* not the one Trump brought in.

So, both 3., above, and 4., below, include Mis- and Dis-Information, news that is actually faked. But more important, they lack Missing Information: important facts, opinions, and issues that are left completely out of sight, because some news executive or sponsor "doesn't think they are interesting," or because they are actually threatening to their interests.

4. The conditions in the real world have changed so much in the last half century, and mainly in the last decades – becoming far more complex and fast-moving – that it has become far more difficult for any citizen to keep up with the reporting; and more important, more difficult for reporters and commentators to stay relevant with in-depth and in-context reporting.

The world approaches a dangerous state in which it is becoming too complex and fast-moving for any entity to accurately describe, or any person, no matter how interested and engaged, to follow or comprehend. This is made worse by the nature of the new media, which have created a serious case of ...

5. Information Overload or what I call the Data Glut. The speed and complexity of the world is mirrored in a flood of mediated news, entertainment, commentary, and real and fake documentary reporting, that is impossible to sift through, trying to understand 4. a fast-moving and highly complex reality, so ...

6. Distraction, and an addiction to media entertainment with minimal meaningful content, makes our attention a commercial product, sold to advertisers, adding a layer to the Data Glut, and making it ever harder for us to understand our world, even when we can find reliable sources and honest reporters.

7. In a trend in the US, politics has morphed from a more-or-less balanced 2-party system, to a corrupt system dominated by Conservative, Capitalist, Militarist, and Exceptionalist factions. The power of Fox News, Hate Radio, and Toxic Internet commentary (Limbaugh, Drudge, Hannity, InfoWars) keeps a large fraction of the public engaged in a divide that just gets

more bitter, angry, isolated, and terribly mis-informed. (This topic is elaborated in the Millennial Divide, back on pages 116-9, and in the History of the Decline of the Left, ahead on page 190.)

8. Everything in this list so far is about what we accept and understand as Information Media in the conventional sense. We'll use that definition – spelled out 3 pages ahead – to start, and then we'll expand on it. We'll look at 2 or 3 kinds of Information that will both stretch and narrow that definition, and will explain different sets of dynamics that will both: make the conversation even more complex, temporarily, and then, hopefully, bring a new understanding of Information that is clearer and more understandable.

As primitive peoples, all our knowledge came to us through our eyes and ears and touch, and through the teachings of parents and elders. As we adapted to more and more forms of external knowledge – stories and books and pictures made by others, in other times – we developed a basic sense of how to judge reliability, by testing it against our own lived experience. But we have now moved beyond the simpler forms of *mediated* knowledge, to find we have to rely more and more on information that we could never experience directly or verify on our own. It's too much trouble to ask "Why?" or "How do you know?" about *everything*. Especially in this accelerated digital media environment.

We approach a dangerous threshold. Across it, all facts and fake news, knowledge, and blind faith *seem to* have the same value. The more we rely on virtual knowledge and the less we engage – directly, physically and mentally, simultaneously – with the dimensional world, in experiential time, we are less and less able to verify *anything* that *we think we know*.

"Reality"? Wait, I'll just Google that.

THE NEW *STUPID*?
This may be a new and special kind of stupid, one that feels like unlimited knowledge – *21st Century Stupid*. We find ourselves

in this dilemma exactly when most of the people in the world need an upgrade in their thinking, just to keep up with their experience, their society, and the world of virtual knowledge. The opposite is also true. To reject all new intelligence and information, because it doesn't agree with something *we think we know is true but isn't,* is equally new and especially stupid, even dangerous. Many of us have a problem accepting new information when it disagrees with our beliefs, even when we don't know how we came to believe them.

FREE WILL, FREEDOM AND INFORMATION

Our desire for Freedom and our trust in Democracy are rooted in our belief in our individual Free Will – the powers to decide, choose, and act without constraint (within the limits of the freedoms of others). We would not care about protecting our liberties if we didn't believe that we possess at least the possibility of exercising personal free will. But personal free will and public freedoms are meaningless without four conditions:

    1) understanding what is going on around us;

    2) recognizing when a decision is necessary;

    3) having valid information and the ability to understand it in context, and to use it to make a timely decision; and,

    4) having the power – personal or political – to put a decision into effect, to have it implemented.

    The Powers to Know, Decide (in Time) and Act. Those are all aspects of the dynamics of Information, Freedom, Democracy, and Change. And they are at the heart of the Eco-Crisis – its causes and impacts, our Denial and our leaders' failure to imagine a plan to reverse it.

FREEDOM FROM, FREEDOM TO

Let's start with the easy part and get it out of the way. There are *Freedoms From*, and there are *Freedoms To*. For example, we would probably agree we'd like to be *free from* crime, disease and exploitation, and to be *free to* choose our own diets, houses of worship, political parties, amusements, career paths and mates.

More broadly, we want to be *free to* think and act independently, and *free from* public deceptions and illegitimate authority. But let's put Freedom in the context of the Global Eco-Crisis.

No one on the planet today is FREE FROM the impacts of man-made climate change.

And none of our children will be FREE TO enjoy a world as stable or as healthy as the one we inherited.

Most of us living today have never had the *freedom to* choose a candidate or a ballot proposition that proposes a long term goal of eco-sustainability, or any long-term vision at all. And for eighty years we have not had the *freedom to* choose a political party or candidate who would stand up to injustice or the corrupting influence of big money.

For generations, only a few of us have used the FREEDOM TO KNOW about the condition of the Earth or the risks of environmental damage.

It's one thing to fail to search out inconvenient truths or to deny them. It's something else to be prevented from access to that Information. But it's different, and much worse, to not know that Information exists, or how crucial and scary it is. Do you recognize that description? *Blind spots do not only hide Information, they conceal the fact that information is missing.*

> *Argument 20:* At the peak of the age, Information essential to critical decisions is delayed, distorted, confused with trivia, ignored, misunderstood, or missing altogether.

> *Argument 21:* We can't have true freedom without a working democracy. We can't have a working democracy without free and full Information. We can't have either when the information media and the government are both corporate-owned, or when facts become partisan.

REDEFINING INFORMATION AS 4 TYPES
• We start with the conventional definition of Information, how we use it – mostly correctly – and why it is confusing, both too broad and incomplete.
• We have to clarify the difference between Data and Information, and to establish why it's important.
• Then we'll go on to discuss a couple crucially important forms of Information that we overlook, underestimate, or never even consider.
• We will introduce a new, broader and more encompassing definition of Information as the *Combined Forces of Change.*

That discussion will carry us into Part Five, where we start to think differently about Power, and create some new Information about Power, in order to understand, and eventually fight those who habitually and cruelly abuse it.

THE CONVENTIONAL DEFINITION:
The way we conventionally think about Information is not wrong or stupid. Paradoxically, and to expand on Argument 19, it is correct *and* incorrect, too broad, too narrow, and incomplete. It's something like this:

> ***The transfer, through education and media, of facts, opinions, entertainment, and knowledge to help us manage our lives and our world.***

In a Democracy, we need access to an ongoing supply of news, current events, updated history, and opinion, to be well enough informed to vote intelligently and responsibly. We need for that information to be *objective*, which has almost become an obsolete idea, as if no one can really be objective; so instead we say *without apparent bias, omissions, or mistaken assumptions*; specifically *without* the thumb on the scale of virtually every sponsored corporate program or podcast.

We need to carry the discussion of *Exformation* forward by making 3 points: One, that our five or six (or more) sensory perception organs are in fact Information-collecting and -processing systems. Another that we may not notice, may forget or take completely for granted, is that all the messages we receive, face to face or over our many media, have to be absorbed through our senses before they can be consciously interpreted. A third is that we may not realize the many layers of decoding and inter-pretation our minds have to do, mostly by unconscious habit, to understand perceptions or messages.

TYPE 1 AND TYPE 2: PERCEPTION AND MESSAGES
Of the 4 types, we will call the first 2 Overt (vs. Covert); we are generally aware of them as Data and as having meaning; we can all basically agree on how they work.

Type 1: Exformation. We established that the process of pat-tern recognition forms the fundamental building blocks for our minds, and the basis for all of our knowledge. The patterns we recognize are all combinations of sensory stimuli: sights, sounds, touch, taste, and body kinetics. We have to accept that process as our first and most fundamental Information gathering skill.

Type 2: Messages. Our definition of *Messages* comes the closest to the conventional meaning. We will need to distinguish it from mere Data, as we generally confuse the 2. We have to start with a digression that will help clarify these first 2 Types, and when and how they are connected.

INFORMATION AS DIFFERENCE AND CHANGE
Gregory Bateson (1904-1980) came before Tor Norretranders, but some of his ideas are coherent with and complementary to the idea of Exformation. Bateson was a biologist, anthropolo-gist, philosopher, and teacher. He would challenge his students to explain how they knew that a leaf, a seashell, a lobster claw or a tree branch was, or had once been alive or part of a living thing. They were stumped. "We just know it." "It's obvious." He prodded, "But *how* do you know?" After a bit more prompt-

ing they realized that they observed a "pattern of growth." See the connection? It's a great example of how we use our earliest knowledge without knowing how we acquired or created it.

Bateson gives us a definition of Information that is essential. It is not complete, but it is fundamental to a new understanding, the idea that Information is best comprehended as a *Force of Change*. It is different from the conventional definition, less inclusive, yet broader, more specific and important in this new context. In addition to what we've laid out so far, we can look more carefully at Sense Perceptions and Messages by observing how we notice newness or difference, and how they create change. Bateson defined conventional forms of Information – our Sensory / Perceptual Systems and Messages – in terms of the *differences* they make in our thinking or our behavior.

DATA AND INFORMATION: At the most basic level, Bateson clears up our confusion about the difference between *Data* and *Information*. In doing so, he describes two significant thresholds or barriers that Data has to cross, in our perception and in our minds or actions, for it to become Information. Bateson said (paraphrased in part):

> **"Information is the difference that makes a difference."** ... *a change in attention that leads to a change in thinking or behavior.*

In a longer discussion of that statement, Bateson makes two clear points. First, everything is *Data*. Every *bit* or *byte* of stimulus available to our senses is part of the *data array,* the combined fields of our experience, the mix of changing sights and sounds, smells, textures, temperature, taste, and three dimensional space that surrounds us – the perceivable world, including of course all messages, media and technologies. It all remains Data until it crosses two specific thresholds.

For a cluster of data – a sight or sound in our presence, or a phrase, spoken or read from a page, or an image on a screen

– to have the potential of becoming Information, it has to cross the first threshold, penetrate the first barrier. It has to *get our attention*, as something different from what we *expect*, something that doesn't fit the pattern of normal experience. Whether it's a baseball flying over the fence from the schoolyard, or a new idea coded in letters on a page, we first have to notice it. It has to *stand out* from the background of our expectations, memory and experience, and from all the things we think of as known or predictable. That's the *first difference*.

And second, to become what Bateson implies and what I think of as *Real Information,* or to be *truly In-formative,* the thing we have noticed has to create a change in our thinking or our behavior. That's the *second difference.* So here's a new definition:

> **Information represents the combined forces of mental and physical change, in individuals, society, the natural world, and in civilization.**

As helpful as the new definition is, it still needs clarification. How much change? The degree of change induced by real Information can be tiny or great. The bell on the stove reminds me to turn off the water boiling the frog ... I mean the eggs. The voice on the phone tells me a sibling has met a violent death. The pixels on the TV make an image of huge buildings collapsing. A subtle pressure in the lower abdomen gets me up from the computer to go pee. A shortness of breath leads to a triple bypass. A random idea in a book changes a life. Or goes unnoticed.

The Difference that Makes a Difference helps us to think a little differently and to form a new, arguably fundamental understanding about *Real Information.* If we are not changed, it is only *Data.* But if we don't notice or pay attention to the difference in the Data, it has no chance of changing us (exceptions to be noted). If we are truly *In-formed,* we think or act differently than we did before (without exception).

There are other complexities among these distinctions.

Our attention is not always reliable, especially in a dense and fast-changing data environment. It could fail us and we might not notice the thing that is really important, a baseball flying through the air toward my head for example, or carbon accumulating in the atmosphere. I would still be *Informed* by the baseball and the carbon, but the noticing and the change would occur at the same time: OUCH! ... too late to duck – or, GASP! ... the planet has become unlivable.

With Global Warming, we generally don't notice the data in our day-to-day lives, unless we live in the Arctic or on a flat island in the ocean ... or unless we pay attention to the science. And in a state of Information Overload, we may simply fail to pay attention to the facts that matter. Within the Eco-Crisis or separate from it, we could notice something and dismiss it as familiar and unimportant – or as impossible – preventing it from becoming potential Information. But then later, something else would make us reconsider, reevaluate and be changed. Or in reverse, we could notice something, find it significant, and change – our mind or behavior – and then later find the data was wrong. We might even find it difficult to change back, even when we discover the mistake. Think about the *Deniers, Confirmation Bias,* and the refusal to admit mistakes.

In that case, finding out we were tricked into believing bad Information would itself become new Information ... *IF we accept it.* It gets complicated. And then it gets simpler.

The relevance to the Eco-Crisis should be obvious. At our present rate of noticing and changing, the entire human race may notice and adjust to the *correct* Information – that radical climate action is urgent and necessary – only when environmental collapse demonstrates that we mis-informed ourselves when we didn't notice or believe that truth. For decades.

INFORMATION, TIME AND TIMING, IN MESSAGES
Important data becomes available to us at a moment in time. It may be complete or missing pieces. We notice it and pay attention, within seconds, days or years, or we don't. We interpret

and absorb it at a moment in time. If we need to make a critical decision, we learn that at a moment in time. The sequence of those events can include life-or-death variables. Incomplete Information can lead to bad decisions.

> *Information received after a decision was needed leads to decisions that are too late or wrong, either useless or tragic.*

Critical Information received after the wrong decision was made, or where no decision could be made in time, is only useful as a lesson, and equally tragic.

The worst case, in the context of decision-making, and in the case of the Global Environmental Crisis, is coming to the stark realization that the emergency decisions – that we now see as essential to our survival – needed to be made decades ago.

> *At this rate, by the time we understand the urgency of the Crisis, or what we needed to do to avoid it, it will be too late to matter.*

LATENCY KILLS: Online video gamers have – or had – an expression for a technological delay between the moments that a decision is needed, made and registered. Depending on the bandwidth or response time in their web-access link, two gamers playing at a distance could make a crucial decision at exactly the same instant, but because of a time delay in the technology, one would register more slowly. Such tiny delays could make the difference between winning and losing. The delay was called *lag* or *latency*, as in "latency kills." Consider this when you think about the missing Information, the power of the Deniers, or the near paralysis in our government.

> *Argument 22: In life-and-death emergencies, even short delays in the Information-decision-action cycle can make the critical difference.*

137

WHAT DO WE KNOW?
     WHEN DO WE KNOW IT?
          HOW DO WE KNOW?

In my Media Fundamentals classes I used to bring Alfred Hitch-cock (the great film director) and Richard Nixon (the disgraced president) together (only in spirit, in my lecture) to make an important point about Information. Explaining his approach to visual story-telling, Hitchcock said, (paraphrased) "It doesn't so much matter what happens to the characters, what they say or do. What's important is what the audience knows and when they know it, relative to what the characters *appear* to know."

The tipping point in President Richard Nixon's downfall was when Republican Senator Howard Baker asked, "What did the President know and *when did he know it?*" This in response to Nixon's claims of non-involvement in the Watergate break-in, when recordings proved otherwise.

> *"What do we know? When do we know it? And how do we know?" Where Hitchcock and Nixon meet.*

To illustrate the idea, I'd show some clips of Hitchcock films that demonstrated how he made stuff so suspenseful. I'd screen some examples of jump cuts and flash-forwards to show how the directors of French New Wave challenged their viewers by compressing and distorting time.

When I put my *Hitchcock Meets Nixon* lecture together I had no idea it would play a part in this book. I was just trying to communicate a point about narrative structure and how it en-gages us over Time. Only later did it became evident that those issues are relevant to theories of Information and the Eco-Crisis and how our government deals with it ... or fails to.

MULTIPLE LAGS: There have been growing lags between: the time the vital Information was available, but hidden or ob-scured, 40-plus years ago; the time when we *began to* get the clear Information that was missing, say around 2000; the time that decisions were needed, well before 2000; and the time they will finally get made, in the very near future, or too late.

> *"What we didn't know and when we didn't know it." may become an epitaph for a civilization that is committing accidental suicide.*

This concludes our exploration of Information in the conventional definition, including Messages and the idea of Exformation, but this side glance at narrative – storytelling – will come up again.

I'm trying something here that I have not seen anyone else attempt: to cover 2 Overt and 2 Covert Types of Information into a new definition in a coherent manner. It is not hard to describe the 2 Overt forms of Information, sensory Perception and Messages, in terms of the 2 differences. It's harder with *Subliminal* and *Subtle* forms. In the pages ahead, I'll try to do that as well. Bateson did not extend his idea into those realms, but the 2 differences still apply, though they occur in different orders in time. All 4 types have different relationships with data and time and change.

TYPES 3 AND 4: SUBLIMINAL AND *SUBTLE* INFORMATION
I call the 3rd and 4th Types *Covert* because they are not evident as (different) Data, and their impacts are generally not observed or understood as being *Informative,* until possibly later.

Type 3: Subliminal Information. We laid the groundwork for a discussion of the unconscious mind (or *subconscious*) in the part about mental Blind Spots and unconscious Denial.

For this to make sense and have meaning, – for it to be *In-Formative* – we have to accept the idea that we all have an unconscious mind, and that it has unknown levels of influence over our conscious minds, unless and until we begin to understand its operations ... a little at least.

Subliminal (or unconscious) communication occurs between people in face-to-face conversations. Unconscious feelings and attitudes are communicated through body language and tone of voice, for example, without conscious intention or awareness. It is used, consciously and intentionally, between performers, art and media programs, and their audiences, but it also has intuitive and unconscious overtones that the artists may not recognize they are using.

Messages are sent, consciously and intentionally, from specific sources to our unconscious minds (in advertising and in propaganda), or through the cultural unconscious, often involving fear, to manipulate our attitudes and habits, from political to personal to financial and beyond.

For example, it's arguably true that we have been brainwashed to think our materialist prosperity is a genuine entitlement, something we have worked for and deserve, and that it has no negative consequences; or to believe that GW/CC is a hoax, or benign, or happening too slow to matter.

This discussion bridges Part Four here, and Part Five, coming up, because the power of the unconscious mind appears in 2 contexts: here as 1 of 2 Covert forms of Information; and later as a possible actor in human nature writ large, in the context of Power. Beyond Subliminal communications, the power of the unconscious will play a large part in our later arguments.

Type 4: Subtle Information. Marshall McLuhan (1911-1980) was a Canadian intellectual and philosopher of communication media. You may recognize his catchphrase, "The Medium is the Message." That is the essence of this 4th type of Information.

I made up the term *Subtle Information* for McLuhan's *Message in the Medium*.

He predicted the Internet 20 years before it was engineered and put into popular use. The prediction was illustrated by his idea of a "global village," a global communication network that would make us all members in a global community. 30 years into the popular use of the internet, we could discuss how much
140

of that has become true, either beneficial or harmful. He could only hint at the possible unintended consequences. We may see them more clearly.

Marshall McLuhan gave us a broad and radical definition of Information as the changes we go through, too fast or slow to notice, individually and culturally, as we adapt to new technologies.

McLuhan's study of communication media explored the broad impacts of the printing press, and evolved to include electronic communications from the telegraph and radio to TV and the computer. His theories went on to include all forms of tools, and he expanded his definition of *media* and *technology* to include almost everything human-made, including toys and clothing, religious dogma and advertisements.

McLuhan often framed his insights and warnings in layers of jargon. He acquired an unusual celebrity status for a professor. It's hard to know which – jargon or actual insights – were cause or effect of the celebrity. The combination made it too easy for his critics – and those who just didn't *get it* – to dismiss him.

As much as I have studied the man's work, I often find new twists and the occasional glitch. For example he found advertising abhorrent, and corporate control of media evil, but he thought Capitalism was fine. And I never fully understood what he meant by *Hot* and *Cool Media*. Nevertheless, my faith in (what I see as) his core ideas stands firm.

Forty years on, in the context of our abuse of industrial technology, and the Global Eco-Crisis, I think we are dangerously late in understanding the *what, how* and *why* of his warnings.

I urge you to research more of the man's work: the idea, for example, that every technology *extends* (or is an *extension* of) a human limb, organ, activity, or skill, into the uses of the technology; and that, in spite of obvious benefits, the *extensions* almost always come with a cost or unintended consequence that remains unnoticed until after we have become habituated – even addicted – to the new tool or system. He also formulated his 4

141

Laws of Media, which we will only skim over, except for the 4th, which is the most crucially important.

He became alarmed at the way we adapt so quickly to new technologies, and at the ways we overlook the side-effects. McLuhan's basic arguments are surprisingly simple and profound, with far-reaching implications. We have yet to understand most of them, or to incorporate them into our culture. McLuhan's followers think he was one of the most eclectic and prescient thinkers in the second half of the 20th century, and that his ideas are more critically relevant today than ever.

I introduce McLuhan here because we can think of the Eco-Crisis broadly as the unintended consequence of an addiction to fossil-fueled technology, and the materialism, waste, and excessive consumption that it has produced. The point is that we were not aware of the huge changes we were making, in ourselves, to our society or the Earth, as those habits formed; we didn't *pay attention* to the *differences,* we only felt the benefits. The data was outside our awareness ... until now, when we find those addictions enormously hard to break.

McLuhan echoed Alfred North Whitehead, who foresaw such issues much earlier. Whitehead said, "We shape our tools and thereafter our tools shape us." In other words,

> **The human makes the tool, then the tool remakes humanity and the world.**

Here are 3 real world examples of McLuhan's Message in the Medium (and 1 more later):

THE AUTOMOBILE: McLuhan said that the wheel, then the horse-drawn carriage, and later the car and its engine, were *extensions* of the foot, the leg, and the heart and lungs that power them. Like many new technologies, the first *Horseless Carriages* were seen as toys for the rich, or as a nuisance.

The first side effect of the automobile was to start transforming the landscape into highways and suburbs. By the time they became necessities for most of the middle class, cars changed the way we organize our lives and became a necessity. They fundamentally altered the nature of the economy – from agriculture to oil – and started to upset the stability of the global climate. We have barely begun to adjust our thinking to the fact that our oil addiction has created negative impacts that far outweigh the benefits of the motorcar. Yes I said it and believe it's true.

At their best and worst, cars are motorized suits of armor with faces and attitudes, projecting our identity, status and power to the world.

We can outline **McLuhan's 4 Laws of Media** (new technologies), as we go through these examples. **McLuhan's 1st Law of Media** is obvious: *Every new technology improves on an existing one.* Cars replaced horses as the power in most forms of local, personal transportation, and competed with trains for inter city travel.

THE BOMB: In the waning years of World War II, the US tasked J. Robert Oppenheimer (1904-1967), a physics professor at the University of California, Berkeley, with managing the "Manhattan Project," the design and construction of the first nuclear bombs. While he had grave doubts about the wisdom of the project, he could not resist the technical, creative, and administrative challenges. This is a key feature in *Subtle Information*.

In public testimony, he later explained away the dilemma faced by most inventors, but acknowledged by very few until after the fact. Oppenheimer said, "When you see something that is technically sweet, you go ahead and do it and you argue about what to do about it only after you have had your technical success. That is the way it was with the atomic bomb."

Once underway, it is nearly impossible to pause such a process of invention, no matter the reason. Questions about side effects and unintended consequences – foresight generally – are all dismissed in the quest for the powerful new thing, no matter its purpose. There is an almost inevitable cycle, from imagining the new thing, to designing, building, and testing prototypes, to mass production, to wide acceptance by the public, then market dominance, and addiction.

After the team produced a working bomb, Oppenheimer was humiliated and excluded from the recognition and appreciation, because of his leftist beliefs and his pacifist qualms. The international Arms Race was launched when other nations acquired The Bomb. It led to an incredibly expensive and dangerous 40-year Cold War. We somehow came to believe that *mutually assured destruction – MAD –* was the only path to stability and peace. Now, after a couple generations of moderation and weapons reductions, Trump has launched a new Cold War with North Korea ... and possibly with other nations like Iran.

> *"Your scientists were so preoccupied with whether they could that they didn't stop to think if they should."* Dr. Ian Malcolm, Jurassic Park

McLuhan's 2nd Law of Media: *Every new technology obsolesces the earlier one – makes it useless.* Also fairly obvious, but not always true. The Bomb was supposed to make global war obsolete, because it would mean total devastation, and no leader would risk provoking it. The threat of nuclear war may have fostered the trend toward many smaller, local, and proxy wars. And it just made total war more competitive and dangerous ... and costly ... with huge unintended consequences: the dual industries of nuclear generation of electrical power (totally overrated, inefficient, leaving massive quantities of toxic waste), and nuclear weapons. And it made local wars and terrorism the new normal. Including the possible use of The Bomb by terrorists.

THE TELEVISION: Television has been called the "bastard child of radio and film," implying it embodies the corruption or the shame of both. Television rearranged our living spaces – by making the TV the focal point in any room – and, later, disrupted shared family time by sending us off into separate rooms to watch our different shows. Television, more than any other medium, transformed advertising from an annoying but benign source of production funding (in print for example), to a pervasive, high-tech form of mind control. Many people think advertising is essential to the success of the internet. I think it is ruining it. This topic will come up again later.

McLuhan said that the TV (expanding on the camera and the radio) is an *extension* of our eyes and ears (but not our mouths or hands), operating exclusively in one direction, from the maker to us, with no opportunity for feedback or a two-way communication ... other than switching channels or buying the advertised products. The cynical joke was, the news and dramas show you all the things you can watch but can't control, and the ads show you the few things you can control.

The wasteful consumer economy that emerged in the 1950s in the US, creating a model for the Western world (and developing countries as well), was dependent on TV advertising for its success. It transformed the cultural *mirror* in which Americans saw themselves (or didn't, depending on their race and socio/economic status) – it made us believe that our well-being, social citizenship, and identity depended on our ability to buy the advertised thing. TV ads helped turn thoughtful voters into passive viewers and responsible citizens into anxious consumers. This happened in parallel with the Great Dumbing Down; the two in combination have nearly killed critical thinking in the US.

The materialist consumer fantasy that advertising promotes contributes as much to environmental degradation as any other factor. TV helps to hide the militaristic base of the economy and the waste inherent to conspicuous consuming, while promoting an illusion of an entitled and privileged *Good Life*. The environmental side-effects are rivaled only by the weapons industry, factory-farmed meat and vehicle emissions. Excessive consumer spending and the military continue to be the two biggest *non-essential* pieces of the US economy.

145

A TOASTER WITH PICTURES?
Mark Fowler was Ronald Reagan's appointee for chairman of the FCC (Federal Communications Commission) in the early 1980s. He argued that critics of the TV medium like McLuhan were deluded alarmists, and argued for the de-regulation of broadcasting. He said that TV was nothing but "a toaster with pictures," meaning it was an innocuous form of diversion and entertainment. The number of commercials children saw per year doubled from 20,000 in the late 1970's to about 40,000 in 1987. And they continue to multiply, in number and in their power over our unconscious impulses, and our children's.

> *McLuhan believers think that the harshest criticisms of the television medium are gross understatements.*

McLuhan's 3rd Law of Media, is not so obvious, and not very important. But it appears to be novel, interesting, counter-intuitive and often true. It says *Every new technology will revive or retrieve an earlier technology,* as a form of nostalgia or art, like an antique. He argues that the TV replaced fireplaces, as the center of the living space, and that the TV retrieves the function of earlier fireplaces – heat and light with almost no content.

> *Someone's grandma, who never heard of McLuhan, was quoted as saying, "We don't need a TV. We still use our fireplace."*

NO TECHNOLOGY IS EVER NEUTRAL
McLuhan says that no medium or technology is ever *neutral*, a mere transmitter of a message or performer of a task. No tool or medium is ever a transparent facilitator.

McLuhan's 4th Law of Media (absolutely the most important): *Every new technology will negate or reverse its original intended function, or will at least come to the end of its usefulness, often suddenly.*

Our adaptation to new tools creates fundamental changes in us and in the world, beyond their intended uses, in every instance, outside of our awareness – as the car, the bomb and the TV did to our lives and our world – until the adaptation has become irreversible.

According to McLuhan, *EVERY NEW TECHNOLOGY* will create three impacts that remain imperceptible ... until it's too late to replace, reverse, or correct:

• Our habitual use of a tool or medium will always distort the intended message or function; and,

• Virtually every prolonged use of a popular tool or medium will have a negative impact on us the users, on society, on the human-made world and on the Earth, often greater than the value of any message or intended function.

• By the time we recognize the unintended consequences, we will have become addicted to the new technology and will find it nearly impossible to abandon. It tends to enforce the ongoing cycle of demand for more and more new technologies ... that we may not really need or even want, except for the demand created by advertising.

These sound like sweeping generalizations and they are. We could say "some technologies" or "comparable changes" or "some of the time," or "nearly irreversible." But here again, we're trying to draw a big picture. There may be exceptions to every generalization, but if we use them to ignore the larger pattern, they are trivial distractions, if not deceptions.

THE INTERNET: Please notice that we are barely beginning to notice the monumental changes that computers, smart phones, and the internet are making in our lives. Aside from the obvious benefits, real and exaggerated, we don't think about the chaos that will be caused if and when such systems start to fail (or are sabotaged). Aside from the social changes cited earlier, we have not started to imagine their other possible unintended consequences. The less they are noticed, the more likely they will be

147

serious. They will affect the value of knowledge and original or critical thinking for a generation at the very least. They have already disconnected many of us from the here and now of our existence in time and space, so we can network socially with friends at a distance or at a later time. Observe how many teenagers cannot stand to spend time alone or without their devices. Try to imagine the impacts on knowledge generally when so much *apparent* knowledge is available online, but will remain incomprehensible without the context that conventional learning provides. To the young people who are already abnormally distanced from nature, the impacts are beyond scary.

Never mind the comedians who produce their version of *Fake News*. The impacts of Trump's false use of "Fake News," combined with Fox and Russia flooding the airwaves, cable and internet with manufactured lies, have already altered what the general public will believe or reject, regardless of whether it is true or not, scientifically or journalistically. Not to mention their gut punch to the core of our Democracy.

Governments have already started to refer to international hacking, including possible hacks of election and financial controls, energy grids and weapons systems, as the equivalent of actual war.

SAVE US?

McLuhan, as I understand him, presumed to take over from the government its failure *to protect us from ourselves* – assuming we can agree that is something government *ought to* do, if and when it can. In the impacts of technological media,

> *McLuhan saw that the roles of the message and medium have been reversed. The purpose of a tool has less of an impact than our use-habits.*

The reorganization of our lives and minds, around media usage, is more trans-formative than any of the meaning we may extract from media programs, and generates more real change in our lives than the actual work that any tool performs.

> *Argument 23: If we believe McLuhan, every technology will begin to reverse or negate its benefits after our adaptation to it has become an addiction.*

And we have not noticed. In a bigger picture, we have missed the vital first difference new Information needs to make; we have adapted to the new Information media without noticing we have done so, or how and how much it has changed us.

Our adaptation to any medium of communication gradually *changes* or *informs* us more deeply than any group of messages that the medium transmits. Our dependence on the simple *thing that is a tool* – airplane, hammer, smart phone – *changes us more* than the work that is done when we use it ... because of how *we adapt our behavior and thinking* to its patterns of usage. What the medium was supposed to help us say or do has been drowned out by the way it transformed our society. What the technology was supposed to do or make has been trivialized by how it has made us technology and energy addicts.

One careful observer says that McLuhan's most valuable insight is to observe, especially in emergencies, that ...

> **... the changes that we fail to notice, or take for granted, are among the most important (and risky) aspects of our lives and culture.**

When we tend to ignore or forget the role of our bodily sensations as Information systems, it diminishes both, our direct engagement with the perceptible world, and our ability to decode Messages. And when conventional Message systems are distorted by the influence of corporate profits, our ability to function as responsible citizens in a working democracy are severely undermined. When we remain unaware of 2 powerful forms of Covert Information, in our minds and our lives, we've invited ignorance and passivity to stand in for our ability to be free persons.

BREAKING NEWS AND A COMMERCIAL BREAK
Between the Part on Information, now ending, and the Part about Power, just ahead, two short additions are needed, one new in 2018, one about 50 years old. One is news. The other is about advertising. The connection between them, BTW, evident on many other pages here, is corruption of the news, and the ethical compromise of *TWO* predominant media business models.

BREAKING (Summer 2018): Facebook executives have been apologizing and scrambling to correct sloppy, possibly corrupt, access to the personal data of millions of us – Facebook users *and* their non-user friends. A variety of practices – hacking, data-mining and -selling, personal profiling, online bot activity, targeted negative messaging, and other new wrinkles in electoral messaging – are assumed to have influenced the 2016 election in favor of Trump. When the methods, the impacts, and the implications of those practices are fully understood, it will be way too late to undo any damage done, like the "election" of Donald Trump, and way too late to prevent the next round of the same thing, unless some honest politicians rise up and demand better internet security. We will probably find entire new generations of algorithms that can do the same stuff differently and better, with different keyholes on our privacy.

It is not only an example of McLuhan's 4th Law, *Negation* or *Reversal*. In my view it warrants a new, 5th fundamental Type of Information (after Perception, Messages, Unconscious/Subliminal, and Subtle, Message-in-the-Medium).

The pattern is related to subliminal propaganda, and it is a glitch within a medium that has advanced to the stage where it negates its perceived benefit, beyond what McLuhan's 4th Law describes. It relies on innovations in software, algorithms, that are completely unethical; these practices escape even the engineers that design the systems that allow them access. But beyond that, they performs actions, and have impacts, unlike any of the other 4 types of Information, and they are a new and distinct Force

150

of Change, beyond our revised definition. They operate on the ability to stack illusion upon illusion, and disguise lie upon lie, within an addictive technological interface. It has made thousands, possibly millions of us believe Fake News, so convincing that the corrections trigger hard Denial.

A World Affairs Council program featured Janine Zakaria, the host Jane Wales, and references to designer Tristan Harris, and brought a man named Roger McNamee to my attention. He was a supporter of Mark Zuckerberg and Facebook from the very beginning, but is now a harsh critic. Among several brilliant observations, McNamee points out that the Achilles Heel of Facebook, its inherent vulnerability to corruption and abuse, rests, from the beginning, in the fact that Facebook's business model has relied, and will continue to rely on Advertising. How and why? Because that system depends on continually stimulating our attention and bending it toward purchases (which is the real product of all advertising) or votes (the product of political brainwashing); that tactic in turns enforces the addictive nature of Social Media generally, because it feeds on spectacle and shock, flash, fear, and impulses to irrational desire; and because that makes us especially vulnerable to False Information. Jump ahead to page 167 to "Are you scared?"

AND NOW THIS (A word from a critic of sponsorship. This section was dropped from the earlier version, and re-imported as a footnote to Facebook's business model.)

MY LOVE-HATE RELATIONSHIP WITH ADVERTISING
As an artist/designer, an avid fan of films, and a teacher of filmmaking, I came to appreciate advertising, on one hand, as a brilliant form of expression. The high-end TV spot is one of the most powerful forms of communication ever imagined or created. The plots and acting rival the dramas and comedies in prime time and on the big screen. The talent, time, material, and energy that go into each Super Bowl ad cost as much as some feature films, $20 million to $80 million. The camera work is

stunning, the editing, a masterful play on our attention spans and our visual perception. The digital effects create imaginary worlds that can be visited by conscious and unconscious minds (while prompting a future purchase). The subliminal impacts are as powerful as they are well-hidden, as impressive as any visual ideology in the world.

> *In my opinion, the 30-second spot is the Sistine Ceiling of the 20th century, the most compressed form of emotion and ideas in the culture.*

I appreciate the visual brilliance, the graphic power, the cinematic style, the humor, wit, and entertainment value of high quality TV ads. Advertising is the only place where the power of the market, the power of Information (of all 4 types), and the power of the unconscious meet and interact, and direct our lives far more than we know, far, far more than we would allow if we understood the connections.

So on the other hand, I realized that television advertising is the most manipulative, cynical and destructive form of mass mind control ever conceived by human beings, including physical torture and internet bots, which are much less effective, because advertising tricks us into being its friend. If the public understood a fraction of the unconscious propaganda they have absorbed via advertising, since childhood, shaping entire mental landscapes, they'd demand another way to pay for their media. So I also harbor a deep and abiding hatred for advertising.

Advertising and political media propaganda play a key role in the Power and the preservation of a destructive, militarist, consumption-and-waste economy. It has an enormous role in the corrupt politics of the United States, from conservative fear-mongering (gays, atheists, abortion, Arabs, taxes) to military adventurism. It is one force that drives the industrial/financial momentum that prevents environmental justice and a sustainable economy.

In an imaginary world, where a majority of politicians are

honest, and laws reflect our core values, and are enforced, commercial media revenues would be seen for what they are, *AN ADVERTISING TAX*, on every item that appears in an ad. When that tax is added up – over $600 Billion annually, and portioned out, it means we each pay $100. to $500. per year (global per person average), just for the ads on stuff we buy. And, like the L-Curve, the global per person average is deceptive, because people in developed nations see and absorb more ads, and spend far more on consumables, than the global average; so for us the tax could easily be $500. to $5000./year.

And that registers only the direct cash costs of the industry. Advertising is also a corrupt and invisible TAX – as in *burden and dissipated energy* – on our unconscious minds, on our politics, on our social interactions, *AND ON THE HEALTH OF THE EARTH*, because advertising, more than any other single force, drives the global consumption-and-waste Economy. Advertising, in my view, exercises Abusive Power comparable only to mass violence and war – especially as manipulated by unseen forces, from Monsanto, Northrop Grumman, and Pfizer, to Russia and the GOP – through the addictive forms of TV and Social Media.

In Part Six we talk about Asymmetrical Information as one of the flaws in the Capitalist system. It's part of the idea that every financial transaction, in addition to the exchange of money and something of value, is an exchange of information that can be transparent, honest and complete or asymmetrical, in which one or the other party suffers from a lack of accurate information. In my mind, Advertising is one of the most blatant and unacknowledged, persistent and intentional uses of Asymmetrical Information.

GLOSSARY FOR PART FIVE

Hierarchy: A system that defines difference in priority, preference, access to power, etc. In this context we look at 3 fundamental unconscious forces, their relative power, and their roles in our lives, politics, economics, and in our widely varying uses of those forces.

Organizing Principle: Used in the context of power, and in politics and economics, for example, Defined on page 156.

PART FIVE: POWER
As An Organizing Principle

Global Warming/Climate Change, the burning edge of the Global Environmental Crisis, is caused by the human Abuse of the Power of fossil fuels. If we had the foresight to act on existing knowledge, in 1962, 1980, or 2000, or if Exxon and the American Petroleum Institute had shared their thorough and compelling research, in 1970 (jump to page 268 for a full explanation), we might have prevented some of the obvious damage fossil fuels have done over that span of time. Men in Power still ignore that knowledge, because they are paid to, while the momentum of industrial waste rolls on and becomes ever harder to stop, slow, or turn in a different direction.

> *Any solution to the Crisis will require a Power struggle. A broad vision of the role of Power in all of our lives will help prepare us.*

We will benefit from a better understanding of Power in all its forms: political, economic, technological, social, emotional, and psychological. And by understanding how Abusive Power is exercised, mostly by men, through anger, violence, domination, and the destruction of the Earth. Men who are unmoved by the natural beauty of the Earth, and ignorant of the fragility of the ecosystem – men who don't care to know about Nature's limited resilience – do not deserve Power over the Earth or its inhabitants, the rest of us. We need to exercise our Power to stop them.

Power is Abused in an illegitimate and paranoid lust for more Power, in the form of cheap or stolen resources, in the exploitation of the Powerless, and in the pointless accumulation of unlimited wealth – Power in one of its most destructive forms. We need to recognize the pattern of wealth extraction, and the destruction left in its wake.

Our Powers are manifested in so many destructive practices, it's hard even to notice the few that express our creativity, without inflicting collateral damage. We listed a few of the most significant, in references to our shared intelligence, back on page 89.

We must recognize Power as a motivating force and as an organizing principle in our civilization and our individual lives. We have to try to understand large scale Abuses of Power and to stop tolerating them. And we have to look for the roots of the need for Power – real, symbolic, rational, irrational, creative, destructive, and unconscious – within ourselves.

> *Argument 24: A "power instinct" is at the mental, emotional, and historical root of most human impulses. Understanding it and changing our expressions of it are keys to managing the Crisis.*

ORGANIZING PRINCIPLE?

You may or may not be familiar with the term. Its general meaning is, *A set of core values that a system is built upon, that define how people and other dynamics interact to fulfill the objectives of the system.*

The term is used in two different but related contexts:
1. A principle or a set of values as defined in advance, in the creation of some entity, like a business, organization, or service, to fulfill predetermined objectives – like a mission statement.
2. A core principle or a set of values that is revealed at the base of an entity *without it having been consciously or intentionally designed* into a system. Its impacts for good or ill can be revealed to be different from the intended or desired values.

Power has evolutionary roots deep in our past, in the *Fight or Flight* instincts at the center of our brains and our guts, and in our need for physical Power, evolving from muscular strength, to hand tools, to fuel to cook our food and heat our homes, to the energy systems that drive our massive technologies. It extends to the financial Power exercised on Wall Street, political Power in

Washington DC, military Power as expressed in our weapons –
directly or as threats – and to our personal and social Powers as
human beings and citizens.

We use the physical Power of our bodies to survive in the
world and navigate our physical environments. We feel Power
in our bodies as health, strength and skills. Our tools "extend"
the physical Powers of our bodies. We use our mental Powers to
try to understand the world and our role in it, through our uses
of the Powers of information and knowledge – to widely varying degrees of success and failure. We exercise personal Power
in our relationships. We feel it as self-esteem, mutual respect,
and confidence. It gives us leverage, weak or strong, subtle and
loving, or sinister and violent, over other people and the terms
of our lives. We feel the lack of it as Fear and insecurity. Almost
every relationship that ends bitterly does so over who has more
Power or is willing to use it to gain control.

We endow our legal and social systems with moral and
ethical Powers, in attempts to establish and maintain justice in
a world otherwise arbitrary and brutal. The scientific method
gives the Power of personal curiosity and discovery a systematic
routine at an institutional scale. Ignorance or Denial of those
Powers dis-empower us all. We speak of the Rule of Law as the
Power that *ought to guide* our Justice system.

We extend the Power of personal autonomy and free will
into the Democratic system. A few countries in the world exercise the Powers of Democracy, fed by education and good Information, to give their people the Power to determine the direction
of their lives and their role in the world. Many other partial and
fake democracies delude their people into thinking they have far
more Power than they really do.

We allow honest, ethical Power to be diluted by prejudice,
corrupted by money, and overshadowed by illegitimate Power,
sometimes even within ourselves. In this once great US Democracy, supposed model for the world, we feel Powerless to make
the system work.

How is it that the Powers of our shared Intelligence are unable to moderate the Power of our destructive impulses? We ought to try to ask that question.

We speak of the *Power of Love, Knowledge as Power* and the *Power of Information,* even though we are disgracefully inconsistent in the ways we use those Powers, or even understand them. We use the Powers of language and media to share our knowledge and our creativity, our different views of the human condition and the world. Money extends our personal and physical Powers into time and space far beyond our direct reach. And it allows others to exercise exploitive Power over us and destructive Power over the Earth.

We feel Power when we step on the gas pedal in our cars. It connects us with our instinct to chase after a desire or flee from a Fear, without our recognizing the source or motive. Such Powers can be intoxicating in very different ways. The Powers of explosives in the canon, the pistol, the rifle, and the bomb. The missiles that send intricate technologies into space and the rockets and drones that rain down death, illustrate how raw Power can further the civilization or dominate cultures and destroy populations. They *OUGHT* to illustrate to us how the exercise of Power becomes addictive, to the point of self-destruction.

We seek Power over death through two very different practices, medical science and organized religion. Too few of the religious exercise the Power of independent thought to question the promises and demands that religions make, and far too few consider the possibility of moral/ethical action or an acceptance of death, outside of religious doctrines.

Religious leaders can be authentic spiritual guides, liberating their followers with the Power of the Word. But preachers and priests, rabbis, gurus, and imams may also abuse their personal Power over the naive and fearful, to usurp their autonomy and control their behavior, or to con them out of their cash; in the worst cases they take sexual advantage of children and justify irrational hatred.

158

Racism, in my view, is the ignorant expression of artificial and illegitimate Power, to cover one's own feeling of powerlessness.

The distinguished African-American writer Toni Morrison made a paradoxical and sympathetic observation on the Power of prejudice, in her New Yorker response to Trump's election:

> *"The comfort of being 'naturally better than,' of not having to struggle or demand civil treatment, is hard to give up."*

The desire for and the acquisition of Power leads almost inevitably to an irrational, insatiable desire for more Power, and to more destructive ways to Abuse that Power, even among those who started out with good intentions, because they are blind to the unconscious corruption infecting their own Powers.

> *Argument 25: Power corrupts. Absolute power corrupts absolutely. But the illusions of power, detached from the real, may be the worst corrupters.*

POWER IN THE UNCONSCIOUS
Sex, Violence, Love, Power, *and another level of thinking.*

Mickey Spillane, the popular crime novelist, said, "Violence will always outsell sex, and the two together will outsell everything else." Spillane, (1918-2006) published 30 novels, and sold 100s of millions of copies in the years between 1947 and 1996. But book sales are not the point. Why are sex and violence such prominent themes in our stories (movies in particular) and often so controversial in their depiction? Spoiler alert: it has a lot to do with Power, real and imagined, and Love, pursued or lost, and a couple of other forces.

Images of physical beauty or suggestive sexuality are exquisite analogs for our Need and Desire for Love. The tension

in Love stories stimulates our Desire to be Loved, our Fear of
losing Love or of being rejected. Scenes of violence and destruction are gut-level analogs for our need and Desire for Power.
Images of the victims of violence enable us to experience the
Fear of the loss of Power, but vicariously, symbolically. Images
of hunks and honeys, or of wealth and confidence, stimulate our
Unconscious Desires for pleasure and security – forms of Love
and Power. Is it possible we sacrifice or distort some of our own
identity when we willingly identify with fictional characters?

> *The dramatic tensions in stories are analogs for forces*
> *within the Unconscious: Power, Love, Fear, Desire and*
> *... something else.*

The chase scene pushes our "fight or flight" buttons in sequence,
depending on who is chasing or being chased. As the image cuts
from pursuer to pursued, our feelings are jolted back and forth.
Stand and fight. Go after that guy. Let's get the hell out of here.
We identify with the protagonist or victim, to experience vicariously their Power or Fear.

Observe how all effective stories have to engage our curiosity. The laugh line or pratfall tricks us with exaggeration or a
sudden shift in meaning. Dramatic tension builds as we wonder
how the hero or heroine will manage the source of the tension
– an essential component and motivator in every story. A story
must grab our attention and hold it, through a maze of complications, delays, and surprises, until it gets resolved. Or doesn't.

Spillane's comment made me think about the relative strengths
and weaknesses among our Unconscious drives. I began to
formulate a *Theory of a Hierarchy* among the forces of the Unconscious. It may seem like a big jump from Global Warming and
the death of the oceans to this hybrid topic. I argue that these
ideas will help us understand the irrational greed and destruction that is the connective tissue in the Big Picture. I don't pretend this hierarchy idea is original or purely my own discovery;

but I don't know of any other work that brings it into this broader discussion of Power, politics, economics, and the environment.

There are dozens if not hundreds of good books on the Unconscious. New research makes many of the more recent ones both mysterious and enlightening. Yet many of our peers don't believe the Unconscious exists, don't believe in its Power, and don't think it can be used creatively or managed. It's another form of Denial. The 3rd Premise from page 1 is about Thinking, as was all of Part 3. The issue of personal Power cannot be separated from Self-Deception, Cognitive Bias, Denial, Anger, Aggression, or Exceptionalism.

Argument 26: If there are Unconscious forces that distort our attitudes toward Power, from industrial to interpersonal, and if those attitudes are often destructive, we must try to understand them.

THEORY: A HIERARCHY OF UNCONSCIOUS FORCES
Three broad biological epochs define the evolution of our present-day DNA and our modern selves. I believe there are relationships between:
- Each evolutionary jump;
- The region of the brain involved in each development; and
- A specific set of unconscious, instinctual drives.

THE REPTILIAN BRAIN is a very real section of my brain and yours, among the oldest and most primitive parts, in evolutionary terms. Traces of the reptilian brain are found in our brainstem and cerebellum. One of its main functions is the coordination of motor control, movement in space. The reptile has a narrow range of responses, which some biologists call the "Four Fs:" Fighting, Feeding, Fleeing and ... Reproducing: fighting for food or dominance, fleeing from other reptiles or predators, or pursuing the opposite sex. Scientists tend to agree that the reptilian brain, being the oldest, is the most rigid and compulsive part of the brain and may also be *THE MOST POWERFUL.*

Its only need (that cannot yet be called a desire) is for Power. Its only fears, fairly muted, are the fears of pain or injury, death or starvation – losses of the most fundamental Powers.

THE MAMMALIAN BRAIN: The larger mammals evolved over roughly the same time period as birds, in the tens of millions of years since the last major extinction event. By necessity they (and we) developed similar mental and social capacities: for adults to nurture and teach, for male and female pairs to stay in committed pair bonds and to form communities, also for language and play. Our instincts for familial bonds, and emotions like empathy, evolved to become essential to our survival and growth. Simply observe the way abandoned birds and baby mammals attach to any rescuer, or how some adults (mammals often, birds rarely) adopt orphans of other species. That reaction is arguably a sign of a survival instinct, and the roots of the emotional and survival Need for Love. The two stages in the development of this mammalian, or *Limbic*, brain – paleo and neo – are responsible for "the motivation and emotion involved in feeding, reproductive behavior, and parental behavior," and for "language, abstraction, planning, and perception," respectively. (from Wikipedia and the website, thebrain.mcgill.ca)

The Limbic brain is also where we make the unconscious *value judgments* that affect our attitudes and behavior. (I speculate it's the area where instinctive curiosity begins to foster conscious learning, leading to higher mental operations. It could also be the location where ideas and emotions begin to mix, to form the roots of belief systems and ideologies.) As structures, the paleo- and neo-limbic brain developed after the reptile brain, building on its more primitive instincts.

So the argument is counterintuitive and opposes our ideals of ourselves; our instinct for Love is less dominant than our instinct for Power.

THE NEOCORTEX BRAIN: The next level of evolutionary development forms in the most intelligent mammals – whales, dolphins, elephants, primates (including us) and a very few others. When brains develop enough complexity to seek knowledge – for its own sake, beyond the need for protection or the search for food and mates, rather than acquire it by random encounter – another level of mental acuity is born, the expression of curiosity. And among the few and rare who evolve to more complex states – like humans and the other most intelligent species – that curiosity is followed by (or coincidental with) a sense of self-awareness and identity. (Similar skills evolve among the most intelligent of birds – ravens and some parrots for example – but the evolutionary process and brain structures are very different from the neocortex in mammals.)

Which of the most intelligent animals develop a sense of time? Which express acquired cultural traits or creativity? Which develop an even higher state of curiosity – to wonder what others are thinking? Only the smartest of those mentioned above ... including chimps. In terms of brain structure, these skills reside almost exclusively in the frontal lobes.

I characterize this set of impulses – to be curious and to be self-aware – as a Desire for Knowledge and a Fear of ignorance or confusion, first about the way the world works, second about who we think we are, or about how the world may view us as different from what we think.

Gorillas like Koko have grown up in hybrid human-ape communities where sign-language has fostered an unprecedented level of inter-species communication. Some exhibit a sense of self, and can tell family stories, as they learn to communicate with people. Scientists work with apes using different kinds of sign language (hand and gesture signing like the sign language practiced by the deaf, and icon languages using cards or touch screens). They have discovered several stunning features: apes will invent their own syntax (putting icons in new orders to invent phrases and ideas they were not taught), and make up their own words; they can teach language to each other better and faster than humans can. It appears possible that learning language helps them

163

develop ideas about time. Apes in hybrid social groups, with human leaders, have been observed asking, "What are we going to do next?" It boggles the mind to wonder how this occurs. It indicates more intelligence than some of our leaders.

Generals are often more reluctant than politicians are to go to war – to invade Iraq for example. The question the politicians don't ask, before the invasion, comes back to haunt them: "What will we do then?" After their greed and Abuses of Power, a lack of foresight and exit strategies are among their worst stupidities.

Koko has either been taught, or learned on her own, that "people are stupid, destroying the world." We all ought to be asking what *are WE going to do next?*

WHY POWER AND FEAR DOMINATE

So, this theory goes, the later layers of brain development build on the previous ones, each creating new levels of control or expanding skills, but *remaining under the influence* of the earlier stages. The most primitive, the Need for Power and the Fear of Losing it (in reptiles) remains dominant; the need for Love and the Fear of Losing it (in mammals) creates familial and social bonds, but they remain less powerful; and the need for Knowledge and the Fear of Losing it (among humans and a few other highly intelligent species) bring out our conscious awareness, curiosity, and higher cognitive processes.

I argue, and much of the science agrees, that the Needs and Fears are relatively weaker in the newer brain structures. Curiosity is later and more *advanced* than Love, but weaker; Love in turn, comes later and is more advanced than Power, but weaker. So, in this theoretical hierarchy, impulses rooted in Power will always dominate those for Love, and the Need for Love in turn will be stronger than Curiosity. Yes, this admittedly contradicts what we'd like to believe about our advanced intelligence and the rational priorities we say we value.

Now, in an echo of Spillane, we can see why, "Violence will always outsell sex, and the two together will outsell everything else." But mysteries persist: how is our curiosity manipulated to stay with the story until it is resolved; and how does our willingness to identify with the characters play off of our images of ourselves?

> *Argument 27: The earliest stage of our Unconscious needs and instincts – a desire for Power and a Fear of losing it – remains dominant over the later ones, unless and until we understand the Unconscious dynamic.*

The need for Power and the Fear of losing it combine as the basenote, (or is it bass note?), the foundation of human emotional and motivational life. Sadly. Tragically. Power is the most basic need. Desire for Power the strongest urge. The Fear of losing Power, and the impulse to aggressively defend it, are the most dominant emotions. Period. With an exception that may prove the rule: Our rationality is only liberated from this hierarchy if and when we develop and share an understanding of the Unconscious dynamics within ourselves. I will argue this dynamic curse extends to the entire human community, and is multiplied in times of large scale emergencies ... and in narcissistic and megalomaniac personalities.

This explains, if you accept it, why Fear is such a dominant force in therapeutic work, entertainment, and social/political spheres. Fear works, in storytelling, advertising, and propaganda – in political advertising in particular – because it stimulates our most basic Power impulse as a defense, outside of our conscious awareness. To the degree that our "rational" and strategic thinking is dominated by an *Unconscious* desire for *Power* and a *Fear of losing it*, that is how much it dominates our politics and our economics, controls the levels of violence we will tolerate, and causes the needless and irrational war and destruction that results.

> **"Nearly all men can stand adversity, but if you want to test a man's character, give him power."**
> Abraham Lincoln

165

It also explains how Power, especially as Abused by men, and especially in undemocratic systems, can grow to become concentrated among a relatively small group. At worst, in the US and its adversaries, in 2018, we can see too many examples of Power being wielded out of total ignorance of its Unconscious roots.

> *The default outlet for the exercise of Abusive Power, mostly by men, is destruction. It's fed by irrational Fear and Anger.*

Beyond the four sources for my theory – the dynamics of narrative, the stages of brain evolution, my own therapeutic treatment for depression, and a lot of reading in psychology – I can cite these common societal examples. "Madly in love" implies that impulsive, romantic Love can and will overpower logic, rationality, knowledge, and even genuine curiosity. Anyone who has fallen *madly* into, and almost inevitably, out of Love should agree. A need and desire for Love often dominates rationality. And the most serious conflicts in Love relationships – many psychologists agree (and to repeat) – come down to issues of Power: who holds a higher degree of Power over the terms of the relationship or over the other person. "You can't threaten to break up with me, I'm leaving," or in the workplace, "You can't fire me, I quit."

Or in Trump's highly conflicted dealing with Kim Jong Un, "You can't threaten to cancel our meeting, I'll do it first." We see Trump acting out this *natural pathology* almost daily. The champion Golden State Warriors turn down his invitation to come to the White House ... so he un-invites them. Can you keep up with the ongoing examples?

"RAPE CULTURE" In late 2017, revelations and delayed accusations of rape and other forms of sexual abuse, by victims of Harvey Weinstein and a growing number of others, including the President of the United States, are flooding the news. Abusers try to deny the accusations or demean the accusers. But that is finally being seen, like the assaults themselves, as further evidence of the Abuse of Power by powerful men, over women, children, and men with less Power, or who dare to pose a threat.

In my opinion, men can feel dis-empowered or threatened by the Power of beauty in women, by the Powers of Nature, by the Powers of ideas they can't or won't understand – about Science, difference, or their own flawed thinking, for example – so they tend to want to destroy those threats, simply because they are elusive or impossible to control. There is a Fear that fundamentalist men of several stripes share (fundamentalist Christians and Muslims, for example), of being exposed to the presence, the exposed hair and skin, or the availability of women. I think it reveals a deep gap in their sense of themselves, a lack of understanding of their own impulses, and a destructive Fear of Desires ... because they fear, or claim they fear, that they can't be controlled.

Is it fair to criticize these Fears and the damage they incur as willfully ignorant, deeply prejudiced, self-deceptive, or destructive of the goodness and grace religion ought to convey? With sadness and deep irony, we will discover other activities in which men in Power claim to "have no choice," but to use their irrational Power to escape the irrational Power moves of their adversaries.

ARE YOU SCARED? GET READY FOR SOME FAKE NEWS
In 2017, neuro-science research tells us more about the feeling of Fear, where it is centered in the brain, and what other brain functions it may influence. Dr. Dave Nichols, president of Heffter Research Institute, says, "Fear activates the Amygdala, which makes people more receptive to misinformation." Disagree if you can, but it reveals the evil effects of Right Wing Fear mongering, now revealed to be tied to their chronic lying. It makes their sinister powers even more effective. Whether by research or random accident, they have found that stimulating our Fear response makes us more accepting of their lies.

But can authentic and justified fear make us more receptive

167

to the inconvenient truth in the Missing Information, hidden right in front of us?

LATE UPDATE: In their July/August, 2018 online issue, *The Atlantic* posts an article by Jerry Useem, *Power Causes Brain Damage.* In it, for background, he writes, " ... historian Henry Adams was being metaphorical, not medical, when he described power as 'a sort of tumor that ends by killing the victim's sympathies.'" Connect that with our ideas about empathy in Liberal and Conservative brains. Useem goes on to cite Dacher Keltner, a psychology professor at UC Berkeley, "Subjects under the influence of power ... acted as it they had suffered a traumatic brain injury ... more impulsive, less risk aware ... less adept at seeing things from other people's point of view." A Canadian neuro-scientist looked inside the heads (literally, with transcranial-magnetic-stimulation) of some powerful, and not-so-powerful people, and found the powerful lacking in mental "mirroring ... the cornerstone of empathy." He concluded, "Once we have power, we lose some of the capacities we needed to gain it in the first place."

We humans grew and evolved out of Nature. We are a part of Nature that has become unnatural, through the competition between our intelligence and our primal need for Power, in the ages of technology and money. We have arguably grown into an Anti-Natural force *ON Nature*, threatening its ability to support us and our children.

You and I and our entire species stand at an intersection of time and space as if on a path that splits in two directions, toward a threshold and doorway, with only vague hints of where each leads. The doorway is a metaphor for a radical collective decision. The threshold, the last step before the edge of a cliff.

As if acting out an almost universal Blind Spot, we can't see the difference until we act and take that step, or fail to. We have trouble finding the mass of Missing Information – or even knowing it exists; we are way too slow to realize that the decisions we

168

didn't know were urgent, needed to be made 20 years ago.

We have to understand that the choice is conceptual, made of ideas. Which is the right step, can we choose it collectively and take it quickly and carefully enough? Or will another common mistake in thinking, or another short delay in deciding, doom us ... and most or all of our descendants?

SO *"WHO IS RESPONSIBLE THEN?"* *

The issue of blame arises. At a point in the late 1960s, or early '70s, I and many of my peers understood that there was no point in blaming our parents for "the mindset that took us to war," or for their contempt for us as war protesters. But forgiveness made no sense either, without their request to be forgiven, which never came.

To give the wealthy Abusers of Power the benefit of the doubt, to let them get away with saying they couldn't help themselves, is to ignore their crimes because they may have been marginally unconscious. They are caught between a Blind Spot and a Mindset that relies on an irrational and insatiable lust for Power, on a finite planet, in an existential emergency that will take them another decade to notice, and another decade to acknowledge, and another to start to fix ... long after we have all tripped over that threshold. If we leave it to them. So, whether we blame them or not, forgive them or not, we have to admit that their Power, their acquisition of illegitimate Wealth and Power, and their Abuses of Power are intolerable and need to end.

We are all responsible.

It would be naive and simplistic to say it's time – we have to break the Blind Spot, find and accept the Missing Information, and decide to rescue our human potential, together, or not decide and surrender to our worst impulses.

But it would be correct.

* "Who is responsible then?" *is a taunting phrase from the end of Alain Resnais'* film Night and Fog *from 1956, a condemnation of the Holocaust and the "good Germans" who said, "I am not responsible."*

GLOSSARY FOR PART SIX

ALEC: The American Legislative Council is an organization of conservative state and national legislators and corporate lobbyists, who promote conservative laws in local and state districts. The ideology is predictably AGAINST abortion, health, safety and environmental regulations, taxes, federal intrusion into state and local issues, the rights of women, immigrants, and ethnic minorities; and FOR limits on voting rights, stricter law enforcement, mass incarceration, and private prisons, and other causes.

Populist, -ism: Like *Fake News*, the term has changed its meaning in the Trump era. **'True Populism** is traditionally applied to any loose-knit group who were opposed to a variety of elites in positions of power. See page 216. Trump has awakened a new sub-type, a group that feels disadvantaged by government generally, but also represents currents of racism, white male power, gun rights, and conservative Christianity. We could call it **Alienated Populism.** It's typical of the Koch-backed Tea Party movement of the 2010s. See page 262 for further definitions.

Asymmetrical Information: A term describing an unequal exchange of information accompanying financial or market exchanges, sales and purchases.

Domino Theory: Based loosely on the USSR's expansionist moves after WWII, it became a NeoCon rationale for military intervention in Vietnam and elsewhere, in the fear they would fall to Communism, like dominoes.

Externalities: An accounting term for factors in extraction, manufacture, sales, and other aspects of businesses, that don't impact the bottom line, but may have other negative or positive impacts.

Globalization: Has different meanings that depend on context and point of view. We could say it started with Chinese and European colonization of countries in the 12- to 1700s. Now it's about the expansion of globalized trade, on a NeoLiberal model (below), with an emphasis on globalized capitalism since the 1970s to now.

Military-Industrial Complex: See pages 198-200.

MAD: Mutually Assured Destruction: Cold War logic for the nuclear arms race.

NeoConservative, -ism: NeoConservative and NeoLiberal are not 2 divergent or competing political/economic systems. The NeoConservative or NeoCon movement is a foreign policy ideology. It was founded in the US by centrist "hawks," expansionists, Republicans, conservative Democrats, and exceptionalists, who opposed liberal pacifism, the Left generally, and pacifists. Their most thoroughly planned, and disastrous project was the Bush/Cheney invasion of Iraq in 2003. NeoCons published their ideas and goals in the Project for a New American Century, or PNAC, now defunct and somewhat disgraced.

NeoLiberal: Is a general term that refers to economic and trade policies that expanded from the western democracies (Europe and the US mainly), to reshape national economies and international trade on a set of market principles, assuming that democracy would follow. The policy sparked the transition away from pure communist principles, in Russia (the former USSR), and China, toward very different forms of mixed economies, with both communist and capitalist elements – 2 examples of the policy's failures.

Supply Side Economics: A theory of free market economics that says the interests of sellers are more important than buyers, that tax breaks for corporations and the wealthy will have an overall positive economic benefit, because the gains will "Trickle Down" (another term for the theory) to the middle and working classes.

Systemic: Refers to all the elements in a system and its workings. **Systemic Failure** means that enough parts of a system are failing to bring the whole system down, even when some parts continue to work. (As distinguished from **Systematic,** which describes human methods that follow a fixed plan or in a specific step-by-step and integrated manner.)

Zero-Sum: The economic principle or theoretical maxim that says that both sides of every transaction ought to be equivalent in value. You can't spend more than you have without creating debt or earning more. Price ought to equal cost plus added value.

170

PART SIX: A SYSTEMIC FAILURE
Money, Corruption, Fear, and the Abuse of Power:
Their Roots and Their Legacy

THE OVERVIEW

There were hand-painted signs at the first Earth Day, and then printed bumper stickers that said, "Capitalism is Killing the Earth." Hardly anyone imagined that Capitalism could actually kill the Earth. We trusted the three branches of government, the ethics of the business community, our free press, and the emerging environmental movement to prevent that possibility. Our trust was betrayed.

When Barbara Lee, US Representative from California's 13th district, cast the *single NO* vote against the Bush-Cheney *Authorization for Use of Military Force Against Terrorism* after 9-11, she said, " ... let us not become the evil we deplore." She was the first person, out of 535 in the US Congress, to have the vision and courage to stand up against what turned out to be the worst US foreign policy mistake since Vietnam. A few other Congressmen and Senators echoed her resistance in later votes. But they could not stop the Cheney-Bush juggernaut that tipped the middle east into its present state of chaos.

Alan Grayson, US Representative from Florida, was interviewed on Democracy Now (mid-April 2015), about the power of corporate money in backing the TPP (Trans Pacific Partnership) trade deal. He said that power is "decisive." Then he repeated what he said when the Supreme Court decided Citizen's United in 2010, "If we do nothing, we can kiss this country goodbye." Then, back to the present, "Well, pucker up."

Capitalism and the environment.
Military overreach based on imaginary threats.
Political corruption buying bad trade deals.

THREE EXAMPLES

What do those statements about militarism, fake enemies, corruption, and trade deals have to do with the Global Eco-Crisis,
with Capitalism, or with each other? There is a telling similarity.
Those statements were all questionable exaggerations when they
first appeared, hard to imagine and difficult to prove. But they
have turned out to have been stunningly prescient. It is not a
coincidence. There are deep structural connections and common
threads among them, and with the causes of the Eco-Crisis and
our Denial of it. On closer analysis, there are other commonal-
ities in practices and impacts with many of the other crises our
world is facing.

I recognize a pattern. I would like to make that pattern
impossible for you to ignore. Those 3 examples reveal cognitive
failures at a grand and dangerous scale. They are united by
corrupt motives, obsolete ideologies, failed thinking, and an epidemic of Denial. If we can combine a closer look and a broader
view, we will see the cognitive and ideological pattern. It will
get more complicated, to the point it feels overwhelming; but if
we can agree on the similarities, it will get simpler.

If you recognize the pattern, you will see that a solution, a
single, coherent, radical but feasible fix, is not only possible, but
obvious, urgent, and absolutely necessary.

Capitalism and the environment. A form of Capitalism that
may once have been less harmful, even beneficial, grew and
became more greedy, aggressive, and warlike until it became
more powerful than the ability of most governments to regulate it. It bypassed its reasonable functions and exploded into a
NeoLiberal myth of materialist progress and unlimited growth,
while ignoring its own destructive side effects, both human and
environmental.

Globalized Capitalism has hid behind economic principles
that were questionable, conditional, and misunderstood from the
start. They have now made themselves obsolete and destructive. Globalization can mean many different things, depending

on your point of view and where your Power is invested. As it exists in 2018, it has fed extremes of wealth and Power into the hands of a few banks and billionaires, about a dozen mega-corporations, several monarchies, dictatorships and proto-democracies, most of which, to this day, answer to wealth and Power first, people and the planet last. Real functional democracies have managed to escape the worst of the pattern. Not ours.

Outlaw Capitalism has become a selfish and brutal bully, dominating the global economy and far too many governments, and acting as a parasite on the Earth and most of human society. It carries us all toward its logical end-point: quantities of hoarded wealth far beyond any sane or ethical purpose, and the extraction of the remaining value from the human community and the global ecosystem. In support of all that, we now have a selfish and brutal bully president.

This reveals an underlying Ideology that justifies concentrated wealth and power, while it conceals the environmental costs and a social rat race behind the mask of progress, the illusion of freedom, the narcotic of material plenty, and the threat of violence and endless war, just to protect the illusion.

Imaginary threats justify military overreach. The Vietnam War and the Bush-Cheney invasion of Iraq are the two most disgraceful recent examples of a mentality of domination in the government, the banking cartels, Big Oil, and the military. You may remember it's a mindset with a name. In retrospect, US President Eisenhower (in office 1953-61, see pages 190, 196-8) was an honest, ethical, and liberal Republican president. But he was either duped or betrayed by Exceptionalist advisors into crushing popular administrations from the Middle East to Central America, and laying the groundwork for Vietnam. In the Vietnam era, Lyndon Johnson was chronically misled by the false optimism of the generals and Pentagon analysts, and so gave in to their endless demands for more money, bombs, and bodies. He saw little choice but to repeat their promises to the public, even after he knew they were lies.

A protester's slogan from 1990, repeated in 2002 said, *"Iraq is Arabic for Vietnam."* Vietnam and Iraq were both *justified* by aggressive campaigns of misinformation, propaganda and engineered fear. For the moment, Iraq and Afghanistan may be less costly than Vietnam, in American lives lost, but their dollar costs may exceed Vietnam. And the ongoing chaos in the Middle East creates exponentially growing costs in lives and money and environmental damage.

But even when Afghanistan, Syria, Egypt, Libya, Yemen, and a few other conflicts are factored in, we still fail to observe they are the blowback to our Exceptionalist military adventurism. In sum, they are the consequences and the logical end point of projecting military power for its own sake, to install barbaric leaders sympathetic to US corporate interests, the oil giants and banks above all.

The US has in fact fulfilled Barbara Lee's warning, *We have become the evil we deplored.* And we are well-puckered-up to kiss our democracy goodbye.

In the early 20th century, the US and allies in Europe sowed the seeds for perpetual conflict in the Middle East. Those seeds grew to become the terrorist networks that now fill the headlines, dominate our attention, and inflate our fears. But that crisis is badly misunderstood. It represents the unintended consequence of a history of military interventions over resources, religion, and economic ideologies, and a mask that hides a deeper crisis.

This reveals an underlying Ideology that claims in secret that aggression, deception, and extreme violence are means that will be justified by an imagined outcome that never happens – the spread of Capitalism in the guise of Democracy. The US appoints itself "Cop of the World," with open resistance or reluctant support from other players. Motives remain taboo: the agreement that war is good business, the deaths of innocents are merely collateral damage, environmental costs can be justified or ignored as externalities, and, if the Cop of the World should turn racist and corrupt, too bad; the consolidation and projection of Power is the point.

174

Political corruption buys bad trade deals. Obama and the supporters of the mid-2015 round of trade deals (TPP, TAFTA, TISA and others) claimed that they would not repeat the mistakes of NATFA, CAFTA and GATT, of 20 years earlier. Yet the terms were made secret, and the text that was leaked proved those claims were false. Most of the provisions were not about trade; they represent a consolidation of international corporate Power: to override local and national regulations over consumer health, environmental damage, food, labor, and chemical safety; to prohibit public protest or intervention, to bar the labeling of GMOs, ban the documentation of war crimes and ecological damage, and to make corporate profits a higher priority than public health, the stability of local economies, the autonomy of nations, or the health of the global ecosystem. And that was under the *Democrat* Obama. Trump may have accidentally gotten one thing right, scrapping bad trade deals or demanding revisions. But if so, he did it for the wrong reasons and ignored the new damage his deal-making would almost certainly do.

This reveals an underlying Ideology that tries to justify the top-down dominance of corporate interests over the public good. Most trade treaties are written by the corporations and banks to benefit their bottom line; they rely on dis-information and lack transparency, they ensure corporate power, while being passed off as keys to freedom and economic growth.

At the root of all three examples, and more to come, are false justifications for an Economy of Extraction, War, and Waste, ongoing Abuses of Power, and the Failure to Address the Eco-Crisis. At the heart of it all, the US has achieved 6 things: the most powerful military in the world, a supposed model for democracies, the strongest economic force in a globalized Free Market, the worst per-capita polluter, the worst public health and justice systems for an industrialized country, and one of the most corrupt governments in the world ... if not the most corrupt.

THE WORLD IS A MESS

When Madeline Albright, (US Secretary of State under Bill Clinton), was asked for a comprehensive summary, she said, "The world is a mess." That was long after 9-11 and well before the 2016 presidential campaign.

The next questions may be, "How big and sticky is that mess?" "How long has it been coming?" "How did we allow it?" and, "What will it take to clean it up?"

I argued in the first few pages that the Global Environmental Crisis will soon emerge as the only issue that matters to everyone in the world, and that ...

> *... all the other crises we think we face are subsets of it, trivial by contrast, or part of a larger pattern we have yet to recognize.*

We are searching for the pieces of that pattern and assembling them, with the goal of finding common causes, and in turn a common solution.

THREE ARGUMENTS reflect the 3 stages that Part Six has to navigate. A comprehensive understanding of them will require us to Think Differently about the world and our role in it.

> *Argument 28: The Ecological and Non-Ecological Crises that the United State faces are the local signs of a Systemic Failure in the whole of Human Civilization.*

> *Argument 29: If we think of each sub-crisis as separate from most or all of the others, with separate causes, requiring different cures, we will surely fail.*

> *Argument 30: If we can identify a common cause, or set of causes, for the crises we in the US face, and if it also applies to the global "mess," it will point to a single, radical but relatively simple set of remedies.*

EVIDENCE OF A CRISIS, A POSSIBLE SYSTEMIC FAILURE, IN
THE UNITED STATES AND IN HUMAN CIVILIZATION

Part Two covered the details of the unprecedented Global Environmental Crisis, and the central role the US had, and continues to have in it. The Global Environmental Crisis includes Global Warming/Climate Change, Bad Agricultural practices, the failing Health of the Oceans, and at least 9 more environmental sub-crises, including dozens of species threatened with extinction. Part Two left us with some hard truths, on pages 63-66. We need to update them with other *inconvenient truths,* and to identify the necessary actions they demand.

Where We Are And What We Now Know We Must Do
When we look at the Big-Picture fundamentals of the Global Eco-Crisis:
• We see we are at the tipping point, after which holding to the 2° C. "limit," without extreme emergency action, will be impossible.
• We understand that *ANY* more emissions will continue to push Feedback Loops and will lead, almost certainly, to 3°- 5° C (5° to 8° F.) *additional* temperature rise, causing massive food and water shortages, by 2100, possibly much sooner.
• We know that will also cause 6 to 10 feet of sea level rise, flooding coastal zones everywhere and making an unprecedented refugee crisis.
• We now understand that if we only reduce emissions, instead of getting to Net-Zero Carbon ASAP, Climate (or Thermal) Lag will continue to push temperatures further up, locking us into more excess heat for decades to come, which will make most of the Earth uninhabitable for most species, including us.
• So we see, to avoid that, we must cut global emissions of CO_2, Methane, and other GHGs to near zero as fast as possible, ideally in a decade or less. And do a bunch of other stuff.
• And we see that *that* appears to be impossible, because of 3 overlapping "reasons," which we now have to evaluate as ...

TRUE OR FALSE ?
1. It will be politically impossible, short of some kind of peaceful and widespread political revolution, or ...
2. It will take too long and Climate Change will still overrun our efforts, or ...
3. It will wreck the economy, or cost more money than exists in the world, and will in turn create more problems than it solves.

Number 1. is true. So we need that revolution. Number 2. is possible; it will come down to how much we do and how fast ... and a little luck. Number 3. is false. The economy is already fragile enough to crash on its own, and Climate Change will surely wreck it. But the economy can be re-engineered to be stronger, more fair, and ecologically sustainable. The rest of the book will explain why and how, and what else we have to do.

Two major factors, themes in the book from the start, will determine the possibility of economic re-engineering: Whether we, as a global species, can agree that the Global Eco-Crisis is in a priority category of its own, *the only top priority*, and whether we make the connections between ecological damage, poverty, an economy of extraction and waste, and failures of government. In the summer of 2018, Trump, his dittohead Republicans, and his racist base, stand in the way of that realization.

WE ARE FORCED TO LOOK AT THE OTHER *non-ecological* crises and issues that confront the US and much of the rest of the world. They compete with the Eco-Crisis for our attention and for remedies, here and almost everywhere. They number at least this 15:
• Abuses of Power and Systemic Corruption in high places;
• Crime in public life, business and politics, local to global, from Skid Row to suburbia to Main Street, Wall Street, Congress, and the international banks.
• Education and Information systems, failed.
• Electoral failures, broken Democracies.
• The national and global Gap in Income and Wealth: poverty
178

or virtual slavery for hundreds of millions, vast and growing wealth for a fraction of 1%, a lack of water, food, jobs, and housing that make systemic poverty dangerous, and often deadly.

• Health care and public services, failing, including new diseases and bad water, like lead in the water of dozens of US cities. Include in this issue the opioid crisis in the US.

• Immigration and refugee issues, sparked by wars, crashing economies, vicious cultural biases, and Climate Change. The homeless crisis in the US.

• Illegal trade in weapons, drugs, resources, hunting trophies, and endangered species. Humans being trafficked for sex and labor slavery.

• Infrastructure lacking, crumbling, or failing to meet basic safety standards.

• Justice, failing: judicial bias, privatized and secret prisons, police brutality, non-judicial killings.

• Political gridlock, caused by Corruption and religious and ideological rigidity.

• Population and its impact on basic necessities, water, and housing, and related pressures for society and politics.

• Racism, sexism and other forms of institutionalized discrimination, including religious bias and hypocrisy, with an emphasis on the abuse of women and children.

• Taxes, government spending and debt, too high, too low, or radically out of balance.

• Violence generally, pointless Wars, proxy Wars, and Wars for profit, civil Wars and rebellions, Terrorism and torture. The psychic toll on millions of children.

ESTABLISHING A BROADER PERSPECTIVE
Nafeez Mosadeq Ahmed is a best-selling author and the founder and Executive Director of the Institute for Policy Research and Development in London. *The Crisis of Civilization* is the title of his book and a film (2010), directed by Dean Puckett. Ahmed's emphasis is "the interconnections of systemic global crises."

I could say that Ahmed's work was an inspiration for this

part of my book, but that would be incorrect. Like many other influences, *The Crisis of Civilization* came along when my ideas were converging around similar themes; but without it, I would not have had the courage, clarity, or knowledge to spell out.

Most writers tie the Eco-Crisis to industry's abuse of carbon fuels, to a destructive economic model, gridlocked or corrupted governments, and failed information and education systems. Ahmed is one of a few who draw militarism and terrorism into a broad and coherent picture of a civilization in crisis. The connections we now can see, among the global economy and most of the many other crises we face, are central to my last arguments.

CRISES: CATEGORIES AND COMPETITION
If, on one hand, we see Climate Change and the other ecological symptoms, as 2 or 3 among 25 or more serious crises – all with different causes, all requiring different solutions, we are basically screwed. At the moment we – as a global species, as a group of nations – are making next to zero progress on all of them; and in the US, Trump is making many of them worse and more urgent, every day. The dozen Environmental Crises, and the 15 or more non-ecological crises will continue to compete with each other for our attention – already divided, distracted, and exhausted – for economic or administrative solutions, and for political decisions, in governments that range from conflicted to unstable to paralyzed. Indecision alone, about the many crises, will make any one harder to fix, and many impossible to manage. Some of them are urgent and desperately need fast and thorough remedies. Many are not existential threats to our world and our future, and might be ignored for a long time without getting progressively worse. The several Ecological Crises, and the crises in the economic and political systems around them, are extremely urgent and cannot be ignored any longer.

On the other hand, if the pattern points to a single central cause, or even a cluster of related causes, we might find we can find solutions for entire categories of crises.

A SYSTEMIC FAILURE

Systemic means affecting all the parts and connections within a system, like a body, an organization, a machine, or a nation. *Systemic Failure* means that enough parts of a system have failed to take down the entire system, even when some parts continue to work. A systemic remedy, like the one this book will propose, is possible. But it will require a quantum leap in our thinking. It presents the best option, maybe the only option, for avoiding the worst possible outcomes.

From here, we proceed on the assumption that the pattern will reveal, yes, a Systemic Failure in, and a Crisis of Civilization. It may shock us into the realization that the combination of crises is far worse than we have imagined, dragging us toward Worst Case Scenarios that are already threatening to beome inevitable.

The object of this section is to reveal a pattern of political and economic causes that may point to a singular solution ... and to name it. We will have to recognize and highlight relationships among: large and small scale, short- and long-term, political trends, economic systems, information, the public interest, psychology, sociology, and the common good, money, Power, influence, and the Earth. That pattern will get more complex, then simpler, then impossible to ignore or deny.

WE ARE LEFT WITH 4 REALLY HARD QUESTIONS:

How did the US democracy get so fucked up?

What undermined the US democracy, leaving it corrupt, paralyzed, and ineffective? This will take a while but is basically easy.

How did the US economy get so rigged?

What turned the US economy into an obsolete and destructive model, that most of the world has adopted even as it approaches collapse? This will require some background but is also easy.

How and when did facts, and clean air and water become partisan issues?
How and why did a moderate Democrat/Republican divide turn into a bitter cultural opposition that splits on science, truth, justice, Climate Change, and the public good? This one's more complex and hard to track accurately, so it will take a little longer. The answer will overlap with other topics.

How do racism, sexism, social biases, and a general fear of difference fit into the pattern?
How and why do a rigged economy and a corrupt government either provoke or worsen social divisions to hold power? The answer to this one may be the hardest to accept, but mainly for less well educated white people, who have probably stopped reading.

We are looking for a pattern of connections among several to many crises, revealing they are caused by just a few obsolete ideas, a few dark examples of human nature, and the insane belief that they were working in a civilized world.

ALL ECONOMIES REFLECT ORGANIZING PRINCIPLES
Because all economies have to balance competing forces – supply and demand, price and cost, profit and stock evaluation, efficiency and waste, free choice and monopolies – they rely on the control of different Powers, or suffer from a lack of control. As mentioned at the start of Part Five, *Organizing Principles* can mean ... *the core values that a system is built upon, defining how people and other dynamics interact to make the system work;* and that *they can be defined in advance ... to fulfill predetermined objectives – like a mission statement.* Or they may define a system, *without ... having been consciously or intentionally designed.*

Some early human economies evolved out of simple systems of production and trade. For example, we know that many regional economies functioned for long periods without currencies (tangible money); because commodities and other things of value were exchanged, borrowed or loaned and paid back with interest, all by bartering the labor, materials and resources in play.

We could define natural systems, before humans, as having a *Natural, Organic,* or *Circular* Economy, in which there were usually enough resources to go around, often surpluses, and some occasional brutal shortages; but without anything that could be called *profit* or *waste.*

POLITICAL ORGANIZING PRINCIPLES, and differences among them are less clear to most Americans (the young and poorly educated in particular); making us less aware of what democracy demands for us to participate in it. For example, the principles of the 2 parties in the US have been shifting, often dramatically, since the Civil War, and especially since the 1960s.

I'll assume most readers know the basic definition of a Democracy. Fewer understand the variations, from Democratic Socialism, to formative democracies that are trying to find their way, to some that were once great and have lost much of their fairness and shared power (through obsolete bureaucracies and corruption for example).

It is hard for present-day citizens in formerly imperialist or colonizing countries – Great Britain, Spain, the Dutch, the US and others – to acknowledge and admit that the current wealth that they share that was accumulated through racism, violent conquest, slavery, and genocide.

PROBLEMS IN MERGING DEMOCRACY AND CAPITALISM

Let's have a brief look at the principles that define the models for different economic structures that compete with each other for dominance in the global economy.

Bigger picture, this conversation started with Freedoms From and Freedoms To on page 130 and will run to and through Parts Seven and Eight.

Free Market Capitalism is often called *Laissez Faire,* French

for *Let Them Do What They Want.* It's based historically on works
by Adam Smith, like *The Wealth of Nations,* where, Capitalists say,
he laid down the great and immortal tenets of the Free Market.
The problem is that most recent and current Free Market zealots
ignored or forgot about Smith's writing on *Moral Sentiments,*
which he said were essential for any economy to run efficiently
and fairly ... to both suppliers and consumers. We, non zealots,
can assume he would be shocked and mortified to see what his
ideas have turned into in the 21st century.

Part of this study is to try to determine which principles
are more Conservative or Pro-Deregulation, which are Liberal,
Progressive or leaning Socialist; which are better for poor people
for example or for the Earth. This is probably an incomplete list:
And, heads up, a whole new twist is added to this discussion
starting on page 238, with Robert Kuttner.

We need to get to the defining principles of the American
model of Capitalism, which, since the late 1800s, and especially
since the end of World War II, have slowly devolved into *Crony,
Supply Side, Disaster, Extractive* or *Deregulated* – or *Trickle Down –*
market principles. At their worst, when they gain more power
than the government's ability to regulate them, they turn into
what I call *Outlaw Capitalism.* And, like organizing principles
generally, some were designed in, some happened by default,
some are correct but have been mis-applied – either too narrowly
or broadly for example – and most have devolved since around
1980, in complete Denial of the growing mass of unintended and
destructive side-effects, inherent to its present form. These are
the principles as I understand them.

• The *Invisible* (but infallible) *Hand of the Free Market* will regulate supply, demand, human self-interest and well-being, money and resources. Any regulations will simply slow it or prevent
its benefits. This economic law was never meant to be absolute;
it has been used to justify deregulation in every industry; it is the
IL-logical basis for the conflation of Free Markets with personal
freedoms; and it has always been set up to ignore ...

• **Externalities,** in corporate and government accounting, are the things that don't affect the bottom line or the budget – like waste, pollution, workers' safety, pollution, product safety, pollution, or long-term impacts – so they don't matter and don't have to be accounted for. We could say that *Black Lives Don't Matter* to Outlaw Capitalism, but that would be uncivil ... and true. Externalities allow for vast profits to be accrued from terribly damaging business practices, whether legal, illegal, or legislated, through corruption, to be "legal." And regardless of *Moral Sentiments*.

• **Asymmetrical Information:** Every financial transaction, every purchase, loan, profit, or penalty, in addition to the transfer of money and value, is a transfer of Information, which may be true and balanced, or asymmetrical: false, missing, or incomplete. This principle is basically true, but has been misapplied, used to explain or justify the false Information that is essential to the workings of Outlaw Capitalism. If it was applied to the whole economy, we would know how and why it is so rigged.

• **Zero-Sum** is the principle we all ought to have learned as children: You can't spend money you don't have. If you want to spend more, you have to save some elsewhere or earn more. As above, it's true, but misapplied. Zero-sum can explain the connection between *Wealth Extracted* and *Damage Done*.

• **Rent-Seeking:** There are basically 2 different principles for making money: In one, you use resources, add value through innovation and work, and produce useful products to sell at a modest profit. In the other, you own something that you can rent out or sell, with little or no work or value added, often at inflated rates (especially if you can monopolize or fix prices on it). It includes owning property that you rent, selling resources high that you bought low, or stole, and renting money, i.e. creating and profiting from debt. It's true, pervasive, often unfair, and, at a large scale, hugely extractive and damaging to a fair economy.

185

Let's look at the ways the GOP/Conservative economic principles distort and corrupt those (admittedly flawed) organizing principles.

• **Taxes and Regulations** are always bad, pulling money out of the economy and *wasting it* (on public services for example) and slowing down businesses or cutting into their profits.

To be Liberal, and honest, taxes are quite simply the dues we pay to live in a civilized society. Regulations are what keeps big corporations from doing more damage, to people, the nation, and the Earth, than they already do. If you can't see the connections between low taxes, low regulations, and endemic poverty or environmental disaster ... well, you have some work to do.

• **Privatization:** Related to a hatred for big government's taxing and spending (supposed Liberal/Democrat sins), it is the idea that the government can never be as efficient in operating bureaucracies or administering funding, for public services for example, as privately held, profit-driven companies would be. The push by the Right to privatize as much as possible, of what the government does, and what we own collectively as a nation, is based on that assumption, which is easily proven wrong, and a form of legalized corruption and theft.

The privatization of many services that supply the military – in the Iraq invasion for example, like laundry, transportation, and a maze of field logistics, including their own security forces – creates bitter injustices, like contractors working next to soldiers who make a fraction of what the private agents do, and cost overruns that are almost impossible to calculate. Take one example. Dick Cheney was an executive and stockholder in Halliburton/KBR, originally an oil services operation. The company expanded into contracted military services under Clinton and Bush II. It made almost $40 Billion in Iraq, much of it through overcharging, and lost comparable sums of government funds through waste and inefficiency. Cheney's share of that may have made him a multi-billionaire.

186

The US Post Office/Postal Service is recognized as a highly efficient and cost effective operation. Republican controlled Congresses have imposed a bunch of unfair restrictions and financial burdens on it, to make it seem inefficient and wasteful. They have borrowed huge sums – in the billions from the USPS, in the trillions from Social Security – to fill in gaps in their reckless spending. They lie about every aspect of this and never had any intent to pay the money back.

The push to privatize everything runs parallel to the Reagan slogan, "The government is not the solution to the problem, the government is the problem." When the GOP dominates the government, they prove it's true. Their propaganda says the GOP is the party of fiscal responsibility, and the Democrats know nothing but *Tax and Spend*. The exact opposite has been true for decades.

.

• **Economic Growth** is touted as the indicator of a healthy economy and the promise of prosperity in the future. But in deregulated Capitalism, growth is worshiped and measured in a way that leads unavoidably to a growing gap in income and wealth – concentrations of wealth for the 1%, borderline poverty for 1/3 of the rest of us. The idea of unlimited economic growth on a finite planet, with finite resources, and a limited tolerance for abuse, is insane.

We ought to be talking about 2 kinds of growth: horizontal economic growth – shared equally by all – rather than vertical growth, as is the overriding trend; and sustainable growth – with waste and pollution kept to near zero – that favors durability, stability, and efficiency, from individual products to the larger economy.

• **Supply Side Economic Theory:** One of the biggest lies and worst abuses of legislative and economic power, it claims that if the economy should be regulated at all – i.e. rigged – it should be for the banks and bosses, not the customers or consumers. If we give big tax breaks to big businesses and already rich investors, it will benefit the whole economy – investments, expansions, raises, better conditions, more profits, and mainly, more and better jobs. Bullshit. It's called *Trickle Down* by anyone with any economic sense. But otherwise, time after time, lying president after lying president, the tax cuts go into the bank or wealth management/equity accounts of the rich, into corporations buying back their own stock to inflate its price, into destructive investments in damaging industries, into money laundering scams (to hide criminal profits) and gigantic real estate purchases, where no one intends to live, just to hide wealth. And the general public is stuck with the leavings: low quality products and services, at inflated prices.

I just learned who first said *Trickle Down*. A brilliant Native American comic and political critic, named Will Rogers, spoke of Herbert Hoover's ideas in 1932, after the crash of 1929 and before FDR's remedies. "The money was all appropriated for the top in the hopes that it would trickle down to the needy. Mr. Hoover didn't know that money trickled up. Give it to the people at the bottom and the top will have it before night. But at least it will have passed through the poor fellow's hands."

And that's a generous description; sometimes it never touches the "poor fellow's hands."

• **The National Debt,** the amount the US owes to a variety of lenders, supposedly inhibits a healthy growth economy, and burdens our children with a legacy of excessive spending. So it's an excuse to hold government spending to hard limits, or to a balanced budget, no matter the nation's needs or the side-effects. Liberal economists only agree in principle, or when the debt reaches a point where interest payments are a drain on the budget. Otherwise, debt is necessary for governments to function, especially in retracting economies.

On the other hand, debt as a "financial product" and a tool to keep the economy rigged, is a vital component of a GOP economy. As with the national debt, personal debt is necessary, at least to some degree, for most citizens. But the terms are

controlled by banks, payday lenders, and credit card companies
who pay Congress persons $100s of millions to let them keep the
"terms" – that we all have to accept – impossible for us to read or
understand, and usually exploitive.

• **War is Good Business:** As much as Republicans and fiscal-
ly responsible Democrats harp on limiting spending to avoid
increasing the National Debt, simply observe a few facts: Since
the 1920s, Republican administrations have *ALWAYS* increased
the National Debt more than Democrats have; they are *ALWAYS*
willing to spend on military expansion, and they are all too eager
to break their own rules about No New Spending Without Cuts
... like to Social Security.

In January and February, 2018, alone, the GOP Congress
approved spending around $4 or $5 Trillion dollars, without cutting anything ... yet. There's more to come about the corruption
that created and perpetuates a whole range of GOP economic
crimes (and Democrat indifference).

I ADMIT TO A BIAS ... OR 2
I was born into a Christian, Republican family, in a 100 percent
white suburb. All of my older male relatives served in World
War II. Several of my uncles and cousins became preachers, as
did my dad for about a decade. Several others were lawyers. I
turned away from Protestant Christianity over the hypocrisy of
some of the preachers I encountered, within and outside of my
family. I remained a Republican, though I wasn't old enough to
vote until 1964. I've been betrayed by both parties, by politics
generally, by an exploitive economy and an inept mass media for
most of my life. So my liberal/progressive bias, and my hypoc-
risy-antennae and BS-detectors have their own history and logic.

The next section recreates a history of political economics
in the US, mostly from the end of World War II to the present,
basically the span of my lifetime. But, for background, we have
to start with a few incidents before the war. Some of it is revisionist history, but it's essential to understand how we got to this

189

terrible state.

Heads up. I think this history is essential. But it runs to 40 pages and you may already know some of it. I've laid it out in an attempt to make it easy to skim.

Andrew Bacevich's comments are excerpts from an article that appeared at TomDispatch and AlterNet.com, in February, 2018, titled, "How We Got (or could have avoided) Trump." Another source is an Infographic from InsideClimateNews that helps us answer that 3rd question (How and when did Climate Change become partisan?).

PIECES OF A HISTORY IGNORED:
The decline of the progressive Left, and the rise of a corrupt and extreme Right-Wing/Conservative GOP in the United States.

Stephen Colbert, in his earlier, fake conservative character, opened one evening's show with,

> *"My guest tonight says that those who don't remember history are ... something something something."*

To finish that thought, if it's not familiar, "... are condemned to repeat it." Some historians prefer, "History doesn't repeat, but it rhymes." German philosopher Hegel had a different take (and may have been quoted by President Eisenhower):

> *"We learn from history that we do not learn from history."*

HELP FROM A HISTORIAN AND A FILMMAKER
On one hand, there's not much point in re-imagining factual events to reflect how we wish they had gone. On the other hand, we need to understand how we got here, what bad decisions were made, which good ones were missed, which ones need to

be corrected or still need to be made, to manage this set of crises – to take our nation and our civilization in a different direction.

Oliver Stone, writer, producer, and director of many films (*Platoon, JFK, Born on the Fourth of July,* and others), co-produced a ten-part documentary that premiered on Showtime in November 2012. It's available online and as DVDs. Historian Peter Kuznick was the co-writer and co-producer. As reviewed at the The Nation by Jon Weiner, "*The Untold History of the United States* demonstrates ... that history is not an iron cage, the keys to which are held by the ruling class. At many pivotal moments, Stone argues, history could have taken a radically different course. The missed opportunities, the roads not taken – these are Stone's central themes, ..."

Stone and Kuznick's point is that little accidents of history can have devastating global impacts, and that it is often only by luck or timing that history did not result in vastly different outcomes, either better or worse.

Tiny variables of knowledge, decision, timing, and luck, at this critical juncture, may seal the fate of future generations.

• **1929-35: The Stock Markets in the US and the UK crash,** bringing on the *Great Depression.* The 1870s through 1900 were called the *Gilded Age;* it continued into the *Roaring* (19) '20s. A deregulated stock market in the UK and the US drove excessive speculation, led to margin buying – gambling on a bull market with borrowed money – and a huge market bubble, which exploded in the dual crash. The period is seen as an example of unregulated Capitalism basically sucking the wealth out of the economy until it collapses. But it's only seen that way by those willing to question Capitalism.

OBSERVE: In spite of the crash and its recognized causes, and in spite of the success of FDR's New Deal (just ahead), Republicans then and now stick to a hatred of government regulations, on almost everything, as a core principle. Regulations and taxes. The deregulation, and the weak resistance from Democrats, continued into the Reagan, Bush I, Clinton, Bush II, and Obama terms, causing or leading to: the S and L Crisis under Reagan, that cost taxpayers 10s of billions, the Mortgage Loan crash of 2008, under Bush II, Obama's failure to hold the banks and Wall Street responsible for it; and, in 2017-18, into the Trump/Ryan/McConnell Tax Scam and exploding Military Budget, together totaling well over $10 trillion.

• **1931-5 General Smedley Butler:** Major General Smedley Butler (1881-1940) was the most honored and decorated military man in US history, when he retired from the US Marine Corps in 1931. He served his country by leading invasions, interventions and small wars in several countries in Latin America and the Far East. He would surely have risen to higher levels of military, civilian, or political power, were it not for his rough personal demeanor and the pacifist views that he came to later in life.

In Butler's post-military book, *War is a Racket* (1935), he revealed that he had been " ... a high class muscle-man for Big Business." "... a racketeer, a gangster for Capitalism." His assignment was to make countries like Mexico, Haiti, Cuba, Guatemala, Nicaragua, the Dominican Republic, Honduras, and China *safe* for companies like United Fruit, Standard Oil, National City Bank and others. The need to dominate countries, their governments, resources, and markets, stemmed from a Fear of Socialism, and hid behind the guise of spreading Democracy. Butler connected the dots and revealed the pattern. He came to hate the trend and then to openly resist it. You can do the research on those interventions: which ones led to Socialist/Communist revolutions, or to US-installed Right-Wing dictators. A hundred years on, most of those countries still suffer the aftermath.

In 1933, a group of powerful businessmen tried to recruit Gen. Butler to help lead a Right-Wing military overthrow of the FDR administration, and the US government. He refused and exposed the conspiracy.

He came out in strong opposition to war profiteering and

of military enforcement of international business interests. He warned us about the dangers of secret alliances between government, the military, and the business community (add in the police, and that pattern is a definition of state Fascism).

OBSERVE: Hardly anyone in Power heard that warning, or cared.

• **1938-50: The General Motors Streetcar Conspiracy:** In the early 1900s, many US cities created electric streetcar systems that ran smoothly and reliably, were cost effective and relatively sustainable, even when they relied on coal-fired electrical power. But General Motors, Standard Oil, and a few other corporations conspired to make sure they were replaced by gas- and diesel-powered buses and automobiles. They bought up the streetcar systems in LA and Oakland in California, in St. Louis, Baltimore, and as many as 20 other cities, and destroyed them, pulled up the tracks and junked the electric streetcar carriages. Most of the companies were convicted of Conspiracy to Monopolize both Interstate Transport (which was not really the point) and the Transit Industry (which was still not really the point). Some were convicted, others not, but the end result was accomplished and stands to today, with LA being the worst example.

OBSERVE: City and state governments and the courts were powerless to stop the conspiracy, in the face of the Power of the oil giants. And don't be surprised, the arch Conservative oil billionaire Koch Brothers are trying to do the exact same thing right now. (New York Times, June 19, 2018) *That* is the point.

• **1932-1945, Franklin Delano Roosevelt's** *New Deal,* is the sum of the radical economic innovations he got Congress to enact, to help end the Great Depression. But, over his 3-plus terms as president, they did not create a prosperous, growing economy, like the Gilded Age and Roaring 20s had been. The policies were seen correctly as a positive correction, and incorrectly as negative Socialist economic principles. They included, for example, extensive federally funded programs to get people working again, social and economic safety nets like social security and unemployment benefits, and a progressive income tax – with rates above 90 percent for the highest earners. Federal revenues rose enough to cover all the benefits and more.

FDR also managed the US entry into WWII and the US's role in the victory over German, Italian, and Japanese Fascism.

OBSERVE: Following the war, Republicans, corporate managers, and the super-rich had a justifiable but exaggerated fear of Communism, which they inflated into an irrational Fear of Socialism, that came to dominate both parties. Until today.

• **1939: The Threat of War, and an Economic Conversion:** The US had started producing quantities of weaponry and war vehicles – ships, tanks, and airplanes in particular – to help the British in their defense against Hitler's Nazi military. The production was also justified as a backup plan in case the US was forced to enter the war. The United States restructured its entire economy to a war production footing between 1939 and the end of the war in 1945. It was called *The Conversion*. We were still at peace until Japan attacked the US bases at Pearl Harbor, Hawaii, on Dec. 7, 1941. It provoked us to declare war against Japan, Germany, and Italy, the 3 Axis powers.

War spending finally lifted the US economy out of the Depression.

OBSERVE: The Conversion demonstrated that the US, unified by a shared cause and a strong government mandate, could completely transform its economic profile in a short period of time. But most US citizens did not observe the bigger picture, that military spending had become a major support for a growing economy. A similar change occurred in the 1950s, for very different reasons.

• **1944: Henry Wallace:** The first episode in Stone and Kuznick's film series features the mostly forgotten story of Henry Wallace.

FDR probably knew he was dying when he ran for a 4th term in 1944. He was proud of the New Deal, and wanted a suc-
194

cessor to continue the Progressive trend. He wanted to keep *Big Business* at bay, to continue the progressive income tax, to resist the growing *Anti-Socialist* wave of fear spreading in the country, and he wanted his social/economic programs to continue. He wanted Henry Wallace, his VP from 1940 to '44, and a strong Progressive (accused of being a virtual Socialist), to be next in line for the presidency.

But his Democrat Party was beginning to feel the pressure of its business-friendly, Socialist-phobic wing (just a few years after the attempted revolt that Gen. Butler exposed). They replaced Wallace with Harry S Truman, a political unknown, in the VP slot. Speculation persists as to whether Wallace would have ordered the first use of nuclear weapons, as Truman did. And there are still arguments about whether most Democrat delegates preferred Truman, or other Democrats, to Wallace.

OBSERVE: The betrayal of Henry Wallace created a model of *Political Power Abuse* that continues to today, in the Democrats' fear of their own legitimate Left Wing, and in the corruption of the Right. It's an early predictor of the Failure of the 2-Party System.

• **The Postwar Economy Slumps:** It took the US's entry into WWII to multiply industrial output and get to near zero unemployment ... actually *negative unemployment,* because the new war industry gave thousands of women their first jobs. But the end of the war created new economic and social challenges.

We can see that racial and gender Bias were not softened by the war. The US failed to elevate the status of minorities after the war. Many black, brown, American Indian – and even Japanese American – war heroes were back in a segregated society before they took off their uniforms. Many women had achieved a clear measure of Power through wartime employment, and resented losing that power. Rosie the Riveter went back to housekeeping.

Truman, to his lasting credit, desegregated the US military.

The high levels of investment and production were no longer

needed for tanks and bombers, but the economy had come to depend on the cash flow. Both consciously and unconsciously, publicly *and* privately, it was understood that the US needed new forms of consumption to keep the economy cranking. Continued military spending for a *Peacetime Army,* though strategically unnecessary, and considered bad policy by many, became part of a new economic foundation. The returning veterans and their families (with the help of a lot of government assistance) filled the remaining gap, by building a powerful middle class consumer economy during the late 1940s and '50s: free college for vets, appliances and cars, travel, low interest loans and home ownership with subsidized mortgages, and enough consumer goods to sponsor a whole new information industry, Television. The veneer of happiness, shared mostly among Whites, gave few signs of the social and political upheaval brewing under the surface.

• **1952: Dwight D Eisenhower, Liberal Republican,** retired Army General and Pacifist, was elected to the presidency. *Ike* (his popular nickname, in the Army and out) called himself a "moderate conservative." He kept most of FDR's New Deal programs in effect, angering a lot of more conservative Republicans. He included FDR's progressive income tax rates, as outlined above, because, in his words (now long forgotten, adjusted to inflation, and paraphrased), "Nobody needs ten million dollars."

In his 1953 "Cross of Iron" speech, he likened military spending to a theft from the public good. Look it up. It is a kind of reckoning.

It is stunning to compare the Republican party platform in the 1950s to either party today. Eisenhower's policies were far to the left of Nixon and Reagan (the next 2 Republican presidents), and even further left of the GOP in 2018. He stood up to the Communist witch hunts of Right-Wing radical Joe McCarthy, and kept the GOP separate from that faction. He took pride in not getting the US into any new wars, and he helped to end the

196

fighting in Korea with a truce, still in effect today. Though he was opposed to military adventurism and secret interventions, Conservative advisors like the Dulles brothers persuaded him into several covert operations. He authorized the overthrow of the popular and legitimate Mosaddegh regime in Iran (see pages 201, 216), and a democratic government in Guatemala, both with the covert help of the CIA. The rationale was the containment or suppression of left-leaning administrations, and, notably, the protection of US business interests. See The Shock Doctrine, ahead on pages 202-4. With the Dulles's influence, Eisenhower also laid the groundwork for Vietnam.

In his exit speech on Jan. 17, 1961, Ike warned of the "grave implications" of the *Military-Industrial Complex*, and its potential to exert a "disastrous rise of misplaced power ..." You can find that speech online too. Eisenhower feared that the corporations that had come to rely on military spending as their life blood might undermine the values at the base of the US Democracy; that they would conspire, consciously and unconsciously, to thwart the best interests of the country in three ways:

1) to make our foreign policy more belligerent and aggressive than necessary or wise;

2) to control more of our national budget than needed; and

3) to obscure public awareness of, and thwart civilian control over the combined workings of the military, industry, finance, and covert intelligence operations.

Do any of those seem familiar today? Which ones?

Eisenhower cautioned, on one hand, that Communism (though he didn't name it in that 1961 speech) was a dangerous ideology that needed to be contained. On the other hand, he warned that an irrational Fear of Socialism, blown out of proportion, might help to rationalize and spread the influence of the M-I Complex, and lead to the kinds of Power Abuse he predicted. It's ironic that Eisenhower helped to create the Military-Industrial Complex, during and after the war, and then began to see its unintended consequences. It may have been too late to stop or control it, even then. Now it will be vastly more difficult.

OBSERVE: Eisenhower actually delayed the Decline of the Democrat Party and the Left. The 1950s were a unique time in terms of dramatic bipartisan progress, including some early Civil Rights legislation. But the Powers of the Military-Industrial Complex, and the Fears of the early NeoConservatives set the US up for decades of militaristic waste and foreign policy disasters ... that could not help but distract us from the emerging environmental problems.

I graduated High School in 1960 and had nothing but sweet illusions about my options for success and the positive trajectory of the world at large. Rachel Carson's Silent Spring was published in 1962. In spite of my interest in environmental issues, I didn't hear of it for another decade. The idea that I was benefitting from White Privilege would not enter my mind for at least 8 more years. But I'm getting ahead of the times.

OBSERVE: The victory in WWII appeared to justify the US jumping into the role of *Cop of the World.* The new Consumer Economy more or less blinded the nation to the possibility of over-consumption and unintended consequences.

DIGRESSION: We are quite riled up, as a nation, in March, 2018, about whether the Russians interfered with the 2016 election, whether Trump knew, colluded, or requested the interference, whether Russian internet bots affected the outcome that put Trump in the White House. Naive or uninformed, too many of us assume such dirty tricks are only done by our adversaries. The press has been slow or silent on our government's interventionist history. The US attempted or succeeded to influence national elections – to the extreme of a few militarist coups – in Iran, Chile, Guatemala, Honduras, Nicaragua, El Salvador, Greece, Iraq, several African nations including South Africa (because Conservatives thought Nelson Mandela was a terrorist), and in other countries.

Only a few of us really understand the impacts on US elections, for decades, of real and fake voter fraud, or GOP gerry-mandering, or campaign finance money, or the Electoral College, or a half dozen other factors.

Conservatives and Fox's Fake News pundits struggle today to clarify the differences between *Sure they did it and naughty them*, and, *Sure we did it but we were right and had no choice – we were defending Democracy ... (um and oh yeah, Capitalism)*.

• **1947 to the present: The Cold War:** The earlier stages of the *Cold War* were the direct offspring of the very hot Second World War. The USSR, Britain, and the US had defeated Hitler and German Nazism, and Italian and Japanese Fascism, which set up Communism and Free Market Capitalism as opponents in a global battle between economic ideologies. The Cold War appeared to be a military standoff between Capitalist and Communist blocs, but it was just as much a competition to see which system could invest more in a consumer economy, and waste more on weapons and armies. When the USSR got the bomb, followed by their successes in space, the economic competition gained a lot of fossil-fueled steam. The space race has worked out to a draw, with the US, Russia, and other nations cooperating on the International Space Station. The weapons race and the consumer economies played out very differently.

The fear of MAD - Mutually Assured Destruction – became a psychological weapon in the Cold War, and – maybe only in my view – is linked with Capitalists' and Communists' *rational and irrational fears* of each other. Attempts by the USSR, and later Russia, to match the US in consumer and military spending led to the dissolution of the Soviet Union, to a hybrid Communist/Capitalist system, riddled with corruption, to an ongoing stagnant economy, dependent on oil.

The nuclear power generation industry in the US was founded as a scam, to make the public think it was a safe and useful way to generate electricity, when it was actually a nuclear bomb fuel system, with tons of deadly toxic by-products that have accumulated exponentially. The US public was promised that the electricity produced would be "too cheap to meter." The unintended consequences, including 3 or 4 meltdowns and vast quantities of radioactive waste, we now find to be *too costly to measure.*

The economic and environmental costs of the nuclear weapons race (aside from the victims of Hiroshima and Nagasaki) are beyond any possible calculation, unless compared to the Global Environmental Crisis ... or (again, now under Trump) the possibility of nuclear war.

The nuclear buildup in the US, costing many trillions of dollars, was almost certainly inflated by grossly exaggerated estimates of the USSR's threats, by (who else?) the Military-Industrial Complex, with the help of the CIA and Defense "Intelligence," and of course a media market getting hooked on real and imaginary threats.

The consumer economies in Russia and China took decades to even begin to compete. And when they did, it led them, paradoxically and in very different patterns, to adopt hybrid Capitalist systems to bolster their economies and compete with the West, in production and pollution ... and to succumb to widespread corruption.

OBSERVE: An objective view, if that is possible, might say that the Cold War was all unnecessary, a paranoid obsession with the accumulation of Abusive political Power on both sides. Ultimately ...

... it belies the possibility (or fact) that each opposing camp had doubts about the popularity or the economic validity of its own ideology.

A SHORT DIGRESSION: Karl Marx (a co-founder of Socialist/ Communist principles, partly to blame for the conflation of the two) was arguably a defender of the environment; he spoke of Capitalism's tendency to destroy the value of labor and the environment for private wealth, and he wrote of sustainable practices. Did you know that the original Marxist had a written correspondence with Abraham Lincoln? I didn't. Marx apparently understood that slavery and race discrimination were ultimately tools of Capital. It's pretty clear Lincoln understood that the South would not relinquish slavery for any moral argument, because it depended on it as a wealth-production system, and because it used racial discrimination to divide poor whites and blacks with a system that impoverished both groups.

OBSERVE: ... the connections between an exploitive economy and race-baiting; and the fact that Capitalism and Communism (with real, flawed, or fake, token or parody Democracies) have both proven to be destructive to the environment; Socialism (almost always in functioning Democracies), in fact, much less.

• **1953: Iran:** While I was sitting in front of a 10" TV screen, enthralled with the Lone Ranger and Hopalong Cassidy – *good guys with guns* on TV – my government, Eisenhower, the Dulles brothers, and the CIA, posed the question that has come up over and over in the years since, mostly about Middle East Arab countries,

"How did so much of OUR oil get buried under THEIR sand?"

US Capitalism was already addicted to oil. Access to it at a reasonable price had become a national security issue, and has remained so *long after it was no longer true or sensible.* The military cost of protecting our *national oil interests abroad* cost far more in money, emissions, and lives, than alternate fuels and efficiency could have saved.

We made solid alliances with some middle eastern suppliers, Saudi Arabia in particular, to keep our habit supplied, with little or no regard to their internal politics or human rights records. But when a popular, secular government was elected in Iran, with Mohammad Mosaddegh as its prime minister, who chose to reclaim Iran's oil resources from US and British oil giants, those countries decided that regime had to go. The

Dulles brothers probably convinced Eisenhower that we could not allow Iran to sell oil to the USSR, and that the new prime minister had to be overthrown, by something that would look like a popular, local *Anti-Communist* uprising. That led directly to the return to power of the dictator Shah, who provoked an Islamic revolution a couple decades later, which has dominated the Persian people to this day.

• **1954: The American Petroleum Institute's** *Smoke and Fumes Committee*, through it's spokesman Vance Jenkins, announced, "The worst thing that can happen ... is the hasty passage of ... laws for the control of a given air pollution situation." (Inside-ClimateNews.org)

• **From 1953 to the present: The Shock Doctrine:** In 2008, Naomi Klein's book, *The Shock Doctrine, The Rise of Disaster Capitalism,* was released. Her 2 more recent books, *This Changes Everything, Capitalism vs. The Climate* (2015), and *NO is Not Enough* (2017), deal directly with 3 crucial topics that are relevant here (the Climate Crisis, the economy, and Trump). But *The Shock Doctrine* is most relevant in this history. It describes a program designed by NeoLiberal economist Milton Friedman and his colleagues at the University of Chicago, often called *The Chicago Boys.*

The Shock Doctrine was a plan to impose a state-enforced, Free-Market/Capitalist economy on selected countries (and eventually on most of the world) without resorting to military action ... unless fake WMDs could be used as an excuse. But invasions and coups d'etat were always a plan-B option. And real Democracy was never on the agenda.

The premise was that radical economic "shock therapy" could be applied to an entire nation, in a short period of time, by an authoritarian regime, when a nation faced a crisis, real or perceived: in national security, internal conflict, political gridlock, leftist movements, labor disputes, or economic recession. A regime under stress could be forced to flip a national economy to a completely different set of principles.

A country was primed, before the fact, with propaganda, bribes and investments, threats, military aid and hired gangs – fake protesters and death squads – to turn the public against the regime in power, or to scare them into submission. The new Capitalist governments were aided by high-interest loans from the World Bank. Trade agreements, taxes, interest, and benefits were transformed to help the US corporations and the local rich, who prospered while economic austerity was forced on the poor and middle classes.

Milton Friedman's Shock Doctrine was nothing less than an engineered plan for global political/capitalist domination, country by country.

The plan had a perplexing range of outcomes over the last forty-plus years. Some earlier examples, like Chile and Argentina, went terribly badly, with some deep, long-term wounds yet to be healed: debt, austerity, chronic corruption, the *disappeared*.

It was news to me that the privatization of government assets after the breakup of the USSR in the 1990s, followed Shock Doctrine principles, as did the Chinese conversion to a hybrid Communist/Capitalist system, around the turn of 2000.

The current outcomes, in Russia and some of its satellites, and in China and other countries, have very different profiles but the same general trends. They appear on the surface to be working. Trade has increased, but has been limited, with Russia for example, by sanctions. But deeper failures and symptoms of collapse persist: corruption, income inequality, and crushing poverty for large fractions of the population, pensions seized and benefits cut, delayed, or eliminated, authoritarian social controls, and unabated environmental damage.

The Shock Doctrine creates a historical bridge between, for example, Iran 1953, Chile 1972, and Iraq 2003; and mental bridges among NeoLiberalism as economic policy, NeoConservatism as foreign policy, and a Right-leaning Congress in the US. It has turned the US into a third world country for the working poor. It illustrates a coordinated, engineered program to undermine popular Democracies that appear to be turning left, including here in the USA.

OBSERVE: On one hand, Naomi Klein reveals a grim reality. Under specific circumstances, it is possible to impose a radically different economic system on an entire population: extractive, exploitive, and authoritarian rather than fair, sustainable, or Democratic. It may achieve its ideological goals, but the negative consequences – human and ecological, political and economic, intended and unintended – are extreme, and, sooner or later, intolerable.

On the other hand, why not imagine *flipping* the strategy? Jump to Parts Seven and Eight.

SHORT DIGRESSION: The 1960s was a decade of social and political divisions in the US (and in Europe and other places): a broad-based generation gap, birth control and women's liberation, resistance to the Vietnam war, racial progress and set-backs, and the middle phases of the Failure of the 2-Party System. The first anti-segregation and voting rights laws were enacted under Eisenhower; the Johnson administration went further, only to face a political backlash and social/racial unrest, especially after the assassination of Martin Luther King Jr. It is notable that across those three administrations – Eisenhower-Kennedy-Johnson – the Republican Party went from being the Party of Lincoln to the inventors of the Southern Strategy; while the Democrats went from covert racism to reluctant support for Civil Rights for blacks. The 2 parties' positions on the war were, sadly, almost identical until it started to go bad, when a few politicians on both sides – but mostly Democrats – joined the war resisters. The social/political shifts may seem paradoxical in hindsight, and are hard to boil down to a summary. But, generally, as one who lived through that decade, I see the beginnings of a Liberal/ Conservative disagreement turning into a bitter Divide – one in which both parties have moved significantly to the Right.

• **1960-'64: Kennedy and Johnson. Politics on TV.** Richard Nixon and John F Kennedy faced each other in the first televised presidential debate, prior to the 1960 election. It was a turning point in the relative impacts of politics, credibility, and TV. The radio audience thought that Nixon won; those who saw it on TV judged Kennedy the winner. Nixon *sounded* reasonable but *looked* stressed and awkward. Kennedy matched or beat Nixon on some points, but he simply looked and acted – how else to say it? – cool. So the visual images of the candidates began to balance, and often to overpower, their voices and words, for good (in 1960) and for ill (through much of the 1980s, 90s, and 2000s). The new format opened the door to a lot of confusion about media truth and objectivity. Kennedy *appeared* to be thoughtful, spontaneous, and truthful. Nixon would eventually fail to distinguish between his corrupt idea of the truth and political crimes and cover-ups. The early 1960s gave birth to the costly, highly persuasive, and often corrupt and dishonest political ad. TV made campaign budgets the new political reality and political messaging a new form of propaganda – unconscious manipulation of a public that still does not understand the internal psychological dynamics.

OBSERVE: The whole process expands the political divide with nasty rhetoric, almost exclusively from the Right, and forces both parties to yield to the corruption inherent to the demands of campaign donors. In 2017 and '18, several rich donors to both parties have threatened them openly with de-funding, if they pass or don't pass certain legislation – tax cuts for example.

The assassination of president Kennedy was a deep and brutal shock to the nation, especially 20-somethings like me, at the time, that we have yet to transcend, and that the 20-somethings of today can barely understand.

At some point in time, Democrats had the option of fighting the betrayals, the degraded principles, and the corruption, from the GOP and from within, but a majority decided they'd be better off joining in selling out to the big donors.

- **1964: Barry Goldwater vs. the *Peace Candidate.***

In spite of Kennedy's alleged intent to get out of Vietnam, Lyndon Johnson allowed himself and the nation to be seduced by the Generals' optimism and a bunch of other really bad ideas. Like the *Domino Theory.* But in 1964, the war was still in the background and Johnson was challenged by Barry Goldwater, the founder of the Conservative wing of the Republican Party. Goldwater was characterized as a sort of nutty war hawk that would expand Vietnam into a nuclear conflict. The Democrats aired attack ads – uncharacteristic of them generally – that effectively spread the fear. So, in my first chance to vote in a presidential election, my only rational choice was Johnson, *the Peace Candidate.* I knew the ads were bogus, *and* that Barry was a little unhinged. But anyway ...

In 2018 hindsight, Goldwater seems a moderate, while his conservative GOP legacy brought us a party slowly losing its mind and relevance, and with Trump, renewed threats of nuclear war.

Goldwater, with all his right-wing credentials, had no trouble calling himself a "strong conservationist" (of nature), something no climate-denying Republican would dare say today. Given the present-day alliances between avowed Christians, oil barons, some local school boards, bankers, weapons dealers, and corrupt Republicans, it is mind-blowing to quote Goldwater from 1964:

"Mark my word, if and when these preachers get control of the (GOP) party, and they're sure trying to do so, it's going to be a terrible damn problem. Frankly, these people frighten me. ... these Christians believe they are acting in the name of God, so they can't and won't compromise. I know, I've tried to deal with them."

OBSERVE: That's a powerful contrast. Goldwater predicted that the (I call them fake) Christians were already on track, in 1964, to turn the GOP into uncompromising extremists. But, tracing from then to now (given my experience with hypocritical and fake Christians in my family), the issue is not so much whether they really believe they are doing God's work. Rather,

> *... if they can convince other real and fake Christians that what they are doing is Right in God's Eyes ...*

– they know they can get and hold Power, and use the system any way they choose, without ethical principles, therefore exempt from criticism, moral guilt, or counter arguments.

FROM THE MIRACLE BULLET TO BUILDING 7
Since John F Kennedy was assassinated in November of 1963, neither the official commission studies, nor the many unofficial follow-ups have convinced a majority that the full story has been told. There were hints that Kennedy had wanted the US to get out of Vietnam even before he was elected. History has not verified that claim. He had given a speech, earlier in November '63, warning of hidden powers that covertly controlled the US government and international finance, with ill intent. He indicated he wanted to end that control.

In retrospect, in the eyes and mind of a skeptical progressive, the official report, meant to explain the Kennedy assassination, looks a lot like the one that was meant to explain the 9-11 attacks. In other words, a lot of significant questions *APPEAR* never to have been answered. Some were never asked.

• **1964-'74: Vietnam, Chicago, Nixon. War on TV:** Here's where it all gets more complicated and way more mean-spirited. It feels like a disservice to my own vivid memory to cut this down to a few paragraphs. I urge you to do your own research.

When the anti-war protests started making the headlines, Johnson dug in his heels, committed to a longer war and started criticizing the press for negative coverage, giving a lot of politicians permission to attack "unhelpful" coverage. Nixon and his VP Spiro Agnew would pick up the theme a few years later.

When a quick, cheap, and honorable end to the war faded, public support began to disintegrate. Making war to keep from "losing face" brought on the nation's worst self-inflicted wound of the last 90 years, with the possible exception of Iraq. With no lessons learned. To. This. Day.

When Democrat Senator Eugene McCarthy announced he would run against Johnson for the presidential nomination in 1968, the overall dynamic started to shift. *OR SO IT SEEMED.* The combined pressures, from the public, the Congress, allies, the failing war effort, and certainly the stress, Johnson said he would not run for re-election. Anti-war activists saw it as an opening for an anti-war president. I canvassed door-to-door in Milwaukee for Gene McCarthy.

Robert Kennedy decided to run against McCarthy and other Democrats, as a second high-profile anti-war candidate. Some saw Kennedy's move as a betrayal of McCarthy's early courage, others, as slightly delayed opportunism. It threw the Democrat Party into what most welcomed as a hopeful conflict. Maybe one more than they needed.

While the Democrats paid lip service to Civil Rights, and in fact fostered some great legislation, they were not receptive to the idea that the progress was still too slow in coming, and severely incomplete. The Democrats, rather blindly, saw Dr. King's message and popularity as a threat to their Leftist credentials; they have never overcome the notion that their commitment to Civil Rights was conditional. And they were slow to connect US's racism at home with the racism of the Vietnam war.

Nixon and Goldwater guided the GOP to withdraw support for minority rights, without being obvious ... to their white base. The Democrats' Civil Rights Act of 1964 gave blacks more guaranteed rights, but it deepened the racial divide in the south. As Johnson feared, it turned the South over to the Republicans, who used code words like *Law and Order,* and programs like the *War on Drugs,* as a covert strategy to put thousands of young blacks and hundreds of white pot smokers in prison.

When Martin Luther King was assassinated, in April of 1968, Bobby Kennedy gave a "heartfelt impromptu speech, calling for reconciliation between the races." (Wikipedia) Only a month later, in May, 1968, moments after he won the California primary, Bobby Kennedy was assassinated in Los Angeles. The Democrats went into their Chicago convention as a divided party, in a city run by an unscrupulous mayor who was already alienating the anti-war faction. The establishment Democrat Party chose Hubert Humphrey, Johnson's Vice President, as the nominee. The anti-war movement felt justifiably betrayed.

1968 was an absolute turning point for many factions in the country, and for our national outlook. It was one step in a long, gradual but stubborn expansion of Conservative control of the country, as waged by both parties, even when Democrats reflected the public's positions on most issues, and when they held or shared power.

"WAIT, OK, I GET THE '60s, BUT WHAT DOES THIS HAVE TO DO WITH CLIMATE CHANGE?" Good question. Answered with a reminder: These histories and their impacts – increasing air and water pollution, anti-war activists, the *Generation Gap* and the *War on Drugs*, rising racial tensions, heightened militarism, the environmental movement and the resistance to it, the early and middle stages of tax reductions and deregulation, and more – illustrate a pattern that is now at the core of our multiple crises. Struggles for political power started to blur the principles the parties stood for. The corrupting Power of campaign finance added to the struggles and the blurring. The Left had started to fragment under Johnson. The Republicans under Nixon clearly put Partisan Power over truth, ethics, and the public good, until Watergate forced a few of them to be honest and patriotic. That tracks the faint beginnings of resistance to Environmental protection and the rise of Outlaw Capitalism. Those issues become more clearly interconnected in the next few years.

The 3rd and 4th Premises for this book argue that we have to understand the connections to understand the growing scope of the combined crises, or to imagine any solution. The Anti-War Movement had begun to feel a core alliance with the Environmental Movement, still in its infancy. I felt a part of that alliance. Together they began to formulate a long-term vision of a world organized around Sustainability, Justice, and Peace.

Folks like me who were young adults during those years say they have never seen the country so divided as it was then. Except now.

• **Richard Nixon:** With the help of Roger Ailes (who co-founded Fox News a decade later), Nixon had remade himself into a more friendly, confident *looking* candidate. Most of the country didn't like or trust Nixon, in spite of the makeover, and, before the assassination of Bobby Kennedy, he had little chance of being elected.

But against all odds and expectations, the Democrats nominated one of the few people who could lose to Nixon. It was a sad predictor of HRC vs. Trump.

It's helpful that Watergate, Daniel Ellsberg, the Pentagon Papers and the Washington Post have been back in the news, as historical entertainment, clearly in response to Trump. Watergate did not just expose Nixon's enemies list and his racism, the criminal conspiracies and cover-ups he ordered; it exposes the rotten roots of 21st century Right-Wing Republicans *TODAY*, and their lack of a moral, ethical, or patriotic core. Every new Republican scandal seemed to signal a Conservative paradox: a combination of guilt, Denial, the public's demand for a reckoning, and both parties' commitment to the status quo. GOP crimes remained somehow un-indicted, while every little Democrat scandal became a permanent scar, and a marker of the party's wishy washy core.

After the Watergate scandal forced Nixon to resign, I thought 3 things had become possible: 1. It would make the GOP reform and never let another lying trickster bid for high office. 2. It would make the Democrat party reform and trust their more progressive wing. 3. It would make citizen-voters more attentive to politics and issues, and demand more from the 2-Party System, otherwise in an ongoing Failure. I was wrong about all 3. In many cases the opposite occurred, leading indirectly, but almost inevitably, to the Trump disaster.

210

Nixon goes down in history as a troubling paradox. He improved relations with China, Wikipedia says, "he was a late convert to the conservation (environmental) movement." But liberals clearly understood it as pure opportunism, or something he felt required to do in response to public opinion.

In the context of the paradox, I'm amazed to find a Nixon quotation I was not aware of. In his (real or fake) justification for signing the laws that created the Environmental Protection Agency, the Clean Water Act, worker protections under OSHA, and other good environmental policies, he mentioned our obligation to make, "reparations to nature for the damage we've done."

Nixon ended the draft and promised to end the US's engagement in Vietnam "with honor." But by then, that was impossible. Two of Tricky Dick's worst tricks, bordering on treason, are left out of most histories, sadly including this one. See the section on Reagan for a footnote.

Nixon turned the funding for Medicare and Medicaid into block grants, reducing federal spending and limiting benefits. He backed the formation of Health Maintenance Organizations, basically Privatizing much of what Medicare and Medicaid had been created to do, leading directly to the extreme inflation of medical costs, the expanded power of private medical insurance, and deregulation of supporting industries like pharmaceuticals.

Nixon's lists of enemies and his dirty tricks, his favors for big business and his hatred of the press, his willingness to demonize blacks and liberals, **to** exaggerate fears to further his objectives, and his paranoid political style – all the things that made him a failed president – found a warm home in the hearts of Republican strategists, lobbyists, and war profiteers. In spite of his impeachment. A few hard right Conservatives still think it was a miscarriage of justice. Many others see it as one of the last signs of bipartisan commitment to principle over party.

WE RETURN to the decline of the Left in the US with a little-known, but lasting and powerful event in the Nixon years.

- **1973: The Powell Memorandum:** Lewis F. Powell (1907-1998) was a high-priced and well-connected corporate lawyer in the 1950s and '60s. He reluctantly accepted Nixon's nomination to the Supreme Court, in spite of his limited experience outside of corporate law. Shortly before he joined the Court, in 1971, he wrote what is known as the *Powell Memorandum* ... or *Manifesto.* It had a huge role in this unfolding history, partly because most of us never heard of it.

Powell's Memorandum was meant to counter what he saw as a gradual but growing anti-business attitude across much of American society. It was addressed to and promoted by the US Chamber of Commerce, a powerful pro-business advocacy group. The Memo circulated among Republicans, corporate CEOs, business lobbyists, and wealthy investors. It represents a big bump to the Power of Money and to the slow rightward creep – of both parties, more or less knowingly, and across the population, almost invisibly. The memo and its impacts are well documented in the 2011 film, *Heist, Who Stole the American Dream?*

I admit to a potential bias. I can't help but think Powell was motivated by a general Fear of the anti-war protesters, racial tensions, and the social upheavals of the 1960s.

The Powell memo prompted several Right-Wing Conservative/Capitalist think tanks to become more aggressive, with money and messages, and sparked the founding of a bunch of new ones. The American Enterprise Institute, for example, was founded in 1938; it did undergo a transition in the late 1960s, and again in the 70s, after Powell. The great and growing influence of many other Right-Wing think tanks, organizations like ALEC, and big money Conservative donors like the Koch Brothers, can be traced directly to Powell's Memo.

Powell harshly criticized the Colleges and Universities that had become bastions for the anti-war movement, and for other Liberal causes. He saw this as a sinister attempt, by the Left generally, to use education as a form of Liberal indoctrination. That move fostered 2 disturbing trends: the idea that education

212

generally is an elitist Liberal program to indoctrinate students
to question authority, tradition, and conventional moral values,
when its purpose (it's implied) ought to be training for profes-
sions and jobs; and beyond that, it represents the middle phase
of the Great Dumbing Down, the public questioning of facts,
science, and history, as mere Liberal propaganda, whenever they
differed from Conservative doctrine.

The fact that intelligent, educated people tend naturally to
support Liberal ideals, and that lack of education tends to bolster
Conservative beliefs, are dismissed as Leftist propaganda.

His Memo pushed hard for Capitalist investors to start
influencing institutions of higher education to better represent
the Free Market ideology and related Conservative ideas, like
opposition to abortion, the role of God and prayer in the public
schools, the suppression of racial and gender rights, and so on.
The NRA (National Rifle Association) for example, became much
more political and strident, and expanded their membership
dramatically, starting around 1977.

Powell was never a Right-Wing ideologue; he was a social
moderate, and an apparent supporter of civil rights, but a critic
of the movement's tactics. Flip side: he saw the young Ralph
Nader, in his role as a "consumer rights advocate," as a flagrant
proponent of Socialism, bent on destroying the Free Market system, and possibly the Democracy.

> **Powell's Memo outed Conservatives' worst fears:**
> **hippies, pacifists, angry blacks, drug crime and critics**
> **of the Capitalist social order.**

The notion that "Corporations are Persons" – meaning equal to
living people in many legal matters – (from a decision in 1898)
has made it easier to grant them free speech rights under the
First Amendment. Can you see where this is headed?

On the Supreme Court, Powell joined the majority in two
cases that opened wide the gates to political corruption through
campaign contributions. One (Buckley v Valeo, 1976) established

a devastating precedent by declaring, "Money is a form of free speech." (That only makes sense if *Corporations are People*.) The second, in '78, (First National Bank of Boston v. Bellotti) carried that trend further by knocking down state restrictions on political contributions by corporations and the wealthy. Those Powell-supported precedents were cited in the majority opinion in 2010, in Citizens United v. Federal Elections Commission. It demolished most of the remaining constraints on legal bribery ... oops, I mean campaign donations ... by opening wider the pipeline of corporate and private money to influence elections. More recent high court decisions have carried the corrupting trend even further (McCutcheon v. FEC 2014).

A DIGRESSION:
TOBACCO IS TO CANCER AS CARBON IS TO THE CLIMATE
In Heidi Cullen's book, *The Weather of the Future: Heat Waves, Extreme Storms and Other Scenes from a Climate-Changed Planet* (2011), she points out the intersection of two Right Wing talking points, rooted indirectly in Powell: all taxes and regulations are evil, and you can't have personal Freedom without Free Market Capitalism. That connection points indirectly to another: the marketing campaign that promoted tobacco smoking, and the coordinated campaign, since the 1970s, to discredit Climate Science.

I have to include the fact that a major public relations firm was behind both of those viciously deceptive campaigns, and that it is the exact same one that *sold* the first Gulf War (the US invasion of Iraq in 1990-91) to Congress and the US public, with false *eye-witness* accounts of stolen incubators and abandoned babies in Kuwait. That firm has been cranking out Conservative/Capitalist propaganda for other toxic ideas for decades.

In his law practice, Lewis Powell helped Big Tobacco file and win a bunch of pro-smoking, anti-regulation lawsuits, before their cancer denial and poisonous marketing strategies drew public opposition.

The conversation about tobacco causing lung cancer evolved

over 50 years. In my teens, real and fake doctors appeared in
TV ads and popular magazines to tell us how safe cigarets were,
even how they could make our lives better. The tobacco companies spent hundreds of millions to keep the conversation locked
in that mindset. By 1964, when the US Surgeon General made
the statement – *cigarette smoking CAUSES cancer* – millions had
died from nicotine addiction and lung cancer.

Climate Change Denial has followed the same pattern as the
pro-tobacco campaign, used the same Mis- and Dis-Information
tactics. The similarities are obvious, shocking and infuriating:
crucial facts are kept from the public, or made to seem unfound-
ed, for decades – about the links between tobacco and cancer,
or carbon pollution and Climate Change. In both cases, severe
health risks are downplayed or dismissed, so dirty profits continue to pile up. In both cases the government, media, and the
courts collude in the deception.

OBSERVE: From Powell until now, politicians of both parties (one much more than the other) will legislate, and conspire
with the media and the courts to delay or obscure bad news,
pump fake economics or Capitalism generally, and lie about the
risks ... *of almost anything.* Politicians' donors threaten to defund
them if they don't vote the right way. When corporate news gets
too close to *An Inconvenient Truth* (the title of Al Gore's film), the
sponsors threaten to switch their ad business to networks that
follow their mandates.

• **1977: A revolution in the National Rifle Association** turns
it from promoting responsible gun ownership and safety, to an
aggressive agent of gun manufacturers, and it's central mission
turns to using the Second Amendment, and Fear-based propaganda, to justify a massive increase in gun sales.

• **1979: Jimmy Carter: Malaise and Solar Panels:** Jimmy Carter was a different kind of paradoxical president. He made great
strides toward nuclear disarmament and peace in the Middle
East. He pardoned the Vietnam draft resisters, and tried, in a

215

rare partnership with Teddy Kennedy (otherwise a bitter rival), to try to get universal health care passed, but failed. He inherited a weak economy which was worsened by a Middle East oil embargo that resulted in severe gasoline shortages over periods of months. In his efforts to promote sustainable practices, he had solar water heating panels installed on the White House.

He gave a televised speech in which he said that the US was experiencing a *Crisis of Confidence*, stemming from the 1960s and early '70s, that was due in part to a heightened materialism and over-consumption, and that the nation would do well to live a more modest lifestyle. The speech was reduced to "the Malaise speech" even though he didn't use that word. It fed into Ronald Reagan's criticism of him, and it helped Reagan pitch his overly idealistic vision of a "New Morning in America," to beat Carter in the 1980 election. But Reagan also dipped into Tricky Dick Nixon's bag of treasonous dealings.

FLASHBACK AND PREVIEW: With the coaching of Henry Kissinger, Nixon prolonged the Vietnam war twice, purely for political gain. Johnson thought it was treason but didn't say so. Prior to his election in 1968, and his re-election in 1972 (just as Watergate was becoming news) he made secret contacts with the North Vietnamese peace negotiating team. In both instances he got them to postpone a pending agreement, promising to give them better terms after the election(s). The two tricks did help get him elected, a little or a lot, but the postponements needlessly extended the war and essentially doubled the total number of US war dead, from 25,000 to over 50,000, and added as many as a million additional Vietnamese, Laotians, and Cambodians to the "Body Count."

Jump to 1979: The blowback from the 1953 overthrow of Mosaddegh in Iran was still simmering in 1979, and erupted in a populist mini-revolution ... that turned huge and dark. It had 2 distinct factions, one more religious, one more democratic. But the Islamist sect raided the US embassy and held 52 Americans hostage for over a year, while the 1980 electoral season got underway. Many historians overlook the unethical steps that Reagan took to turn the *Hostage Crisis* to his favor. The Islamists were about to release the hostages near the end of Carter's term. But Reagan persuaded them secretly to postpone it until after the election, promising to give their regime better treatment. The negotiations worked, but remained secret ... long *enough*; the compliant Information Media let it escape the public's awareness. It was a little harder to keep the *Iran Contra Scandal* out of the news. Reagan operatives sold weapons, illegally, to Iran (part of the hostage deal), then used the money to support *Death Squads*, illegally, in Nicaragua, to help suppress a Socialist revolution.

- **1978: A Five to Ten Year Window:** James Black of Exxon* says that, " ... man has a window of five to ten years before the need for hard decisions regarding changes in energy strategies might become critical." (InsideClimateNews.org)

* Note that many oil companies were buying each other and merging over the last half century. Exxon, also known as ExxonMobil, is the present-day name for the combination of earlier separate companies Standard Oil of New Jersey, Esso, Enco, Sohio, Humble and others.

PREVIEW: THE EXXON DECEPTION
In the years spanning the Carter and Reagan administrations, and likely going back to the early 1970s, we now know that the large oil companies were conducting their own, very detailed and thorough research on CO_2 emissions and GW/CC, including the projected costs of trying to slow emissions, or, failing that, to repair the predictable damage. It was also during that period that lobbying began expanding its influence, by plying politicians with campaign donations to further their agendas.

OBSERVE: Exxon will feed into the topics of Partisan Truth and a Zero-Sum solution in several ways. Already we see glaring examples of how the US's oil addiction was influencing foreign policy, covert actions, and what passed for truth in the public conversation. This topic picks up on page 268.

• **1980: Ronald Reagan and Voodoo Economics:** Reagan campaigned against Carter's *Malaise* position, and for the general principles of American Exceptionalism, saying it would bring a happy and prosperous *New Morning in America*. Reagan's opponent in the GOP primaries was George HW Bush. (The father of George W Bush, he is only mentioned in a few details in this history.) In the 1980 primaries Bush Sr called "Reaganomics" "Voodoo Economics" because it was based on Supply Side (remember, from page 187?). Bush ended up as Reagan's VP in 1980, and was elected president in '88. *Voodoo Economics* was never mentioned by a Republican again. But Supply Side / Trickle Down is still a fake rationale for Trump's *Tax Scams* in 2017-18.

Reagan came into office in the middle of the economic recession that had dogged Jimmy Carter. One of his first acts was to have Carter's solar panels taken down and destroyed.

In his inauguration speech, Reagan said (about trying to fix the economy), "Government is not the solution to our problem; government is the problem." That phrase has become the rallying cry for Conservatives and Libertarians. The original thesis was that Liberals created "Big Government," raised taxes on everything, then spent it all and more on stuff we didn't really need or want, and that it regulated too much – like pollution, worker safety, and banks – which killed jobs and profits, for no reason. A side argument was that Liberals had made government too big to manage, or even make work.

That basic argument started to morph into, "We don't really need most of what government does, and could better spend the money that taxes take from us. "

• **1982: Roger Cohen of Exxon says,** "... the results of our research are in accord with the scientific consensus on the effect of increased atmospheric CO_2 on climate." (InsideClimateNews.org)

OBSERVE: How Exxon was not saying this in public (the quote is from an internal document) and how Exxon had officially started to say the exact opposite in public. That pattern continues a year into the Trump administration.

FOOTNOTE: (On the middle stages of the Failure of the 2-Party System.) The League of Women Voters in the US was founded in 1920 to support women's right to vote. Among many other activities to advance Democracy in the name of women, the League started to sponsor, host, and moderate presidential debates in 1976, and continued in the elections of 1980 and '84. In 1988, preparing to host the debate between Bush Sr and Mike Dukakis, the League rejected a plan from the newly formed, bipartisan CPD, or Commission on Presidential Debates. Representatives of both parties wanted to help pick (or reject) the moderators, to preview all the questions to be asked by them, to exclude questions on a specific list of topics, and to otherwise steer the debate away from subjects that were controversial or potentially damaging to one or both candidates. The League issued a statement saying that the debate format would "perpetrate a fraud on the American voter" and that the organization did not intend to "become an accessory to the hoodwinking of the American public." (Wiki) While it's hard to document, it's almost certain that 2 of the taboo topics were Bank Deregulation and Environmental regulations.

Since 1988, presidential debates have been controlled by that same ad hoc group, created by both parties, to limit the debates to what the candidates find comfortable. It's an indicator that the divisions were becoming artificial, that voices on specific issues were being suppressed, and that the 2 parties colluded to avoid hard topics like crime, militarism, and pollution.

• **1988-92: George HW Bush:** Though Reagan's apostles like to credit him with ending the Cold War ("Mr. Gorbachev, tear down this wall."), the wall actually came down during the GHW Bush presidency. His campaign for president was highlighted by the promise, "Read my lips, No New Taxes." But because Reagan's Supply Side ("Voodoo") economics had cut taxes, but had not reduced spending as promised, and had increased the National Debt by $220 billion, Bush I had no choice but to agree with a Democrat Congress to raise taxes, and implement several other Progressive spending programs. He was in fact stuck with a Democrat majority in both houses, so ended up with a legislative record that looked pretty Liberal; including new or expanded rules on limiting oil pollution, expanded clean air protections, and increases in legal immigration. The darkest blots on his record were: the Gulf War invasion of Iraq (1990-91), and the fact that the whole invasion was based on engineered lies (mentioned back on page 214). A strange foreboding of his son's crimes, and Cheney's, in Iraq, 12 years later.

• **1992-2000: Bill Clinton: Democrats become GOP-LITE:**
I was so sick of 12 years of Republican government, that when Bill Clinton was elected, I trusted that things would generally improve and I disengaged from politics. Big mistake. I was barely aware of the good or bad things Clinton did. I didn't like his decision to bomb Bosnia, but accepted his rationalizations. I didn't think the hyper-criminalization of crack cocaine was a good idea, even though a few African American leaders asked for it, to help cut inner-city crime. No one knew how it would balloon the prison population, with mostly black men, except the Republicans whose pressure Clinton seemed to welcome.

I assumed that Al Gore, as VP, would have a dynamic role in raising environmental controls under Clinton. Big disappointment. I was impressed that Clinton reduced the national debt and came closer to balancing the federal budget than any president in the last 30 years, but I didn't like that he radically cut federal assistance to the poor to do it. Clinton left a budget surplus of nearly $90 billion to George W Bush, which he immediately started wasting on tax cuts and an illegal war.

Clinton caved to the GOP and the banks in sweeping deregulations that set the stage for W to push them further, opening the door to the mortgage loan crash of 2008.

• *Who Killed the Electric Car?* ... is the title of a film from 2006, released through Sony. It documents how General Motors launched a courageous and innovative fleet of fully electric cars in 1995-6. They were available as a lease-only experiment in a few cities. The people who got to lease and drive them loved them, but GM withdrew them all and scrapped them in 1999. Wonder why? Look it up.

Andrew Bacevich sites the situation as decisive in postponing the wide availability of electric cars until the Chevy Volt and Elon Musk's Tesla, in the 2010s. Could Al Gore have done more? Would wider acceptance of electric cars have blunted Trump's Climate Change Hoax idiocy? We'll never know.

OBSERVE: ... the Power of the oil industry to subvert the public good, to destroy any innovation that might cut into profits, and to limit the government's ability to stand up for peoples' choices or the Earth.

PERSPECTIVE : Clinton's election and the GOP's de-evolution, during his 8-year term, in my view, reveals an insidious trend, and several sub-trends. The list that follows includes several examples of the GOP's increasingly aggressive and dishonest tactics, from around 1994 to today, and continues with examples of the oil industry's gradual shift from truth to lies about Global Warming and its impacts.

• **More vicious, brutal and corrupt tactics help drive the GOP:** It's almost impossible to trace this trend directly to the Koch brothers (who were staying out of the spotlight, but working hard behind the scenes), or the Powell Memo, but it's impossible to observe it without realizing it was part of a new GOP national strategy to create a Permanent Republican Majority in the US government. A major tactic was the use of ALEC as a powerful lever on local and state governments; Right Wing ideology drove a flood of regressive legislation, more or less purchased with huge campaign donations. And the GOP started using more radical gerrymandering methods so Republicans could select their voters, instead of the other way around.

The GOP had basically started to out-smart, out-lie, and out-cheat the Democrats, without their resistance or reply.

- **Newt Gingrich emerges as House Speaker and attack dog.**
He quickly became an expert at deepening the divide, to favor
the GOP and make Democrats appear unpatriotic and worse.
Gingrich made the word *Liberal* synonymous with evil. Many
true Liberals have tried to reclaim the titles as a badge of gener-
osity and tolerance but still have a long way to go. Many Republicans suddenly wanted to learn how to "Talk Like Newt."

  Gingrich also became a legislative bomb-thrower, prompting the first government shutdown over economic and ideological differences.

- **The language gets more partisan, devious, and divisive.**
Gingrich's protege Frank Luntz was only too happy to help,
listing and spreading new adjectives to use whenever talking
about Democrats, like: *bizarre, decay, disgrace, intolerant, incompetent, sick, shame, pathetic, traitors, radical, cheat, betray,* and *hypocrisy.* Hypocrisy!? Really!? I see Gingrich, Luntz, and Grover
Norquist (below), as 3 of the most dishonest, hypocritical, and
ruthless players on the Right, at least until Bush, Cheney, and the
GOP *Clown Car* of 2015-16, including Trump.

  Luntz (I call him a *Language Whore*, but *Rhetorical Pimp* is just
as accurate) had become an established pollster, focusing mainly on the more divisive issues, to color everything Democrat as
evil, and everything GOP as godly. He admits that his agenda is
to re-frame issues in terms that will deepen the partisan divide
– especially ones that are already *Hot Buttons* or *Dog Whistles*
– by appealing to unconscious emotions, mainly fear, racism,
and greed. His influence extends from the Clinton years to the
Trump fiasco. He's built a career on inventing Right-Wing propaganda language. (Look up George Lakoff, a Liberal linguist
who takes an opposite, much more honest, but ineffective tack.)

- **The Hard Right Echo Chamber is launched.** Fox News,
founded in 1996, and other Right-Wing media, helped to make
Luntz's engineered vocabulary into accepted parts of the public
conversation.

To Luntz, the term "Orwellian" is a good thing. It's from Orwell's dystopian novel, *1984*, published in 1949, about an authoritarian regime in an imagined future where an entire population is subjugated to the will of *Big Brother*. There's a stark difference between Orwell's fiction and today's fact: in *1984* everyone is forced to listen and watch while Big Brother pounds them with oppressive and deceptive propaganda; in the era of Fox News and Limbaugh, millions watch and listen voluntarily.

• **Pro-Pollution, Anti-Democrat Propaganda:** Luntz got Republicans, then many among us in the public to: change "oil drilling" to "energy exploration," "inheritance tax" to "death tax," and "Global Warming" to "Climate Change," because it sounded less threatening. George W Bush wanted to pass an early Cap and Trade scheme to reduce air pollution, that would have actually increased it. Luntz named it the "Clear Skies Initiative." He was paid millions to get the media to call Obama's Affordable Care Act, "Health Care Rationing," and " ... a government takeover," which Politifact called the "Lie of the Year" in 2009. He terrorized millions with the threat of "Death Panels" where Socialist Doctors would decide who could and could not get medical help. The deep and tragic irony is that Republicans, with help from a few Democrats, have forced the entire Health Care industry, from insurers to Big Pharma to doctors and hospitals, to become real Death Panels for millions of US citizens.

Luntz also got Republicans to call every Democrat economic proposal, "a Job Killer," and every Republican push for Free-Market expansion, "Job Creation." For decades, Luntz has effectively promoted the notions that the "science isn't in" about Climate Change, or is "inconclusive" or in doubt, and that environmentalists are radicals and extremists – even *Eco-Terrorists* – bent on killing the Free Market and American prosperity.

• **Cut Taxes, Starve Civilization:** Running parallel with Luntz over the last 20 years is the influence of Grover Norquist, who founded *Americans for Tax Reform* at Reagan's request. He's the guy who wants to make, "government small enough to drown it in the bathtub." 60-Minutes correspondent Steve Kroft says, "Norquist has been responsible, more than anyone else, for rewriting the dogma of the Republican Party." He's done that by forcing GOP politicians to swear to a pledge that they will never *NEVER* vote for a tax increase that is not paid for by budget cuts elsewhere, for fear of being "primaried" by others further to the Right, who take the pledge. You can bet that the Koch's are among his most avid and secret sponsors.

Beyond the anti-tax madness, Norquist worked in assisting or whitewashing: George W Bush's presidential campaign, uniting religious and ethnic factions with the "free-market community," the Tea Party, Jack Abramoff's money laundering (he went to prison for corruption in defrauding Native American tribes), Reagan's illegal support for the Nicaraguan Contras (death squads fighting a Socialist revolution), and opposition to the anti-apartheid movement in South Africa.

• **Lock Step, No Thinking, No Dissent:** In the context of the Never Tax Pledge, GOP leaders in both Houses have become enforcers of a strict and inflexible opposition to everything Liberal or Democrat, whether it's good for the people or the nation's status in the world. With a little occasional resistance from the Freedom Caucus, the party leaders have made their team obey orders in lock step, without resistance or complaint. It has worked amazingly well in the Senate in particular, under Mitch McConnell, who declared, right after Obama's inauguration, that his prime goal (and the GOP Senators') would be to make Obama a "one term president." It became a Party-Over-Country movement that is truly unprecedented. It reveals the level of corruption that Republicans have come to rely on as the ticket to the funding they need to keep running for, and undermining, elected office.

• **Get more aggressive in suppressing Democrat voters.** Tom Delay was sentenced to prison for the antics that set the model
224

for actual *Voter Fraud,* (as opposed to Conservative lies about fake voter fraud). They were still skewing election results in 2016, and are likely to continue that until an opposing political force can set things right. Delay was out on bail when his conviction was overturned, then appealed, and then finally rejected in the Texas (of course) Court of Appeals. As a Deputy Minority Whip in the US House, he worked with Norquist and other rabid Right-Wingers to start the K Street Project, which became an enormously powerful and well-funded Conservative lobbying campaign.

Delay forced through an illegal redistricting plan in Texas, that Gerrymandered the state so extremely that it almost eliminated Democrats – who had been dominant in Texas – from all state and national elected offices. He helped "Gingrich orchestrate the Republican Revolution," (Wikipedia) that stuck Clinton with 6 years of a GOP-controlled Congress, and still holds power, in spite of several party splits since then. Delay's imitators passed voter ID laws, purged Democrats from voting rolls, and expanded radical Gerrymandering to nearly every Republican state. The tactics continue to cheat Democrats out of their own base voters. See Jeb Bush in 2000, below.

• **Cut Spending on Everything ... Except Killing:** It's beyond sad and tragic that the one area where Democrats have consistently fallen into line with the GOP, is in voting for increased "Defense" spending, and refusing to exercise their Constitutional authority to declare war, in spite of the lessons *not* learned in Vietnam, Iraq, and a dozen other avoidable conflicts.

OK that collects several *Dots* in the 18 years since Bill Clinton's terms. We need to go back and pick up the historical narrative, and the other topics, in 1997.

• **1997: Exxon Starts to Change It's Tune.** Lee Raymond of Exxon says, "Let's agree there's a lot we really don't know about how climate will change in the 21st century and beyond. We

225

need to understand the issue better, and fortunately, we have time." (InsideClimateNews.org)

OBSERVE: How many lies can you count in that statement?

• **1998: The American Petroleum Institute Follows Suit:** "Victory will be achieved when average citizens 'understand' (recognize) uncertainties in climate science." (InsideClimateNews.org)

OBSERVE: Can we 'understand' (recognize) the Pattern? I have not found a smoking gun, a paper trail, or a specific date. But the mid-1990s are the years in which Republicans realized they were facing a serious problem – whether or not to acknowledge Climate Change. They had to decide where to stand on GW/CC, and had to face the political implications. As you see, the political implications were recognized as more important than the facts of what is now called the Climate Crisis.

• **1998 to 2010:** "Boosted by a grant from Exxon, the Competitive Enterprise Institute" (funded by Koch brothers and friends) "organized the *Cooler Heads Coalition*, bringing together more that 30 conservative groups ... into an influential echo chamber of climate denial." (InsideClimateNews.org)

OBSERVE: Imagine how much campaign cash those groups funnel from oil profits to US Senators and Representatives.

• **2000: Voter Fraud in Florida:** One of the GOP's obsessive talking points has been "Voter Fraud." They claim that masses of US residents have: voted illegally, including as deceased but still registered voters, voted multiple times in one or more districts, and otherwise committed voter fraud to elect undeserving Democrats. The hypocrisy of this position is almost impossible to overstate. There is very little, approaching zero, information to support their claims. Minuscule numbers of voters have ever been shown to have registered or voted under false pretenses. Over the years, those few turn out more often to be Republicans.

So the very real Voter Fraud that occurred in Florida in 1999 and 2000 (and in Ohio in 2004, and in at least 3 swing states in

226

2016), will stand out in history as markers in the death of fair elections in the US, indicators of the failure of the press to document or the Justice Department to intervene in an enormous injury to the US democracy, our military, our economy, our status in the world, and the health of the Earth.

Jeb Bush, W's brother, had "promised to deliver" Florida to the Republicans in 2000, in spite of the fact that urban and elderly voters had turned the state to a Democrat majority. The only solution was to disenfranchise and neutralize, totally illegally, huge numbers of that majority. Jeb, with the help of his Secretary of State, Kathleen Harris, hired a computerized data analysis firm to review the voter rolls in several Democrat majority districts, and, using a list of names of convicted felons, to strike from the legitimate voter rolls, *ANY NAMES THAT APPEARED TO BE SIMILAR,* even those with different spellings, addresses, ages, and other verification data. The company refused, saying they were being asked to perform an illegal task that would break federal fair election laws; they turned down the contract, estimated at over $1 million. So Bush and Harris just upped the ante and hired a different company, for $2.5 to 3 million, and they did the job. (This and other atrocities to the US Democracy are well documented in 2 or 3 films titled, *The Best Democracy Money Can Buy,* by Greg Palast and his investigative reporting team.)

So the ballot issue that took weeks of headlines and network leads, about a 500 vote "discrepancy" in one district (that had to be solved, by hand count and visual judgments about "hanging chads"), was bullshit. The real scandal, only reported by Palast and a few other brave journalists, and in a very few independent news outlets, was the fact that a huge number of Florida Democrat voters – estimated at well over 50,000 – had been robbed of their right to vote. George W Bush became president only because real and massive Voter Fraud in Jeb Bush's Florida went unchallenged. Now think about the consequences of that election, in the context of foreign and environmental policy.

• **2000: Dick Cheney Picks Dubya's VP:** Andrew Bacevich reminds us that after George W Bush was nominated (and before Jeb stole Florida for him), he tapped Dick Cheney (Defense Secretary under Reagan and Bush Sr. and virulent NeoCon) to scan the field and pick a Vice President. Anyone who was surprised shouldn't have been. He picked himself.

Rachel Maddow hosted a program on MSNBC, "Why We Did It" in 2014 (meaning why did we *do* Iraq?). In it she explains, among other things, that the Cheney/Bush gang was dividing up Iraq's oil fields, among US and British oil companies, *MONTHS BEFORE 9-11.*

Bacevich fleshed out the story. Bush and Cheney weren't really interested in protecting US citizens from "evil doers" like Saddam Hussein. They were obsessed with protecting Iraq's oil from Iraq ... and, oh yeah, expanding the US empire of military bases. Bush had promised, if elected, to pursue a "humble" foreign policy and forego nation-building. Without Cheney, Donald Rumsfeld, Paul Wolfowitz, and others, who took the wheel from Bush, he might have stuck to that course, even after 9/11. Instead, we got the misguided 'Global War on Terrorism.' Adds Bacevich,

> *"No single action played a greater role in paving the way for Donald Trump to become president."*

• **2000: But the Supreme Court Also Played a Role.** Bacevich says (and I strongly agree) that if the high court had picked Al Gore instead of Bush, the US might have avoided the Iraq disaster and the 15 years of chaos that followed, *with or without the 9-11 attacks.* And with no Global War on Terror, the GOP had very little to advance their *FEAR-BASED* propaganda, and Outlaw Capitalist agenda. So in turn, Al Gore might have started a bold fight to slow Global Warming, rather than put it on Crack as W did.

When George W Bush *was not elected* in 2000, but was given the presidency anyway, and got a GOP-dominated Congress as well, Republicans started thinking that their "permanent Conservative majority" might be at hand. But without Bush's stolen elections, it would have been far less likely that Trump, or any other Republican, would have had a chance in 2016.* It makes Trump's minority popular vote "win" an even dirtier joke.

* Look up Ken Blackwell and the hacked voting machines in Ohio, 2004.

OBSERVE: As Stone and Kuznick *might* say, Whether it was 500 hanging chads, or 50,000 caged voters, or a Supreme Court flip of the coin, the random events that put Dick Cheney and George W Bush in the White House altered the history of the United States and the future of life on this Earth, more than any other set of factors could have done at the time. In a Worst Possible Case, the year 2000 may have been our last chance to avoid a critical Tipping Point. So Trump may simply be the factor that pushes humanity irreversibly past that point.

But then, in the Right's *Unethical Tactics Handbook*, political crimes, white collar and war crimes are only punishable when done by Democrats, blacks or other minorities, or the non-rich.

• **2003: Willie Soon, Professional Climate Denier,** appeared in the US Senate, "I am here today to testify that the climate of the 20th century is neither unusual nor the most extreme." (Inside-ClimateNews.org)

OBSERVE: The alleged *3% of scientists who disagree with the 97% of scientists,* who *KNOW* that GW/CC is a serious threat, are either: A. Really stupid. B. Heavily invested in Fossil Fuels. C. Being paid by Big Oil to act stupid. D. Not scientists. E. All of the above.

By the time that the lies about WMD in Iraq and the projected costs of the invasion made the news (now pushing $5 Trillion), and by the time a larger minority was waking up to the climate threat, the public was finally fed up with the GOP.

• **2008: The Obama Backlash:** So against all odds, they elected an African American. The political pendulum had begun to swing in a much wider arc: from Carter to Reagan, from George HW Bush to Clinton, from Clinton/Gore to Bush/Cheney, and then from Bush/Cheney to Obama. But the oppositional swing was never as great as it appeared; Reagan had pushed the country and the GOP to the Right, Clinton pulled the Democrats to the Center-Right, and W – clearly riding on our reaction to 9-11 – took the nation into a NeoConservative global nightmare. So the swing to Obama can only be thought of as "Leftist" to a very limited degree, because Obama and his State and Justice Departments supported the Cheney/Bush insanities, foreign and domestic, and protected the bankers in the worst financial crash since the one FDR had to fix ... with Socialism.

Andrew Bacevich imagines that if Obama had not bailed out the big banks and the brokerage giants and let them collapse from their own fraud, and if he had instead bailed out the homeowners who got defrauded, the economic outcomes would have been far more fair and productive.

• **2010: Mitch McConnell Wallows in the Swamp.** Politicians in both parties have been accused of putting Party Over Country, or Power Over Principle. But Senator McConnell took the habit to a new low when he announced that "the single most important thing we want to achieve," was to make Obama a one term president. McConnell's obedient troops fell in line and tried to block everything Obama or the Democrats tried to do. A few Republicans – mostly those who were retiring in disgust – said that they were ordered to do that, "regardless of whether or not it was good for the country." McConnell managed to hide his racist motives behind the passion for GOP dominance, even when in a minority.

But McConnell found an even lower low. 8 months before the 2016 election, when Justice Scalia died, Obama nominated Merrick Garland to replace him. McConnell's treachery was unprecedented, even among dozens of other acts – not to mention totally unconstitutional; his GOP Senate refused to give Garland a hearing, so Trump could nominate, and McConnell and crew could approve, arch-conservative Neil Gorsuch.

• **2016: The Backlash to Obama:** In spite of appearances, and as hinted above, the Obama election was not so much a full pendulum swing to the Left, as it demonstrated that the authentic Left, the Progressive wing of the Democrat Party, had been reduced to a few voices shouting from the wings, virtually barred from the political stage. The election of Donald Trump exposed two vicious strains of American racism: the suppressed racism of many whites – rich, middle class, and poor – and the unspoken, barely coded, Republican Party's Institutionalized Racism. It did not expose, so much as amplify and accelerate the GOP's unwavering Loyalty to Corporations and the Rich.

• **2017 The Stupid and Bought-Off 3% Takes Over the US Government.** Joseph Bast of the Heartland Institute says, "Carbon dioxide is not a pollutant. More CO_2 leads to faster, more robust plant growth, including staple food crops. Moderate warming, should it occur, would have a positive effect on humanity ..." (InsideClimateNews.org) President Trump says, "As of today, the United States will cease all implementation of the non-binding Paris Accord and the draconian financial and economic burden the agreement imposes on our country."

Nobody is surprised when a Senator brings a snowball into the Senate to prove Global Warming isn't happening, or when a different Senator says wind turbines will use up all the wind and change the climate worse, or when southern states start to tax or restrict all forms of sustainable energy alternatives.

OBSERVE: The Systemic Failure of the US Democracy to function, in the face of the single greatest challenge in its history.

Republicans claim that government is the problem – incompetent and wrong-headed. Then they get elected and prove themselves right.

PART SIX: A SYSTEMIC FAILURE

The single biggest factor in the corruption of State and National
governments in the US is, indirectly, the need for and the cost
of media advertising in every campaign, and directly, in the
legalized bribery of legislators, through the lobbying industry. It
is easy and shocking to research the quantities of cash given to
Representatives and Senators, in the tens of millions, by a variety
of big corporations (oil, pharmaceuticals, private prisons, banks
and investment/wealth management outfits, military contractors, and others) and to compare those amounts with 2 other
amounts: the *public servants'* salaries (fractions of the lobbying totals); and the returns that the donors got for their "investment in
democracy," in the form of new laws that enriched them. It's in
the billions. It is one of the most lucrative investments possible,
usually paying $10. to $1000. back for every $1. donated.

John Boehner, the former Speaker of the House, was observed handing out large checks, from a single corporate donor,
to legislators, on the Floor of the House, prior to a vote that
would help that corporation.

LATE UPDATE: We may never know which force or factor
played the biggest role in the (popular vote minority) election
of Donald Trump. We could say the Electoral College failed
their job, by not keep a dangerous person out of the office. We
could blame the Democrats for subverting their own internal
selection process and cheating Bernie out of the nomination
he earned and deserved. We could blame Hillary for ignoring
huge regions where she assumed her "base" would vote for her,
regardless of whether she asked them to, or gave them reason
to. Comey's late comments on the Hillary investigation certainly
cost her votes. We could blame the GOP for putting up 17 or 18
candidates, none of whom could appear any more competent
than Trump. And the biggest unknown is the degree to which
Putin's social media hack of the election actually changed votes.
At least one major career Intelligence Officer (James Clapper) is
convinced that Putin did in fact tip the election to Trump.

The US democracy has been getting weaker for decades. If
232

Putin wanted to demonstrate to the world that the US and Euro-zone democracies are unstable or ineffective, the 2 party system in the US, and the rightward tilt that rose up against immigrants in Britain, Europe, and Scandinavia gave him a big head start and an edge.

What if Russia and China chose different paths to a more globalized economy and culture? Rather than conform to the (late Shock Doctrine) NeoLiberal economic model, what if they held to their Marxist ideological core, and chose rather to liberalize their social freedoms, their attempts at democratic choice, and increased government spending (which China did in the extreme), without caving to the widespread corruption and the bigger gap in income and wealth that globalized Capitalism brought? Another crucial question that will remain unanswered.

In the Party of FDR, Progressives in 2018 awaken to the fact that the moderate Democrat Party insiders, like 98 percent of the GOP, care more about holding on to party power than to doing right by the Constitution, or what's best for people or the planet.

In the summer of 2018, Chinese billionaire Jack Ma says the US wasted Trillions on warfare instead of investing in infrastructure.

CAN THE 4 QUESTIONS FROM PAGE 181-2 HELP GET US TO A SUMMARY?

"How did our democracy get so fucked up?"

Answers: The Republican Party decided, consciously and unconsciously, over 35 to 50 years, that money and power were more important than Democracy, compromise, the rule of law, human rights, justice, or the Earth they would leave their kids.

The GOP twisted its former ideology – respect for tradition, family values, conservation of nature, limited government, moderate respect for labor and human rights, concessions to economic justice, respect for the rule of law – to foster a union among the rich and powerful, a faction of Christians, militarists and exceptionalists, in order to neutralize the US government and create an oligarchy: a nation, a government, a people, an economy, and a justice system controlled completely by an elite cadre of millionaires and billionaires.

With a lot of help from the Powell Memorandum, the Koch brothers, and organizations they helped to found, and funded, like ALEC, the American Right Wing used a coordinated attack on Liberalism and the Democrat Party. They xeroxed dozens of "Conservative" (meaning racist, classist, sexist, fear-based, exploitive, and fake moralistic) laws, and started bribing local governments to pass them, or funded candidates that would. They gerrymandered and *de-registered* legitimate Democrat voters, and erased their electronic votes, so that a GOP minority could take over state elections, in order to help rig national elections. They gradually came to realize (a lesson from Nixon) that the worst crime is getting caught, so they also made a lot of crimes "legal." The Citizens United disgrace, from the Supreme Court, gave them the last and biggest lever of power they would need.

The Democrat Party either did not observe what was happening, or, more likely, decided that the best way to fight the GOP was to abandon their traditonal base – women and minorities, the poor and working classes, unions, the well-educated, and the victims of injustice – and try to beat them at their own corrupt game. They failed to observe that by caving to the same donor base the GOP relied on, they would welcome the lying and cheating that they were afraid to call out, across the aisle, because (after years of unchallenged Right Wing propaganda) they were afraid of being called *Socialists* ... or of *appearing to be equally corrupt,* or, in a final hypocritical irony, *uncivil.*

In the age of GW/CC, it's an idiotic and amoral betrayal for the Democrats to pursue a few centrist Republican voters, rather than welcome and work for the millions of citizens who support

progressive policies, but have no one to vote for. Like the GOP,
they pretend to be shocked and angry to find some of their former supporters calling them corrupt and indifferent to the needs
of a majority of voters.

And the mass media decided that ratings and advertising dollars – not to mention access to the offices of power – were more
important than the truth, the public interest, or their role in the
foundation of Democracy. The executives in 95 percent of the
mass media outlets that are corporate/commercial-sponsored
(including PBS) made that decision, consciously and unconsciously over decades, and ignored or persecuted the few whistle
blowers who tried to out them for it.

"How did our economy get so rigged?"

Same answer. That was pretty much the point. Both parties
agreed to not argue about economic injustice, or the gap in income and wealth, or the inherent legal biases against minorities
and the poor, or the rigged tax code, or the profits of the Military-Industrial Complex, or Climate Change.

"How and when did facts, clean air and water become partisan?"

It is clear in retrospect. Clues are scattered through the History
of the Decline of the Left, peaking sometime in the mid 1990s,
when Climate Change forced the GOP to face 3 big challenges:
   One: Any effort to fight Climate Change was going to result
in: bigger government, more regulations, a shift in economic
principles, including limits on the Capitalist economic model, a
loss for their coal, oil, and gas bosses, a win for the Democrats
and a threat to GOP Power ... that could bring it down. They
could not possibly foresee that they would do that themselves,
even if it would take Donald Trump to finish them off.
   Two: Then they knew – with the help of the American Pe-

troleum Institute, and the new polarizing tactics of Newt, Frank, Grover (pages 222-4), and others – that they had to make the whole issue disappear. Any wavering in their own ranks, on any of that Climate regulation stuff, would open them to widening cracks in their Power. So they needed to lock arms and recite in unison: *Climate Change is Not Happening, or if it is, Humans are Not Causing it, and if They Are, There's Nothing We Can Do About it, or if There Is, It Will Wreck the Economy and Upset Stable Society Like Nothing Else Could (Except for the Climate Crisis that We Have to Keep Denying ... or maybe Nuclear War).*

Three: So it has to be a Chinese plot, or a Liberal myth, or a Socialist – make that Communist – strategy to destroy the American economy, our fading Democracy, and our abundant lifestyle.

It might have been headed off, had the Centrist Democrats (I call them GOP-LITE) not surrendered to the same campaign donors that keep both parties obedient to the Outlaw Capitalist agenda.

That last thing was probably the easiest to foresee and make happen. The donors saw it coming too and were all too ready to keep the Democrats divided and compromised. The GOP and the compromised Democrats trusted that scaring the public about creeping Socialism would do the trick. It almost worked ... for a while.

"How do racism, sexism, social biases and a general fear of difference fit into the pattern?"

To keep the vast majority of us *NOT* thinking and talking about the gap in income and wealth, or injustice, or pointless and endless wars, to keep us from complaining about an Economy of Extraction and Waste, or gun violence, or failing schools ... whether you call them the Ruling Class or Big Brother or the 1%, *THEY* have to keep us divided socially from each other. But it's no longer just Blacks vs. Whites, it's every identity group being alienated from every other identity group: the uneducated from the conceited coastal elites, the rich from the middle class, the middle class from the poor, the small town Christians from the Big City atheists, everybody against any dark-skinned person with an accent, women from the men who can't help but try to keep them down, gun rights nuts from gun victims ... you ought to recognize the pattern.

There's a powerful racist aspect to Environmental destruction, GW/CC, and most of the other dozen Eco-Crises. The people inflicting most of the damage are white English-speakers, historic imperialists, descendants of slave traders and mass murderers of dark skinned people, whose resources they stole and resold at a big profit. Most of the direct impacts of extreme heat and sea level rise, like floods, hurricanes, and droughts, already affect poor and indigenous populations most directly, just like drilling and mining, over fishing, and deforestation have been doing. Most toxic dumps and deregulated pollution zones are easiest to allow when the people they harm are black or brown.

While it is impossible for a white person to understand the depth of the terror our ancestors applied to dark skinned people, to attain dominance, it is possible for a few of us to point to a mindset too may of us share, unknowing. A few pages ahead.

THE SHORT ANSWER TO ALL 4 QUESTIONS: 35 years of GOP subverting Democracy and the economy, 35 years of Democrats being unable or unwilling to point it out or counter it, and too many other nations taking that as a viable model. That defines ...

A Systemic Failure of the 2 US parties, the courts, and the press, to competently manage the dozens of merging and accelerating crises,

... or to understand how they are connected to each other. The US's role as a world leader was already tainted by our military excursions, our levels of consumption and pollution, our racial tensions and the deep biases in our legal system.

Noam Chomsky sums those failures up broadly ... and brutally, just by shifting the context.

The GOP is "literally a serious danger to human survival." due mainly to their rigid ideological stances, including climate denial.

Chomsky explained that by saying (paraphrased), "The GOP knows they cannot win on their ideas, so they have no choice but to resort to lying, cheating, and spreading irrational fear." And I say, *the Democrats enable them.*

It has become a talking point among Progressives like me who rightly feel shut out of the Democrat Party's decision-making process. Political comedian and online blogger Jimmy Dore sums it up this way: Democrat insiders would rather lose elections to Republicans – year upon decade – (from 1944, or maybe 1968, until today) than to cede an ounce of power to the Progressive wing. The Democrats have become willing accomplices in their own demise. They won't admit it, but they don't want to get the money out of politics, because, just like the GOP, it would threaten their campaign budgets and their hold on Power.

A DIGRESSION: CAPITALISM'S TIPPING POINT

In April 2018, historian Robert Kuttner has been doing the interview circuit with his new book, *Can Democracy Survive Global Capitalism?* I wrote to him, asking why he made so few references to the causes or costs of Climate Change. He answered graciously and wisely, "The environment is a hugely important topic. ... There are plenty of left scholars for whom the environment is the paramount subject. In the last chapter, I do address the need for a green transition as the centerpiece of a reinvestment program." OK, thanks for that.

Kuttner makes the point that when Capitalism (already showing outlaw tendencies) became globalized, several unintended consequences began to threaten democracies new and old, and many less than democratic nations. Globalized corporations have expanded accepted Capitalist strategies, that used to apply to regional and national economies, to global levels of power greater than most governments can regulate or control.

238

(I observe something I haven't yet found in the book: Corporations didn't have to dictate those Free Market strategies; countries voluntarily accepted them via trade agreements, in exchange for more revenue dollars and global cred.) Back to Kuttner's work.

Capitalist Globalization provoked an accelerated race to the bottom. The combined impacts of expanded corporate power and trade deals provoked a new glut of externalities, and has now destabilized local economies, frozen wages, promoted outsourcing, removed workplace health and safety regulations, and undercut resource management and environmental responsibility. Why and how? Because the trade deals prioritize profits over all other concerns including legality, sustainability, and the sovereignty of many nations.

Kuttner makes some brilliant and vital observations about subtle side-effects that turn low income residents (whites in the Eurozone and the US for example) against immigrants, while blaming it on their races or religions, or threats of crime, because they feel doubly exploited – underpaid, losing beneifts, and edged out of their only remaining assets, their social status, citizenship, whiteness, and religious dominance. It shines a little light on the conflicting "populisms" we see in different contexts. Just observe that those impacts are part of the legacy of Outlaw Capitalism.

It's clear to Professor Kuttner, and now to me, exactly how Globalized Capitalism limits the powers of the real democracies that failed to see the pattern forming, in favor of Monsanto and Dow Chemical, Raytheon and Halliburton, Exxon and GE.

Kuttner seems to say that the NeoLiberal trade deals that gave Capitalism the keys to the global economy, were done with good intentions. If dictatorships and communist regimes were allowed to participate in global markets, in theory, they would sooner or later become more liberal and democratic. Of course that was based on several clearly false premises, including the idea that Free Markets and Personal Freedom are joined at the hip – one either leads to the other, or dies without the other.

In interviews, Robert Kuttner makes the point that once the powers of corporations passed a certain limit, beyond the reach of local or national regulation, this was the nearly inevitable outcome. I don't remember if he said this or I imagined it, "It's like Globalized Capitalism couldn't help itself, and governments didn't react until it was too late."

What if neither the men or the system "could help themselves?" Does that excuse one or both? Or condemn both as unwitting evils?

As clear and important as Robert Kuttner's analysis is, as brilliant the writing and as thorough the history, he still misses the point I think is essential.

Whether Democracy can Survive Globalized Capitalism matters less than whether we and our Earth can survive the failure of both systems.

It was assumed that a combination of national and international regulations on trade and finance would make a level and fair playing field. But the NeoLiberal economic engineers failed to foresee that banks and corporations would find ways to write the regulations or dodge them, then tailor tax loopholes to their needs, so that they could hide profits and wealth in anonymous, offshore accounts and shell corporations. They did not foresee that smaller countries (like many US states) would host those legal cheats for their own profit, or that Wall Street players would become proxy banks to help companies avoid the regulations of actual banks.

The Human Pattern of Assuming too much and Failing to Foresee consequences has become a threat to Democracy and life on the Earth.

That may explain why our parents and grandparents didn't see it coming. But it doesn't excuse a system that could not help

240

but turn corrupt; it was based on the fallacy that greed is good, and will eventually benefit the public. Men who could not see past the profit and power were blind to the fact that the system, built on obsolete principles and stupid assumptions, would not only self-destruct, but would have bitter consequences far and wide. The explanation doesn't excuse those men or the system, just because they couldn't help themselves. There were clear and forceful warnings appearing periodically from 1929 through 1962, 2002, and 2016, from thousands of us who predicted those outcomes and could not make our voices heard.

Argument 31: The erosion of the US Democracy, and the dominance of the US model of Outlaw Capitalism in the global economy, point to the core of the Systemic Failure.

SO WHO IS TO BLAME?
The men who designed the system? Or those who put it in practice without even trying to foresee consequences? Or the men who rode it to a level of insanity to satisfy their own lust for wealth and power?

Whatever. Blame and forgiveness have both become ir-relevant. Even proper blame will not help correct the damage, though it may help prevent the ongoing destruction. Forgive-ness is only relevant when guilt is admitted, and it is requested.

What matters is recognizing that those men, their uncon-scious fear and greed, their corrupt principles, and their orga-nizations, in combination – now either failing or failed – have brought civilization to an existential tipping point.

In McLuhan's terms, their tools – the theft of wealth, the destruction of value, and the abuse of power – have brought them and their system and our civilization to a state of *negation* or *reversal*. Whether they were right at the time or wrong, evil or naive, law-breakers or corrupt legislators, acting for or against religious ideals, ignorant or pretending to be, motivated by conscious or unconscious impulses, the men and their corrupt system have created a debt to humanity and the Earth, that is an

241

order of magnitude larger than the world's total debt. But not the world's total wealth.

Could Globalized Capitalism have worked with different core principles, or different men, or more women, running it? Could it have protected people and the planet and made a Neo-Liberal dream? That doesn't really matter either. The Failure is Systemic, and rapidly approaching irreversible.

The systemic solution is nothing more or less than separating the men from their political power, and putting different women and men in charge, so they can shift the system's obsolete and destructive principles to Human Rights, Sustainability, Efficiency, and long-term Resilience.

In a functional and responsive Democracy, separating those men from their positions of Power ought to be easy. It should take one election cycle, two at the most. It's why Democracies exist: to give an educated public power over the representatives they hire, in elections, and to demand that the government be more powerful than corruption, bad laws, obscene wealth, and bribery. The US needs to get its Democracy back.

The NeoCons and hard core Capitalists were not listening when John Kenneth Galbraith updated John Maynard Keynes (both liberal economists) by saying,

> *"The modern conservative is engaged in ... man's oldest ... moral philosophy; ... the search for a ... moral justification for selfishness."*

We need to understand the combined crises from at least three points of view: the conscious and unconscious impulses of the men, the Outlaw Capitalists; the history of Capitalism's devolution over a century, from a risky system that might work if properly and strictly regulated, to the virtual dictatorship of stolen wealth and illegitimate power it has become; and the quantity of that wealth that is a very real debt to people and the planet.

WHAT ARE WE MISSING?
These last arguments and ideas point to a number of factors that comprise one complex but coherent cause, which in turn points to one broad and simple, radical but feasible solution. Parts Seven and Eight spell that all out.

But they also point to a kind of an Exceptionalist Mindset turned greedy, corrupt, and abusive. We need to look a little deeper into that mindset, deeper than the flaws in the system, hiding in the minds of the men who are addicted to the Abuse of Power.

> *Some critics have referred to the Trump/Sessions policy on separating children from their refugee parents as "gleeful cruelty."*

That's one expression of this mindset.

A set of values was embedded in Capitalism that would inevitably turn corrupt if not moderated by Moral Sentiments. And there have always been 2 classes of men, and more than a few women, who either: fought bitterly and ruthlessly for abusive power; or, who fought honestly and intelligently, non-violently (even with love and understanding) against the abuse. The latter group has been losing, chronically and tragically, almost forever, because (remember the hierarchy) irrational and abusive power will never yield to logic, law, fairness, love or intelligence. It's only motive and objective is more *POWER*.

Whether they were raised in racist families, or taught critical thinking, whether their parents were role models for hate or for curiosity, for cheating or for ethics, (if power corrupts, and if absolute power corrupts absolutely) they were vulnerable to the temptation to acquire unlimited Power, and/or unlimited Wealth, and to exercise the freedom to Abuse them, when they acquired the political power to make that legal.

The term "Toxic Masculinity" emerges from the Me Too/Time's Up movement, among the women who are standing up to sexual bias and violence, discrimination and rape. It's an indicator of an unconscious Complex, shared, almost exclusively among powerful white men and others who wish they were. So it's no surprise to see it's related to White Privilege. The common thread, among all the important crises we face, can be summed up in a set of unconscious impulses that guide and empower a mental complex that, I argue, lies beneath the revised version of the Military-Industrial Complex (ahead on page 266).

The Angry Aggressive Greedy Corrupt Amoral Hypocritical Racist Sexist Unconscious Toxic Masculine Need for Abusive Power ... Complex.

Sure we could just call it the *Trump Complex* but that would relieve too many people in both parties who ignored his racism, misogyny, incompetence, amorality, and corruption. We could call it Rape Culture or Gun Culture or Institutionalized Racism, but those would all ignore their common threads, source and solution.

It's important to observe that one commentator says the *Toxic* tag isn't enough. Toxic Masculinity is also *Brittle* because it relies on the bully's threat of anger and violence, assumed to be expressions of power, but actually a cover (like greed) for an emptiness within, a lack of character, a weakness that cannot be acknowledged, an insecurity, like the hollow need for false validation, and the fear of inferiority *in one's self* that drives racism.

True masculinity is a subset of Humanistic values. It will recognize and *R.E.S.P.E.C.T.* its feminine side and its feminine partners in the world; it is capable of critical thinking, self-questioning, and of conscious and intentional Changes of Mind.

Toxic/Brittle Masculinity seldom has a creative use for the Power or the Wealth that it feels justified in extracting from Humanity and Civilization. The Power and Wealth exist only as an illusion of Power, like the threat of abuse vs. actual abuse. It includes a contempt for beauty, because beauty possesses a power that cannot be bought or controlled, short of destroying it. The exercise of the Wealth and Power are merely defenses for a brittle ego. They are illusory and temporary, and need constant expansion and justification. Now one of the most brittle and toxic men in the class has barged and stumbled his way into the Oval Office.

Evidence of that Toxic Greed and Contempt can now be seen everywhere on Earth, from the stratosphere to the Marianas Trench, by anyone who can escape the engineered epidemic of Denial that gives false release from responsibility. It's evident in Iraq, Syria, Yemen, Libya, and a dozen other pointless proxy wars. It is gruesome and obvious in the innocent and unarmed black men murdered by racist cops, and in the rape of billions of women and children. It is obvious in the billion tons of plastic choking the oceans, the heat and acidity killing the coral reefs, the methane being vented faster than it can be measured, and the atmospheric heat that rises exponentially, in the worst imaginable feedback loop. It will continue to be seen in the damaged live of millions of children abused by toxic fathers, by drought or war or border agents, as they grow into adults who will have to fight the PTSD and the toxic men who remain in power.

I wonder if you have asked, as I have, stupified for decades, *WHAT IS WRONG WITH THOSE MEN?* ... that they cannot be satisfied with a simple life lived in love and a quest for self-realization? ... just living a conscious existence on a unique and beautiful Earth? How did their curiosity die when they learned how to make unlimited piles of money? Why can't they or won't they look within themselves for the roots of the mindset that came to control their lives? And ours. I couldn't have finished this work without trying to name and shame the syndrome head on.

The most *successful* Toxic Males found their perfect tool in the ideological pair, Capitalism and brutality, now evident at the root of our Systemic Failure. It made them hollow men who can only work as greedy bullies. The combination leads to

245

a dictatorship of the worst human impulses and prevents any oppositional power. And now the presidency is occupied by the perfect fool, a toxic TV boss. In a self-perpetuating feedback loop of profit, corruption, destruction, and Denial, this pattern of behavior will continue to spiral out of control, exactly like Global Warming, unless and until radical change stops the cycle.

A CONCEPTUAL EMERGENCY
More than a decade ago, the International Futures Forum, a Think Tank in Scotland, called our global predicament a *Conceptual Emergency*. They argue that the complexity of global civilization, the speed of change, and an interconnected maze of crises combine their impacts to "challenge human competence in areas of government, economy, sustainability, and consciousness." While they don't point to Capitalism, as I and many others do, that is a description of a Systemic Failure.

> *"... the world we have created has outstripped our capacity to understand it."* The International Futures Forum

FROM OBSOLETE MINDSETS TO DIFFERENT THINKING
Wangari Maathai (1940-2011) founded the Green Belt Movement in Africa. She won the Nobel Peace Prize and the Right Livelihood Award for her environmental activism. She said,

> *"In the course of history, there comes a time when humanity is called to shift to a new level of consciousness. ... That time is now."*

She said that at least 8 years ago. We wrote and read about Levels of Thinking in the context of Metaphor, Empathy, and Irony, as examples of flexible thinking, and about the opposite, rigid and fearful thinking, specifically among Conservatives and the Dumbed Down. So what would a global Shift in Consciousness look or feel like? Would it, could it follow the pattern of Paradigm Shift as observed by Thomas S Kuhn? (pages 96-7)

WHAT SCIENCE AND FACTS CANNOT DO
I cited James Gustave Speth in the part about Exponential
Growth and Hockey Stick graphs (pages 104-6). As a scientist,
he confesses to one limit in the science community's frustrations
with Climate Denial, the urgency of solutions, and the resistance
to trying to imagine them. From Speth,

*I used to think the top environmental problems were biodiversity loss,
eco-system collapse, and climate change. I thought that with 30 years
of good science we could address those problems. But I was wrong.
The top environmental problems are selfishness, greed, and apathy, and
to deal with those we need a spiritual and cultural transformation –
and we scientists don't know how to do that.*

So, apparently, a majority of us may believe the science and take
the risks seriously, but we will still need to push for a broader
and more profound leap in Thinking, a *Global Mind-Shift* (the
name of an organization and website that addresses these issues
as problem in Mindsets).

EVERYTHING WE FEARED ABOUT COMMUNISM, ... that we
would lose our houses and savings and be forced to labor for
poverty wages, only to funnel more wealth and power to a cadre
of corrupt plutocrats, oligarchs, and party bosses, with no voice
in the system – all *this* has come true under Capitalism. Sure it
may be worse in Russia, but by how much? With how much of a
future?
    The myth of the *Good Life* in the *American Dream* turns out
to be nothing but a carrot and a stick: false fears prodding us to
chase empty desires, which turn out to be a soul-crushing delu-
sion for most of us and a death sentence for the Earth.

EVERYTHING WE FEARED ABOUT BIG BROTHER (STATE
FASCISM), ... that we would lose our privacy, be forced to live
under the authoritarian thumb of a paranoid elite, be prodded
by hate and fear and punished by corrupt cops for questioning

the system, forced to live in an economy of false scarcity, competing for status, resigned to continual war, seeing our neighbors taken to private prisons, or shot in the streets, while the natural world dies around us: *this* is the gift of the *World's Greatest Democracy* and the *Infallible Hand of the Free Market*.

We find Big Brother has an electronic agent in our pockets, telling the corporate state where we are, what we are thinking, and what else we can be made to buy. Too many of us are addicted to a fake sense of connection, to distraction, and a narrow slice of a flattened society, while we lose sight of what actually matters – our health, our connections to each other and to Nature, and a viable future for our children.

Real information is edited and hidden behind a screen of trivia and advertising, while we wait to see how close the next school shooting comes to our kids. We've forgotten – or never learned – how a functioning Democracy works or what it demands from us. Sure it may be worse in China, but only for a while.

WE COULD PROBABLY suppress our contempt for our government, we could be patient until enough votes can overwhelm the gerrymandering, we could write letters and march until a few ethical Senators guilt-trip the others – the corrupt, greedy, incompetent hypocrites – into doing their jobs.

After all, someday, somehow, Trump will be removed from a position of power and our government will have a chance to redeem itself, its promise and its tattered legacy. But by then it may be too late to save civilization or most of the life on Earth.

BUT WHEN WE, as a nation and a species, face annihilation from that corruption, greed, incompetence, and hypocrisy, we may have to unite in a backlash in the streets. See what billionaire Nick Hanauer says about pitchforks ahead on page 288.

WE COULD PROBABLY struggle along in an economy of false scarcity and fake quality, scraping day-to-day and week-to-week to catch up with the rent, hating our jobs and our bosses, praying we don't get injured at work or sick, and hoping that we don't end up living or lying or dying on the street.

We could think that we got a good education and we've just been unlucky. We could let ourselves be divided by institutional racism and fake fears, and fail to see we need each other, if we are to recognize and avoid the most fearful reality directly in our path. We may discover the shreds of truth between the lines in the news and the ads and the Data Glut. Our kids may even learn to distinguish Fake News Humor from Fake Fox News. But when we see our kids will have a harder life than we do, not a better one, we may awaken to why honest government and fair taxes are good.

We might find that a modest life well-lived is enough. We may gain satisfaction from just being here, as long as "here" means a livable Earth. We may be able to bridge True Populism with Alienated Populism and drive the corrupt Congressional bastards into the streets. We may rediscover our own curiosity and be less seduced by spectacle and distractions on our screens.

BUT IF WE wait to see how urgent a radical solution is, those compromises will prove deadly. And anyway, by then it will be too late. We need to see we're in a Systemic Failure before we can imagine a Systemic Solution, or realize it is just a couple good ideas and bold decisions away.

WHEN WE FIND that the choice of a modest, curious, loving life is not on the ballot, that it has been snatched from us and sold, by men who can't imagine that kind of life has any value, we may finally see that far too many of the wrong people are in jail.

YELLING AT THE MEDIA

When I catch myself yelling at the TV, the radio, or for God's sake the Internet, it's almost always a reaction to a missed connection that I think ought to be obvious ... to almost everyone. That missed connection is the crux of the final arguments. It is,

249

or ought to be, the undeniable red flag on the Global Eco-Crisis, and the key to a solution.

That crucial missed connection is between, on one hand, the damage done to the global ecosystem and to human rights, and on the other, the global gap in income, wealth, and power.

Economists and political pundits ramble on endlessly about how the banking system got rigged, how we can't seem to un-rig it or what we would have to do to try, how it continues to suck real and imaginary value out of the recovering economy, and how the Congress is frozen by bad habits and old ideologies, boggled by the power of dirty money. The barrage of statistics and examples is mind-numbing, completely detached from our experience. At best, a liberal economist squeezes in a mention before the host goes to commercial. "And there will also be environmental costs." Or some political insider mutters, "How are these hacks ever going to deal with Climate Change?"

"JESUS!" I shout, "Can't you fuckers see that the environmental costs and the financial rigging are *two sides of the same coin?* ... and that corrupt politicians and polluters are simultaneously choking Democracy *and* the Ecosystem?" The *coin* is Outlaw Capitalism.

Two issues – 1. the global gap in wealth, and 2. the damage to human rights and the Earth – are the mirrored impacts of one Extraction Economy.

Even the patient eco-alarmists play down the risks while missing the other point. "We have to do something soon." "It will have to be a large-scale effort." "If we don't act in a decade we'll really be in *deep doo-doo*." "If we keep postponing action, the problem will just keep getting harder to solve." So, OK, a few people seem to know we're in a Race Against Time ... far too few.

"Mother of God!" I scream, "Can't you say the consumer growth, war-and-waste economy is the problem? ... Just once?" (Oh right, I remember, the sponsors don't like that.) My voice
250

starts shaking. "Can't you say we all have to get off carbon as fast as humanly possible?" My wife says, "Shh, you're scaring the dogs." "OK. Sorry."

"Please for the sake of life on the planet," I whisper at the pixilated screen, "admit that the US has to model a sustainable economy for the rest of the world, and get them all to join in, as fast as we can."

We simply have to stop consuming and wasting so much.

Argument 32: We can't talk about the Economy without admitting it is based in Nature, far more dependent on water than oil, for example; or without considering the Environmental impacts of the consumption and waste demanded by Outlaw Capitalism.

Argument 33: We cannot talk about the Global Environmental Crisis, or about how to address it, without including the role of a global Economy based on Extraction, Corruption, War, Waste, and a constellation of other destructive principles.

An endless string of post-Marxist and Progressive analyses explore every economic angle: monetary policy, wage stagnation, corporate greed, political corruption, the erosion of human rights under austerity, union-busting, saving the insurers vs. single payer health care, infrastructure, the 1% and the 99%, trade deficits, bumps and dips in commodity prices, and the possible influence of speculators ... you name it, without a single word about the connections – causes or consequences – with environmental collapse.

On the flip side, environmentalists talk and talk about carbon caps and taxes, coral reefs and by-catch, carbon sequestration and nuclear waste, fossil aquifers and droughts, rising sea levels and climate refugees, food shortages and methane venting – you know the list – without a mention of the vast wealth generated by those impacts, nothing but vague speculation on how much it will cost to correct any of it, or where the money will come from ... (and then the ultimate ironic lunacy) ... "without wrecking the economy."

At best, we get the few examples cited in a random book or on-line discussion: environmental debt, corporate liability, incentives and penalties, divest and reinvest, the price of stewardship or the cost of consumerism.

The fact that this connection is not yet part of the public conversation is an indicator of how far our understanding lags behind the dual realities of the Climate Crisis and the Gap in Wealth, and the small number of obvious radical actions that can actually address them both. It is crystal clear to me that Outlaw Capitalism is the common driver of both: the hideous gap in income and wealth, and the Global Environmental Crisis.

I didn't know there are *ecological economists*, even though I imagine I am one.

> **"There is something fundamentally wrong in treating the Earth as if it were a business in liquidation."**
> Herman Daly, ecological economist, University of Maryland

There's a growing interest among young people in Socialism, and a higher tolerance for discussing it among many others. In the wake of the Bernie Sanders campaign, and independent of it, many in the US are beginning to criticize Crony, Disaster, or Outlaw Capitalism, for its impacts on their personal finances, on the larger economy, and on on the Earth.

Bernie Sanders clearly defined a Democratic Socialist government as one that is elected to manage the corporations and the banks, rather than be controlled by them. More of our peers have begun to notice how Outlaw Capitalism, as legislated by a corrupt 2-party system, *cannot help* but extract all the excess value from the economy and funnel it to the richest 1%.

We need to update Bill Clinton's campaign slogan from 1991. The phrase, "It's the Economy, Stupid," misses the point.

It's the Capitalism, Stupid, addicted to War, Waste, and Consumption, driven by False Fears and Fake Desires, indifferent to consequences.

THE WORDS *ECOLOGY* AND *ECONOMY* are both based on the Greek word *Oikos*, meaning, generally, *Family, Home* and/or *Property*. *Ecology* is most often used to mean the study or management of our natural home, the Earth; *Economy*, the study or management of property and tangible value. The fact that we have failed, as a species, to see the connections between them, in almost every human activity and decision, is a key to the giant Blind Spot at the core of our civilization's existential crisis. We have come to think (whether we know it, admit it, or not) that the Economy has a higher value and priority than our Human Rights or the health of the Earth – while we continue to take both for granted. The reverse ought to be a basic principle of Civilization:

The Economy must serve to manage the value of the natural home, the foundation of life, in order to preserve the rights of the human family.

ARE THERE MANY CRISES? OR ONE? With many causes, or one? Requiring many different solutions, or one?

We are doing next to nothing about the Global Environmental Crisis, or about the political paralysis that cannot deal with it. It's a feedback loop of corruption, bad law, privatization, and 15 percent skimmed off of everything, to pay the bribes.

Carbon Dioxide and other GHGs, the Consumption and Waste Economy, a Congress paid NOT to act: all are driven by corporate and bank profits.

Where else can we find the fingerprints of a corrupt economic model? Wars, civil wars, proxy wars and endless bombing campaigns and drone strikes? US weapons makers and sellers

253

who profit from them all? The fact that we are still threatened by chemical weapons and nerve agents and nuclear conflict?

In other words, are wars caused by the fact they are profitable to fight, or because they have profitable outcomes? Or both?

Are those signs related to the rise of authoritarian movements, within democracies and separate from them, from China to Turkey to Poland to Philippines? And their reliance on injustice and racism? Does Capitalism inevitably brutalize the disenfranchised, rely on authoritarian regimes, and cripple democracies? Is all that – plus the environmental damage – enough to indict Outlaw Capitalism and its operators? If not, why not?

It would certainly make a recovery – a total and global solution – simpler, and a little easier, if that is true. But only if we can imagine attacking Outlaw Capitalism as an overriding mistake, and if we can offer an alternative. Fortunately there are many good examples. They are mostly among the northern European and Scandinavian countries with the highest standards of living and citizen happiness, the best education and the most effective health care, truly democratic governments, and mixed economies with high taxes, small militaries, and high government spending ... to achieve those standards.

The point? There are many models of national economies. Most of them can manage supply and demand, promote horizontal growth, and allow everyone to participate. The questions are: Which ones are equally fair to everyone? Which ones have crashes, windfall profits, waste, and an expanding gap in wealth and austerity for everyone else? Which ones are sustainable over time?

Capitalism is not a force of Nature, it's not like weather, water, or the climate. It definitely reflects aspects of human nature, from the good – innovation, investment – to the terrible – aggression and greed. But it is not an inherent and inevitable condition or destiny that humans cannot escape. It was invented

254

by men, mostly white Europeans. It was expanded and adapted to a world in flux. It drove industrialization and accelerated the pace of change for 2 centuries; apparently to satisfy a growing population; actually to produce vast wealth and concetrate power among a tiny minority, and borderline poverty for a billion or more.

Argument 33: The Global Environmental Crisis ALONE ought to be proof of a major problem in our civilization.

Argument 34: Combined with the other, non-ecological global crises, a Systemic Failure of human systems is undeniable.

A SUMMARY: BARBARIANS IN THE SEATS OF POWER
A Systemic Failure of the US Democracy, and flaws in the US model of a super-power, have allowed a destructive economic model to dominate the world, most specifically the relationships between people and the Earth.

We can think that there was a moment in our recent past, when human civilization was approaching a high point and a stable state of resolve. I'd put that moment in the early-to-mid-1990s. Others may think, more realistically, that we are still far short of that state. Given the Outlaw Capitalist system, and the men running it, we must open our eyes to the fact that we are regressing, moving backward toward a more primitive and barbarian condition.

Most liberals and progressives are too optimistic to say this, (or too committed to keeping the conversation *civil*, though many believe it):

Too much of our civilization is now dominated by the abusive power of half-civilized men, virtual barbarians in expensive suits.

They own the powers of politics, money, and technology, but

255

lack the moderating Moral Sentiments. Unstopped, they will freeze the human experiment in a state of Pre-Civilization that cannot take the next step toward a mature and resilient, fully civilized, global culture. Combine that possibility with the unknown but severe risks of Climate Catastrophe, and it's painfully easy to believe we are being impelled through the last tipping point by men who can't see it or deny it exists.

A few hundred Mostly White Men, likely raised as English speakers, have accumulated enough illegitimate power and ill-gotten wealth, to bring down enough of the Civilized World to make it Fail Systemically.

They find civilization to be a distraction and a barrier to their objectives. Their ideology is rooted in a toxic combination of conscious and unconscious impulses: Fear disguised as Greed, Aggression in the mask of Leadership, Authoritarian control claiming to help the disenfranchised. The system has made the men inherently incorrigible and unrepentant. They cannot adjust their bad behavior because they can't question or understand their own motives. They are completely incapable of looking for the roots of their aggression and greed in their own formative pasts or their brainstems. It is impossible for them to imagine they have ever been wrong.

Civilization is being driven toward a dead stop against a brick wall or over a cliff of oblivion, by the most rabid carriers of Toxic Brittle Masculinity, because they could not care less about what civilization is, could be, or ought to be.

IF THIS DOES NOT PROVE A SYSTEMIC FAILURE of the US government, and a Crisis in our Civilization, with Globalized Outlaw Capitalism as its primary cause, nothing else can ... until the symptoms become undeniable, and it's too late to matter.

The simple solution – to *BOTH* environmental disaster *AND* the global gap in income and wealth – is to move away from Outlaw Capitalism as the global economic model, to a post-carbon, sustainable economy, with limited horizontal growth and zero waste.

256

We need a global shift in consciousness to see ...

We never noticed the First Human Right: the Right to Pass to Our Children a Planet in No Worse Shape Than the One We Inherited.

The unexpected and beautiful consequence will be to find that the solution to the Global Eco-Crisis will make many of the other *de-civilizing* crises we face easier and quicker to solve than we can imagine. Parts Seven and Eight will spell that out.

The information that is missing, the knowledge that is hidden, right in front of us, is that we, as a species, have everything we need to solve the Global Eco-Crisis, and most of the other serious and chronic problems we face, if we can only recognize that fact and muster the political will.

I WILL STOP YELLING when every conversation in the news, and every new book on politics or economics folds in the essential connection between environmental destruction and a rigged economy.

ADJUSTING OUR PERSPECTIVE
Rachel Carson mustered the courage to stand up to the chemical companies, to give legislators the "wake up call" that led to much tighter regulations on pesticides, even if her warning faded to a faint echo. She saw the clues that would lead to an ecological nightmare, from subtle impacts on eggshells, to sickening human beings, to weakening entire ecosystems. She saw the forces of profit and power overturning the rights of the public to know about the dangers and to have a democratic choice.

Rachel Carson fought the chemical companies' power to pollute, their fake science and their lies about the profitable poisons they sold.

Bill McKibben has become her 21st century disciple.

> *McKibben understands that getting the money out*
> *of politics is an absolute prerequisite for getting the*
> *carbon out of the energy economy.*

We connected the concepts and dynamics of Time, Information, Decisions, and Change, on pages 60-6, to help understand
Information as a combined Force of Change. The crucial issue
then and now is Timing: the urgency of extracting the necessary
decisions from systems that are paralyzed by corruption, partisan polarization, and tactical delays at every step.

FIERCE URGENCY: Dr. Martin Luther King Jr. had an uncanny
ability to see into the complex and destructive undercurrents of
American society, politics, and economy. It's clear in hindsight
that he had no choice but to call out the deep vein of racism in
the US, and to demand that change needed to happen faster than
his *political allies* would allow. He observed and pointed out the
pattern in the US's 3 Sins: Racism, Militarism, and Materialism
(as a form of *Economic Injustice*). The pattern is the same one that
is emerging here, now including the *4th Sin* of Ecological Destruction.

In his *Dream* speech, he challenged us to imagine both the
experience of chronic injustice and a society that could choose to
transcend it. Without his insights, his dreams and his demands,
we would still be mired more deeply in racial and class discrimination than we are. He put US Racism in the context of US Exceptionalism and the Militaristic mistake of Vietnam. He included Materialism with the need for perpetual violent conflicts. The
Vietnam war that he opposed finally ended, but too many others
have been launched, not as big, with fewer American dead, but
equally ill-conceived. And we have still not learned the lesson.

Some of his words ring with a righteous echo today, as a
stand-in indictment of our lack of action on the Environmental
Crisis. In his phrase, "the fierce urgency of now," he condemned
the slow pace of incremental reform. It makes sense to quote
him at length.

"We are now faced with the fact that tomorrow is today. We are confronted with the fierce urgency of now. In this unfolding conundrum of life and history there is such a thing as being too late. Procrastination is still the thief of time. Life often leaves us standing bare, naked and dejected with a lost opportunity. The 'tide in the affairs of men' does not remain at the flood; it ebbs. We may cry out desperately for time to pause in her passage, but time is deaf to every plea and rushes on. Over the bleached bones and jumbled residue of numerous civilizations are written the pathetic words: 'Too late.' There is an invisible book of life that faithfully records our vigilance or our neglect. 'The moving finger writes, and having writ moves on...' We still have a choice today; nonviolent coexistence or violent co-annihilation."

Dr. King saw that the 3 Sins were rooted deep in the American psyche, influencing every aspect of the national system. His most telling assertion was that any significant change in US policy – on racism, militarism, materialism, or economic justice – would require,

> **" ... a radical redistribution of economic and political power." MLK Jr.**

He spoke those words several times. Some may have been in the mid-1960s, as he began to connect civil rights issues with economic injustice and the war. It's possible he uttered them for the last time in the hours before he was assassinated in 1968.

I imagine that at some point Martin Luther King stopped trying to understand racism, how deep it ran in American culture, what its causes may have been, or how long it would take to cure itself. He simply made the connections between racism, materialism and militarism and attacked them as a nexus, a locus of bad ideas turned into a covert national ideology. He had the courage and saw the need to call out the unlearned lessons of American history. The next logical step would be to see that meaningful change would not happen unless it was radical. Which did not happen. Now the Global Environmental Crisis makes it even more likely that we are headed toward "co-annihilation," with an "E" added, "Eco-annihilation."

> Argument 36: The global economy follows a model of Capitalism that demands profit be extracted from every human need and desire, and insists that the waste and damage produced do not matter. It forces our leaders to become liars and criminals, and to pretend they are not. The system destroys more value than it creates. It robs us all of our humanity, and our children of their future. .

A historian and political analyst, who can remain nameless, recently offered up the idea that there has been a gradual transition in the moral values embedded in politics and the range of moral/ethical changes they can induce, more or less worldwide. His (or her) premise is that politics, from after the Civil War, and through Vietnam, exposed huge differences that could, at the time or later in retrospect, be seen as straight-up *Good vs. Evil.*

I would say the edges started to blur around the time of, and in the destructive politics around Vietnam specifically, but continued to the time of Cheney, Bush, and Trump. So I am unclear, at least about the chronology of the premise.

Now, by contrast, he or she says, most political decisions are uncomfortable choices among limited degrees of change – subtle shifts within *slightly better* and *slightly worse* – and that *whew, thankfully,* we are no longer burdened by having to choose so often between an ultimate *GOOD* and an unmitigated *EVIL.*

I could not disagree more. I cannot help but believe that the last couple decades of a Right-ward shift in the US (enabled by the Democrats' cowardice and indifference), culminated in Trump, and now represents the last clear choice we may be able to make between *PURE EVIL,* and an admittedly compromised and delayed *UNIVERSAL GOOD.* It follows my belief that the Millennial Divide is quite simply the signpost at the path of human

destiny diverging in two directions, backward into fear, ignorance, hate, and oblivion, or ahead into a future of possibilities
that we must create, decision by decision and dollar by dollar, to
preserve and expand civilization.

If we, as a species, continue to deny and delay the need for a
radical shift in economic power, in order to preserve the Ecosystem and our children's future, we will choose ignorance by
default, and remain comfortably blind to our denial of the *PURE
EVIL* that impels us toward Eco-annihilation. It may be the only
meaningful decision we have left, and our last existential choice.

GLOSSARY FOR PART SEVEN

Common Wealth: Like the term **The Commons** (used in Parts Seven and Eight), represents the physical features and benefits that ought to be shared fairly by all citizens and inhabitants. The typical use applies to the Public Square (real or virtual) and public parks for example. It runs counter to the general conservative principle of Privatization, the belief that most human-made and natural forms ought to be privately owned.

Plutocrat, -tocracy: Plutocrat is a generally negative term for a person of great wealth; A Plutocracy is a society or nation ruled by such people.

Populist, -ism: continued: Bernie Sanders, appeals to an emerging group of young people and leftists, including Democratic Socialists, who demand economic justice and environmental action. We can call them **Progressive Populists.**

Reverse Engineer: To design a system in reverse order to the way it works or the way it might be designed without a clear end point in mind. To start with the necessary final result or objective and design backward through all the necessary steps.

PART SEVEN: THE RECKONING
Zero-Sum and a Systemic Solution

None of us should be surprised, 15 months into the Trump presidency, the GOP continues to lower the bar on blatant and incessant lying, and rather than clear the swamp, turns it septic. But after the passage of the Trump Tax Scams and the new billions thrown at the military, to be told the government can't afford to pay out the benefits we paid for in our taxes makes my blood boil. Whatever they actually say, this is what I hear:

Now that we've done our duty to our owners and Transferred another shipload of Wealth to the military and the already super-rich, we're shocked – SHOCKED! – to find that the government is broke, and – we're really sorry about it – we can't afford to pay for Food Stamps or Children's Health Insurance, and – oh darn – we'll have to start cutting Social Security and Medicare. Can't you see how that's better? What's the matter with you?

Let's look at one of the GOP's most persistent and destructive lies in the context of the 2 big dots we connected in Part Six:

It's pointless and self-destructive to try to "fix" Climate Change; it will balloon the size of government, the national debt – that our children will have to pay back – and the burden of job-killing regulations. We can't afford it. It will be so expensive it will crash the recovering economy. And it won't help anyway.

The truth may need repeating ... several times over.

First, if the economy is recovering at all, it's mostly for the 1%, who continue, thanks to the Trump Tax Scam, to extract the biggest shares of economic growth for themselves. *Second*, the costs of mitigating and adapting to Climate Change, and the other ecological sub-crises, are pennies on the dollar compared to the costs our children will bear if we do nothing; it will make the "crushing" National Debt look like pocket change. *Third*, the economy is going to crash anyway; the signs are already emerging: more bank deregulation, wages still nearly stagnant or shrinking, the Tax Scam payoff to the already super-rich, trickle down pennies for the rest of us; the huge flood of additional cash into the overblown military and the balloon in growth of "financial services," and the flow of cash *away from* public services, education (except for a few promising teacher strikes), justice reform, and infrastructure ... not to mention the blowback from Trump's trade war, and so on. *Fourth*, the government is not broke, it has been raided by the same Outlaw Capitalists who buy companies, load them with debt, fire their employees, strip their assets, and force them into bankruptcy.

FIFTH, and most crucially important, notice that after the Tax Scam and the Military Industrial windfall, the GOP uses a *false* Zero-Sum argument as an excuse to cut public programs and vital social safety nets that are rightfully ours. We will construct some true and relevant Zero-Sum arguments as we go ahead. There are several minor points to be established, dots to be connected in a larger, simpler pattern, to get to the point.

Lobbyists force both parties to guarantee corporate profits, no matter how excessive or destructive, while the corporations bank their new tax breaks, buy back their own stock to inflate its price, and profit from environmental destruction and workers' stolen wages. But those are just symptoms.

It's obvious the 1% has no idea what to do with their excess wealth, except find new ways to launder it or avoid taxes on it ... or plan how to hide out from the chaos the Eco-Crisis promises to deliver; one of their main worries is how to feed and pay private security forces, and keep them loyal. What is not obvious but ought to be: why can't they imagine investing in fixing the maze of crises their greed and corruption created? That begins to point to the core issues behind the symptoms.

FORTUNES AND CRIMES
In the 1900s, the French writer Baudelaire once said, "Behind every fortune there is a crime." Since then, the fortunes and the crimes behind them have grown exponentially, and we still have not observed the connection. Updated to the present, we can now say,

Behind a dozen great fortunes, there are a dozen great crimes.

WHICH DOZEN? HOW MUCH WAS EACH ONE WORTH? A TRILLION? OR MORE?
1. The removal of Native Americans from their land, by forced migration or massacre and the value of that land as US Capitalism's first Net Worth.
2. The Slave Trade and the vast wealth extracted from it over 400 years.
3. Railroads built across stolen lands, driven by coal extracted from stolen lands, leaving the first layer of coal ash and Mercury contamination.
4. Wage slavery for every race and gender of workers, including children – only marginally better for white men – since before the Industrial Revolution. Prison for debtors and the destitute, or starvation, or suicide.
5. The Nuclear Weapons industry, fed by Uranium mining on stolen lands, leaving radioactive contamination that remains toxic for centuries.

Is it really a crime if it's not written down in the Rule of Law? Can ignorance of Moral Law be used as an excuse for Moral Crimes?

6. Enforced Debt and lack of basic services for the middle and poorer classes. Democratic Socialism would have done better.
7. The theft of retirement funds through engineered bankruptcies and privatization.

265

8. The quantities of wealth extracted from the economy *ONLY* for the purpose of further corrupting the Congress so they will legalize other forms of unethical and immoral behavior.

> *What's our definition of Corruption? The abuse of personal or political Power to enrich one's self, rather than serve the public good.*

9. The profits from uncharged Externalities like pollution, lax labor laws, gutted unions, dangerous working conditions, and 8 million tons of plastic waste dumped in the oceans *every year.*

10. The ongoing abuse of women and children, in sex and labor slavery, in too many forms to list.

11. Auto and gas industries that skewed the entire economy to their profit, by opposing efficiency and public transportation.

12. Medical care and pharmaceuticals, priced out of the reach of half the population; the lack of universal health care (without the middleman of private insurance). How about the family that bribed Congress, with millions, so they could make billions off the Opioid Crisis by making it profitable, legal addiction?

13. A housing crisis created by mortgage fraud, with nearly 10 million homes seized, and as many as 5 million homeless, including children and veterans; and an inflated rental market that puts a basic apartment out of the reach of a full-time minimum wage worker.

14. A corrupt and racist, 2-tiered Justice system that openly discriminates against minorities and the un-wealthy, and rarely prosecutes or punishes white elites.

15. The wealth extraction and waste, the profits made on illegal invasions, oil grabs, and weapons sales to dictators; the "cost" of millions of innocents killed; the price of US Exceptionalism and the distorted foreign policy caused by the ...

> *Military-Industrial Pharma-Chemical Political Homeland-Security Agribusiness/GMO Fossil Fuel Prison Nuclear Education Media Banking Complex.*

266

OK that's already more than a dozen and I'm not done, but I'll stop. But how much profit and *fortune* did those crimes produce? $12 Trillion? $15 Trillion? $100 Trillion? Half a Quadrillion?* Please observe that the Fortunes/Crimes allegation relies on a Zero-Sum argument.

* *Different countries use different names for these gigantic sums. The American version goes in this order, with each jump 1000 times the previous: thousand, million, billion, trillion, then 1000x 1 trillion = 1 quadrillion.*

And now ask yourself, How many of those would have turned out different and better, today, if the economic model the United States used, since before it was the United States, had been based on a respect for human life, economic justice, horizontal growth, minimum waste, and total sustainability? (Or even on the original founding principles?) Hint: All of them.

Granted, our middle and upper classes might be a little less rich than they are, living more modest and peaceful lives. There would be no billionaires, far, far less pollution and waste, maybe fewer pointless wars. And we wouldn't have to ignore and deny the centuries of injustice and greed, or the damage done. But revisionist history is only good for comparison, background, and maybe to improve our foresight. Otherwise, it's not the point.

THE COST OF GOING GREEN GLOBALLY
An info-graphic appeared in my Facebook feed five years ago, *The Cost of Going Green Globally*, from the *Inhabitat* website. Researchers at NeoMam Studios** (as in *new mammals*), in Manchester England, added up the total costs in British Pounds of converting all the world's fossil-fueled industries and facilities – homes, utilities, manufacturing, transportation, etc. – to *green* (renewable and sustainable) energy systems (solar, wind, wave, geo-thermal, hydro-electric – in spite of an argument that hydro, requiring dams, is not green).

** *I have informed them that I cite their infographic in the book and they have allowed it, but they do not know specifically how I apply their logic.*

The info-graphic is still online, you can Google it. But that is only half of the point.

They broke it down as percentages – by segments of the economy and by types of fossil fuels – that add up to the total cost to go from fossil fuels to renewables, *GLOBALLY*. They came up with a thoroughly researched, large but credible number: £29 Trillion (British pounds), or about 48 Trillion US Dollars.* Quoting the graphic: " ... seems like a lot, but it's only 21 percent of total global wealth."

WHAAAAAAAAAT? TOTAL GLOBAL *WHAT?*
NeoMam Studios used the words *total global wealth.* And by giving us that ratio – 21 percent – they tell us that their estimate of Total Global Wealth is around $250 Trillion. There is evidence it's more, possibly much more. Getting closer to the point.

---

* *The value of both currencies have varied since those calculations were done. The £ total (British pounds) probably changed, and the exchange rate (£ to $) is different. So the total in USD would now be around $44 Trillion, not $48 T. Remember that number for 3 or 4 more pages.*

Adjusted for currency fluctuations, and minimum inflation, the Cost of Going Green Globally in 2018 would be about $44 Trillion.

THE EXXON DECEPTION
In the History that started on page 190, we included a sequence of statements by oil company CEOs, API lobbyists, corrupt and fake scientists, about what they knew or didn't know, said or didn't say, or lied about, relative to the dangers of Global Warming. You'll recall, (or in case it wasn't clear) the API, Exxon, and other oil giants were doing their own research into Climate Change, the dangers and the potential costs, and the risks if it went unregulated. Their public announcements over the years went, in the 1950s, from *caution about overreacting* to air pollution; in the late 1970s and early '80s, to *agreeing with the scientific consensus*, based on their own fully researched studies (that the

problem was real, human-made, and likely to cause severe social and economic upset); in the 1990s, to the *skeptical approach* (we really don't know enough about it, the science isn't conclusive); then, in the late 1990s, to *total denial*.

When I first learned of (what I call) the Exxon Deception, I thought that Exxon's research had started in the early to mid-1970s. New evidence came to light in early 2016 (InsideClimate-News), that the oil corporations' research and wavering conclusions can be tracked back to the same time period as the TV show cited in the Introduction. Their research actually started in the mid- to late-1950s and was conclusive by 1978. Exxon, API, and other oil giants like Shell, found on their own that Climate Change, in a worst case, could upset the global economy and cause widespread social unrest, that it would cost $Billions *to adapt to* in advance and $Trillions *to mitigate* after the fact.

> **And then they proceeded to conceal that research,
> deny the results, and claim that the science on causes,
> costs, and risks was inconclusive.**

They paid their lying CEOs extra millions in bonuses to keep up the Denial. They spent millions more telling the public and their stockholders that the claims of Climate Change were false, or unverified, or open to question. That practice continued into 2016, *even after the deception was exposed*. But it prompted a group of Exxon stockholders to file a class action suit against the company for deceptive stock evaluations. In early 2018 that suit remains unresolved.

OBSERVE: Big Oil invested tens of millions over decades to convince the public and the Congress that we live in an *Oil Economy*, and *the good life* in America relies on an endless supply of cheap oil, long after they knew that the oil economy was doing major damage, that it would crash sooner or later, and that it might bring large segments of civil society down with it.

The truth is that we live in a Water and Oxygen Economy, and oil and its byproducts are poisoning the water underground,

269

in rivers and lakes, choking the life in the world's oceans, and upsetting the global water/carbon/oxygen cycle, and the climate.

> *Was it more criminally corrupt to deny their own research, or to spend millions bribing legislators to join in the denial?*

Big Oil has been warning us, over the same 4 or 5 decades, that a Carbon Tax will be a huge burden on all transportation and markets, that it will ruin family budgets, upset the economy, and fail to affect emissions anyway; while they have been calculating it into their budget projections. Eco-literate friends of mine will complain about a 20- or 50-cent rise in gas prices, when we all ought to know that gasoline's externalized costs ought to make its price $8 a gallon or more.

WHAT IS A CARBON TAX and why does it matter? It looks like (MIT professor) David G Wilson will not get credit for being the first person to define and advocate for a Carbon Tax. He started around 1973, when the OPEC oil embargo was starting to mess with the US economy, and well after Exxon and the API had reached their early conclusions. Nobody picked up on it for decades, and when they did, they didn't credit him. But he's a humble man, and has done a bunch of other great stuff that he got credit for.

The oil companies don't want anything to push the price of gas up, or demand down, or profits down, in spite of the fact ...

> *... that government subsidies are basically EQUAL to the total of oil company profits.*

Yes you read that right. The government has been supporting oil exploration and market fluctuations with taxpayer funded handouts for decades. That's a near Zero-Sum equivalent. (Consistent low gas prices were the intended benefit, but they have always been an illusion to support the *Oil Economy*.) The amounts are equivalent to *the highest profits any corporations have ever extracted in the history of the world ... before the deregulation of the big banks.* That equivalence is a predictor of the point.

In the context of a hyper-political, fact-denying GOP government, it's confusing and ironic that a group of Conservative businessmen and statesmen have proposed a Carbon Tax, better than anything Democrats have imagined or proposed. The *Climate Leadership Council*, in a paid Wall Street Journal ad in June of 2017, proposed a *Carbon Dividends* program that would charge a gradually rising tax on carbon, the revenue from which would be paid back out to all Americans, making it revenue-neutral; it would roll back existing regulations (which may be good or bad); and (my interpretation) create a more level playing field for consumers and producers – including wind and solar – while cutting emissions.

The few others who talk about a Carbon Tax say it should start at \$10./ton and gradually ramp up to \$40/ton over a decade, and then continue to rise. The CLC's *starts* at \$40/ton. That number, coming sooner or later, is based on low estimates of the actual costs of the environmental damage CO_2 emissions continue to cause, per ton.

A Carbon Tax will be a huge and essential factor in any attempt to slow our CO_2 emissions. It may be like the CLC's or different, and it may come sooner or later. Theoretically and ideally, a carbon tax would become part of international trade agreements and be uniform globally. It will raise the market prices of every fossil fuel, in proportion to its carbon footprint (or better, its heat retention potential): coal, diesel, gasoline, propane, and other forms of natural gas. And it will inflate the costs of everything that relies on fossil fuels for production ... for a while. But mainly, it will fund a rapid expansion of alternative fuels and sustainable electricity generation, and other sustainable systems like public transportation. That's getting closer to the point.

271

The most severe problem is that a Carbon Tax has to be enacted in 5 years or less, and has to have a major impact within 10, or, like our other lame efforts, it will be too little and too late to matter.

SO WHAT? WE DON'T HAVE A CARBON TAX YET
On one hand, revisionist histories – imagining *What If* the past would have gone differently – are somewhere between wishful thinking and pointless. On the other hand, we need some *What If* to understand how we got here. One of the points is that *we ought to have known* about the long-term impacts of allowing CO_2 emissions to be *externalized* for all these years. We *ought to have been* taxing carbon since we knew it was damaging the atmosphere, impacting the climate and pushing huge environmental costs into the future. We *ought to have been* subsidizing wind and solar more, and gas and oil less, ever since we knew – *ought to have known* – that oil subsidies, in the billions, were insane, given the climate impacts. But the corruption of the US Congress, by the oil giants and others, has kept those facts out of the news and off of any legislative agenda. It has prevented even a conversation about a carbon tax, and continues to perpetuate the criminal myth of the climate change hoax.

> *There is a jaw-dropping Zero-Sum equation hiding inside this story.*

We're connecting 2 big dots here: the Cost of Going Green Globally, from a few pages back, and a Carbon Tax *What If.*

IF we had implemented a Carbon Tax in 1975 – around the time Exxon's research reached the conclusion they would then deny – how would it have changed the intervening 4-plus decades? How would it have changed what we're facing now?

OK, since 1975, the world's fossil-fueled industries have emitted more than 1.1 Trillion tons of CO_2. If that quantity had been taxed at $40 per ton, over that 40-plus years, it would have produced total revenues of *over ... 44 TRILLION DOLLARS.*

Why does that number – $44 Trillion – seem familiar?

And *that* would have done 3 monumentally important things:
• It would have reduced consumption by a significant amount, possibly by *HALF,* in turn cutting emissions by half, and limiting the actual warming of the climate, possibly by 1/2 of 1° C. ... which in turn would give us some breathing room – *and TIME,* a decade to 25 years or more – to cut emissions further and deal with the rest of the Eco-Crisis.
• It would have generated enough revenue to compensate for the economic and social disruptions – the public demand for energy, jobs lost in the energy sector, and other costs – by subsidizing wind and solar, public transportation and batteries, instead of oil and gas, for those same 40-plus years.
• Bigger picture, it would have allowed us to take the first big steps toward a Post-Carbon Economy.
 OBSERVE: That is a crucial Zero-Sum equation that will help us recognize the point.

A SENSE OF PROPORTION REVISITED
We know how many of us live on this planet, within a few percentage points, how we are distributed geographically, and how we are distinguished by ethnicity, language, cultural practices, and governing/economic systems. We know how many nuclear power plants are still in operation, how many are decommissioned, and where the tons of nuclear waste are being stored – temporarily and insecurely. We know how many pipelines are pumping oil across the landscape, how many are likely to leak (all of them), and how many tankers are burning bunker fuel to move oil and other cargo across the oceans.
 We can calculate what percentage of the US military budget for one year it would take to provide permanent clean water systems for every community in the world that lacks them (it's 15 percent).
 But we don't have a clue what Total Global Wealth actually adds up to, or what fraction of it was extracted illegally, immor-

ally, or unethically, from the working economy – human labor and resources – through 50-plus years of banks and corporations cheating the system, by bribing Congress to deregulate them so they can extract more. We have no idea where that wealth is located, how much of it is hidden to avoid fair taxes in one or more countries, or how much of it is being recycled back and multiplied into yet more wealth through money laundering, gaming the financial markets, and gigantic real estate scams – the newest trick to launder and protect excess wealth (just ask Trump's Russian buddies). We just know it all must add up to hundreds of trillions of dollars. But that still isn't the point.

TOTAL GLOBAL WEALTH?

There are a lot of different ways to estimate global wealth, in parts, or as some astronomical total. To try to set up the next argument, I came up with an estimate. Total global debt, plus total global gross product, total bank liquidity plus total stock market capitalization. (Admittedly some of those sums overlap or are duplicated in others, but there are other Trillions those categories can't count.) Round it up to the nearest ten trillion and pick a number. I came up with a ballpark total, a thousand Trillion – a *Quadrillion* dollars, about 4 times what NeoMam tells us in their calculations (back on page 268).

I found several online videos tracing the history of the world's largest banks, most having originated with one family, the Rothschilds. Estimates of the total wealth held by the family's present-day descendants, including half of the big banks in the world, are around $500 trillion, and they guess that that amount is half of total global wealth, making *that* sum $1Q, or 1 quadrillion US dollars – close to my estimate.

For the purpose of this argument, *Total Global Wealth* is somewhere between an unrealistically low $250 Trillion, to something around $1000 Trillion. (The higher number would make the global cost of Going Green Globally only 5 percent of total global wealth, not 20 or 21 percent.)

One online video makes the point that these banks make millions of dollars every day just on transaction charges from lending and trading, interest and fees on every dollar that moves through their computers and across their balance sheets. Given the millions of stock, bond, securities and derivative trades that turn over in fractions of a second, the fees on every trade, the lack of taxes or regulation on those transactions, and the near impossibility of estimating hedge fund totals or off-shored accounts (until we have new regulations, laws and accounting methods), a quadrillion could be a low-ball estimate.

So for all we know, Total Global Wealth could be $2 to $4 Quadrillion. Or more.

TOTAL WEALTH, TOTAL DAMAGE, MORE OR LESS?
Take the Zero-Sum principle, take 2 steps back, and apply it to the global wealth acquired over the last half century. We have the right to speculate: there *must* be an equivalence between: A. the value of resources extracted on the cheap, bought, stolen, or destroyed in externalized practices, plus the eroded value of human labor and life, lost through exploitation, and in resource wars; and B. the excess wealth extracted as profit from those unfair, corrupt, destructive, exploitive, and criminal practices.

We acknowledge that much of the world's wealth was earned ethically and properly. But there still remain, somewhere, huge fortunes that were acquired "legally" only because percentages of them paid corrupt legislators to write the laws. And, it's fair to ask, why wasn't the legitimate wealth invested more fairly, rather than hoarded? Let's split the difference and make the claim: about half of Total Global Wealth was earned honestly and ethically, and half of it ought to be seen as 2 gigantic debts: 1. Environmental Debt, and 2. Human Rights Debt to billions of human survivors. Totals for each are easily in the $100s of Trillions. Up to $400 or $500 Trillion, combined.

AND THAT IS THE POINT
As a global species, we have assaulted the living Earth to the limit of what it can tolerate. Illegitimate and abusive bosses have exploited others beyond what anyone should have to tolerate. While each of us bears some responsibility for tolerating the assaults, or standing by, mute, the real blame is on the leaders that don't lead, or lead in the wrong direction: dirty politicians, greedy businessmen, bankers, crime bosses, and corrupt judges, who are in it for personal gain without limit, and to abuse their illegitimate power, with nothing but contempt for the rest of humanity or the precious and polluted Global Ecosystem.

We have the technological, financial, and informative means for everyone to know as much as they need to, to participate in local, national, and global democracies, and, even at this late date, to correct the senseless damage our leaders-who-won't-lead have inflicted on us and our Earth. But the same leaders-that-won't-lead prevent us from using that power, because it would threaten their choke-hold on their stolen wealth, their illegitimate and abusive power, and on our future.

It might force them to pay back some of their wealth and curtail their Abuse of Power as necessary, in order to repair the damage done, and to start to build a sustainable global economy.

You might take a minute and revisit pages 59 and 63-4 for *Where We Are And What We Now Know We Need To Do,* and think about *why* that is thought to be impossible. Let's *reverse engineer* what we know we have to do in terms of what it will take to get there:

THIRD: We need to get to Net Zero Carbon in a decade to have a 50/50 chance, if we're lucky, of stopping Global Warming before the ongoing GHG emissions, Feedback Loops, and Thermal Lag, force us past the last tipping point of a spiraling, irreversible Global Heating Climate Catastrophe. That will be hugely expensive and require massive international agreement and co-management.

SECOND: Doing that will require a different set of Organizing Principles for the Global Economy, based on efficiency, sustainability, human rights, horizontal growth, and the circular feedback of value back into the common good, instead of a vertical growth economy based on Carbon, Corruption, DD, EE, PP, War and Waste ... and *especially Excessive* Wealth.

FIRST: And *that* will require a nonviolent, widespread, popular and (both kinds of) populist political revolution, to oppose and remove the foul remnants of the Trump/GOP Revolution, and its echoes in destructive, authoritarian, toxic and abusive neo-fascist trends around the world,

We need a revolution like that and more, if we are to create a sustainable – and peaceful – economy. It's what a true Global Leader would do, if one existed or could be reawakened.

And if you still *think that is OBVIOUSLY IMPOSSIBLE,* you haven't been Paying Attention, you still haven't Recognized the Pattern because it is *ABSOLUTELY NECESSARY* to save ourselves. Sooner or later a different group will control the Congress and the White House. They will have to update the US Constitution. The Bill of Rights may have to get revised and reorganized. The justifications for slavery, and for counting African Americans as 3/5 of a person must go. The references to what every "man" is equal to or what rights "he" is endowed with, must become "every person." And Corporations must be ejected from that category. Citizens United has to be overturned or made obsolete by new laws. If we are going to convert the global economy to a sustainable model, we have to describe it clearly, and outline a process of getting from here to there. And we have to get money out of politics so a new government can do it.

Certainly it will be expensive and difficult, and may seem impossible, unless and until we compare it to what will happen if we continue what we are doing ... next to nothing.

1967: WHEN THE OBVIOUS NECESSITY WAS IMPOSSIBLE
The Vietnam war protesters were met with many logical reasons
why their simple demand to Stop the War could not be granted:
national security, momentum, saving face, the domino theory,
logistics, investment, politics. It was just not possible. What did
the protesters expect? Their simple, insanely idealistic answer:

"Turn the boats around."

To physically reverse the direction of the boats, planes, fuel
supplies, ordnance, and reluctant draftees lined up at the docks,
would have been easy. The only things that made it impossible
were the hardened mindsets and chronic blind spots of our leaders: the senseless pursuit of military dominance, in an irrational
fear of a non-Capitalist economy, and the failure to imagine the
emerging worst case – obvious to the anti-war crowd – that the
war was headed for a disastrous dead end.

In August, 2018, it's fascinating to hear: When a US district
court judge heard that an immigrant mother and child (who
were in a case he was hearing, over Jeff Sessions' new asylum
restrictions) were on a flight back to their home country, he ordered the airline (in more legalistic terms), *Turn the plane around.*

So when we are told that a peaceful political revolution is
impossible, or that a sustainable economic model is ... unimaginable, even insane, we have to compare both with the very real
possibility of human extinction, in a century or less. When we
consider our population, the total value that has been extracted
from human well-being, and from the health of the Earth, only
to accumulate illegitimate Power and obscene wealth for a tiny
group of autocrats and billionaires, it ought to be obvious. It is
essential to our survival to understand,

> *Argument 37: The existing Economic Model is the Problem.
> We have to turn it around if we are to save ourselves and
> the Earth. And we have to do it fast.*

FEAR OF THE WORD *REDISTRIBUTE*

The GOP has successfully conflated – intentionally confused – Free Markets with the value of personal freedoms. So the right to private wealth is the rallying cry for anti-Socialist fear, and the notion of *Redistributing Wealth* is their bogeyman. They have scared most of us into thinking high taxes and government spending are not only wasteful and counter-productive, they will lead to a totalitarian Communist takeover before you know it. The GOP seems to actually believe it. The Democrats have been frightened or bribed into pretending to believe it out of a fear of being called Socialists.

Capitalists and Free Market ideologues hold to the notion that private property and private wealth are and must remain untouchable by any government or agent. We worked for it. We earned it fairly. Whatever advantages we had, or whatever biases favored us, it was all legal. Taxes are inherently unfair. It's our money. The government can't touch it. Period.

Now we have to counter that fake and flimsy position with these questions:

Who Distributed the Wealth in the first place? On what basis? Where did it come from? Where is it now? Why can't we reclaim it?

The Democrats have forgotten or ignored the fact that taxes are the dues we pay to live in a civilized society. Look at the countries with the highest standards of education and quality of life (both material and intangible), the least crime and happiest populations: they all have Mixed Economies, variations on Democratic Socialist governments, high taxes and generous funding for the full gamut of public services and safety nets. The idea of a universal minimum income is new and spreading – a basic wage for everyone poorer than middle class, working or not, is an obvious and possible method to end poverty and begin to equalize the gap in wealth.

279

We must identify the wealth extracted from the value destroyed – in human well-being and the Health of the Earth – and Redistribute it.

The GOP admits in private that they'd rather corner the wealth and power than use any of it for the luxury of a civilization, beyond what benefits them. They understand that an unstable and divided society helps support their fear-based agenda.

Argument 38: What hardcore Capitalists condemn as a "Redistribution of Wealth" must be renamed, "Correction of Wealth Mis-Distribution."

ASSET SEIZURE / CIVIL ASSET FORFEITURE
US citizens live in a country and an economy that prize Private Property above most other social values. Did you know that it is legal in many states for local police, state troopers, and prosecutors to seize your personal property, including especially cash, without ever convicting you of a crime – *without even charging you with one* – only because they suspect you of something ... that they do not even have to reveal, much less prove?

A Jon Oliver This Week Tonight episode on HBO recorded state troopers asking a driver they have stopped if anyone in the car is carrying large sums of cash. They threaten obstruction of justice if the driver and occupants are found to be lying. Cops love to find large sums of cash because it's accepted as default rvidence that those with the cash must be involved in some criminal activity, and therefore ripe for prosecution. (It's not the first time fortunes and crimes were found in tandem.) It's a policy rooted in the failed War on Drugs. Trump's Attorney General Jeff Sessions (is he still around?) thinks we have to expand that feature of America's Just Us System.

Did you know that total asset seizure in the US claimed more property in 2014 – in cash and belongings – than all the burglaries in the country in that year? It probably does not exceed the total value of houses fraudulently seized, in any one year, in the Mortgage Crisis. Either way, local cops, the FBI and state troopers can also seize your home, whether you or the bank actually own it, over the suspicion that a crime may have been, or may be about to be committed. Chew on that for a while. You or your parents could end up owing the bank for your house, but never getting to own or live in it, because some cop thinks you might commit a crime.

Be creative. Imagine if the justification for this is extended to the whole of the national, or even global economy. I suspect Outlaw Capitalists of committing some of the greatest crimes in history; can I seize their assets? How about if I get a badge?

ASSET DESTRUCTION AND BAILOUT

When the big banks go bust over some fraudulent practice that blows up in their faces, or when the stock market suddenly drops 1500 points and your (or your parents') retirement account loses $40,000, it's often given the benign name Asset Destruction, as if real value can just disappear, evaporate into thin air, when it's actually been stolen. They should call it Asset Disappearance Magic. (Don't look behind that curtain, or at those offshore accounts.) It's seen as an unfortunate side-effect of bad business practices, which have become the norm, that no one really expected to turn destructive, except those that did, that could not have been avoided, except by the regulations that got cut. It's like asking about the 2008 bank bailout, Where did the $13 trillion GO? It went to the inventors of the financial innovations, the investors who cleared their profits before anyone suspected a problem, and those who knew it was coming and shorted the housing market before it actually crashed.

What is it called then when the well-being of millions of people is looted for profit? Or the vitality of the living Earth liquidated for a stock price? ... other than the worst forms of asset destruction, both engineered and unintended? Is it an unfortunate side-effect of short-sighted Capitalism, or is it premeditated fraud only disclosed after the value – money or resources, personal wealth, or a viable ecosystem – has simply disappeared?

281

Should we think of it as an Externality to the (illusion of the) Good Life? And what is the remedy? Total Global Bailout?

LET'S LOOK AT TOTAL GLOBAL WEALTH ANOTHER WAY: GLOBAL CORRECTION OF WEALTH MIS-DISTRIBUTION

If our estimates are correct, that total global wealth is around $1000 Trillion, and if we agree, just for argument's sake, that it was ALL accumulated through unjust and exploitive practices, then what would it look like if we could redistribute that wealth, equally to everyone on the Earth?

OK, divide $1000 Trillion by our population, around 7.6 billion in 2018. Every man, woman and child on the Earth would get a check for around $130,000, enough to help each of them pay for a fair economic role in a civil community and an economy on the path to sustainability: clean water, far less waste, reliable food and housing, jobs, health care, and education, and Climate Change in retreat.

As you did with the $44 Trillion number, remember $130k.

A DIGRESSION AND A SET UP FOR PART EIGHT: REPARATIONS?

Reparations is almost as scary a word, to Conservatives, Republicans, and most billionaires, as the word Redistribution.

Essayist Ta-Nehisi Coates caused a stir in May of 2014 with a piece in The Atlantic, *The Case for Reparations*. Coates makes an articulate and persuasive case, but it's not a new idea. The argument is for the payment of reparations to black people in America, the descendants of slaves, for the loss of labor, life, income, property, and rights over 400 years, since the beginnings of slavery through Jim Crow, up to and including discriminatory practices still in place today. It belies our denial of our dark past, or of our white privilege, so we will argue the merits of reparations to blacks, without considering how much more wealth, proportionally, might be owed to Native Americans, for what our ancestors did to and took from theirs.

Many progressive whites agree in principle. But there is a

large and bipartisan team always prepared to debunk the idea
with several standard reasons: it would cost too much for the
little benefit to be paid; it would be impossible for it to be done
fairly – every African American citizen would have to prove
their slave ancestry, possibly even the percentage of their DNA
that came from actual slaves; also, there are far better ways to
improve the economic conditions for poor blacks; and reparations paid to blacks would ignore the many poor whites and
refugees who might also deserve reparation, even if for different
reasons and from different sources.

And none of the proponents, to my knowledge, have come
up with a fair or feasible notion of how it would be accomplished.

REPARATIONS generally means compensation for abuse or
injury, usually as compensation paid to persons in the form of
money or other property of value.

Let's look at Wikipedia's summary of the "United Nations ...
Principles and Guidelines on ... Reparation for Gross Violations
of ... Human Rights ... and ... Humanitarian Law." They describe
five categories. (Italic notes in parentheses *are mine.*)

1) **Restitution** serves to "restore the victim to the original situation ..." before the violations occurred. This can for example
include the reinstatement of liberties taken away, a protection
or renewal of human rights, the return of a residence, of employment, and the return of other property, including money.
*(Obviously dead people, like extinct species, cannot be restored to their
original situation.)*

2) **Compensation for Damages** is intended to compensate for
damages that can be evaluated proportionally, such as: physical
or mental harm, lost opportunities, material damage, and loss
of earnings, moral damage, and the costs of such services that
might alleviate the harm done. *(Obviously compensation cannot be
paid where no funding exists.)*

3) Rehabilitation provides for follow-up aid in the form of direct medical, psychological, social, and legal assistance to victims and related parties, to alleviate the impacts of harm done. *(Going Green Globally, or flipping the global economy to sustainable principles, would cause massive economic and social disruptions, with massive costs.)*

4) Satisfaction includes actions to assure the cessation of abuses, truth-seeking, attempts to return persons or remains, judicial sanctions, apologies, etc. *(This sounds like South Africa's Truth and Reconciliation process, which gave amnesty to perpetrators of Apartheid who admitted their roles in the damage done.)*

5) Guarantees of non-repetition are meant to assure the prevention of future abuses, including new administrative controls over whatever forces had carried out the abuses, and systems to monitor protections from further abuse. *(Imagine extending this guarantee to the future impacts of economic and industrial systems. It's the equivalent of 'Sustainable.')*

EXAMPLES: East and West Germany (divided after WWII, now reunited) have paid for or returned the property of Jews, including works of art stolen during the war, and have paid large sums of money to Jews for other abuses and lasting impacts of the Holocaust (of WWII Europe). Some of those monies were used to create the foundation for the economy of the State of Israel.

In spite of the standard arguments, it is possible to add up the fortunes that were made on the backs of slaves, from the 1600s through Emancipation. We could add in the riches extracted from blacks in the intervening years, from lands seized during Reconstruction, through voting rights lost, not to mention thousands of lynchings, to job discrimination, enforced poverty and criminal injustice today. Ta-Nahisi Coates documents a Virginia country club, on land once legally owned by blacks, that was illegally seized by whites and is now their property.

284

40 ACRES AND A MULE

Here's another way to think about it. At the end of the Civil War, some state and federal programs promised "40 acres and a mule" to every adult male freed slave – about 3 million men at that time. Most slaves, before or after they were freed, imagined it would give them a shot at an independent economic future. I thought it had actually been implemented. But of course, like so many treaties made by the US government with Native Americans, once some white guys in power thought it over, those plans, like those treaties, were abandoned. And those dollar values, for mules and land, stayed in the rich white hands that controlled them.

As Dr. King pointed out in 1968, at the same time the US government reneged on its 40 acres and a mule promise, it was giving millions of acres of Native American land in the west to white European immigrants, building them land grant colleges, and extending low interest loans to them to help them build, manage, and expand white family farms.

But anyway. The present-day accumulated value, in 2018 dollars, of 40 acres and a mule, times the number of adult male slaves freed, is $6.4 Trillion. Let's remember that they all would have had families that would have benefited from the gift, and that any such gift would inflate in real value over the years. If we imagined paying reparations, using the value of that one broken promise, every African American person (with slave ancestry) in the US would be owed $160,000.

Is the similarity of that number to $130,000 purely coincidence, or is it another true calculation of wealth extracted from people who were exploited by the system? You decide.

IMAGINE: IF WE WERE ALL MEMBERS OF ONE OF THREE FAMILIES, after the Civil War, who all magically escaped its racist aftermath. Each might in turn resent or take comfort in the economic injustice that was the aftermath. One family is brown-skinned, starving and sick in the aftermath of a flood. One is white or Hispanic, working hard on dry land, with limited resources, barely getting by. And one is white, super-rich, hoarding vast wealth, residences, resources, in-house medical facilities, and the Power to do most anything they want to do.

If most Americans can relate to the middle group, and if they still possess basic American (and/or Christian, or otherwise moral) values, of human equality for example, it's easy to imagine they would share some of their limited lot with the dark-skinned family in crisis, even if they are immigrants, refugees, Muslims, or Black Africans.

So imagine that the wealthy family also sees themselves as having a responsibility, even feelings of empathy, for the family in crisis, they would give all that is needed, to rescue the black family from their distress. They would even share more of their wealth to help the middle family improve their lot.

It's certainly easy to imagine the opposite, that the wealthy family would never be that generous voluntarily, or humane. It's also easy to imagine that the poor-to-middle and lower classes would find themselves competing with each other for the pennies that trickle down, for example, from working for the rich. They have been conditioned to do that. It is how the rich and the super-rich keep the rest of us, competing to survive, distracted from the idea of economic justice.

LIKE US, THERE MAY BE 3 OR 4 CLASSES OF PLUTOCRATS
There are many millionaire and billionaire examples of our negative stereotype: families like the Kochs (fossil fuels), the Waltons (WalMart), the Cargill MacMillans (giant commodity conglomerate), the Sacklers (bribed Congress to legalize Opioid addiction), Robert Mercer ($11 million donor to Ted Cruz's campaign), the DeVos-Prince family (Blackwater, Amway, US Dept of Education), David D Smith (head of Right-Wing Sinclair Broadcasting, which is moving to dominate local TV broadcasting across the US), and Sheldon Adelson (casinos, funding right wing candidates in 2018 to the tune of $30 million), and hundreds of other CEOs, investors, inside traders, and bankers, fraudsters and money launderers, opioid dealers and indicted sex offenders –

and oh yes politicians who became millionaires before or after they retired from public service: they may not admit to gaming the system, benefitting from rigged inheritance laws, or even Congressional bribes. They think their privilege is earned and deserved.

There are a few in between, who made vast sums through standard business and investment practices – like Warren Buffet (giant conglomerates including real estate), Bill Gates (Microsoft), and George Soros (hedge funds) – who may feel some responsibility for having gamed a rigged system, but who have chosen to give back huge sums for valid philanthropic causes. BTW if you don't know, both Gates and Buffet have asked to be taxed more, AND are giving away most of their fortunes to public works charities.

There are a few like Trump, who inherited millions, blew most of it on luxurious self-aggrandizement, lied and cheated in every possible legal and illegal way, and ended up desperately unhappy and unfulfilled, without ever even wondering why.

And there are growing numbers of genuinely humble and empathic million- and billionaires, who know they got rich on a rigged system; they see the little damage they may have done and the massive damage many of their billionaire buddies have caused. They choose to question the system that brought them their fortunes, they condemn the corruption of many of their peers, they make good on commitments to give back, and make a model of doing well to do good.

This group includes Nick Hanauer (an early investor in online businesses), Tom Steyer (hedge funds), and many others. I just became aware of Roger McNamee, a mid-range multi-millionaire, early investor in Facebook (and current critic of it), with a brilliant mind for the impacts of technology.

Tom Steyer is a billionaire with a heart and a mind and a case against Trump. You may have seen his TV ads – framed as *NEED TO IMPEACH* – calling on us all to sign his petition to start impeachment proceedings. I would choose a different tack, but it's great that Mr. Steyer is forcing the public conversation.

Nick Hanauer confesses to enjoying many of the perks of huge wealth – he owns a private plane and a "very large yacht" – but he's willing to criticize the plutocrats who want to squeeze the middle class and the Commons to further enrich themselves. He is quite conscious of the damage that unregulated Capitalism is doing to the Earth. He has lectured his billionaire buddies on economic injustice, and warned them, in a memo for Politico magazine online in mid-2104, that *The Pitchforks Are Coming ... For Us Plutocrats.*

PITCHFORKS ?? !! Hanauer has created a True Patriot Network that promotes, "country above self, service to others, stewardship of resources, shared sacrifice and other progressive values." (Wikipedia) He tells his "Fellow Zillionaires" that the gap in income and wealth is turning the US into "a feudal society ... (like) 18th century France. Before the revolution." *

It's worth a brief historical note. The French Revolution resulted in the overthrow of the aristocracy and the privileged class. It followed two expensive wars and years of bad harvests. (Wikipedia)

Hanauer challenges other entrepreneurs to face up to some hard facts: the gap in income continues to widen, the US is becoming a divided society facing collapse, or something like a police state. He says that when the chaos comes, the plutocrats think they can escape ... but they won't. He also says it would be easy to fix with New Deal style programs and policies – higher taxes on the wealthy and the big corporations, more government spending on public benefits.

As Hanauer suggests, many of the super-rich have started to buy or build walled retreats, or underground bunkers, with caches of water and supplies, around the world, so they can imagine they will survive a global collapse ... of everything. It adds significantly to their already huge carbon footprints, and it won't work anyway.

Remember the mention of the Bush family back on page 76?

We cannot ignore the fact that most of the multi-billionaire plutocrats ignore and demean rebels in their midst like Hanauer, Steyer, Gates, and Buffet. They believe – or lie as if – their "earned" or inherited wealth was fair, and is irrelevant to the idea "that all" (men and women) "are created equal ... endowed with inalienable rights ..." and so on. They are certain – or can convince each other – that their wealth was all earned without damaging the Common Wealth or harming any persons. They are blind to their own greed, the damage their extracted wealth has caused, and whatever insecurities and hatred their wealth may mask.

In a fair, equitable, and sustainable economic system, in a working democracy, in a country with a moral core and leaders who respect founding principles, the economy we are suffering under, the economy that is killing the Earth, would never have been permitted to devolve to its present state.

WE NEED TO ASK THE PLUTOCRAT CLASS (what they ought occasionally to ask themselves): How do you see yourself in a global vision of a world we all share equally? Can you picture humanity as a group with fundamental and common experiences – like birth, struggle, happiness, parenting, suffering, and death? Do you believe we all ought to have equal rights ... to the benefits that you have? Do you think ...

Ultimately we are all in the same boat and ought to act like a large, interdependent human family.

Or,

This is my boat. I bought it fair and square. I don't care what your problem is. I have no desire or intent to pull you out of the water.

The fair and humane response to *that* answer is,

Share the boat with the family or get out of it. Swim or Sink. Your wealth is not a life preserver. It's been extracted from our lives.

In other words, we can at least give the worst of the amoral plutocrats, climate deniers, and corrupt Senators the option: Do you choose to be part of a human brother- and sisterhood? Or do you see yourselves as separate, superior, and justifiably privileged, without responsibility to the rest of us? Members of a distinct class of humans?

Before you answer, understand you can't change your mind when the rest of us grab our pitchforks.

WHAT CREATES VALUE AND WHAT DESTROYS IT?
There's a Karl Marx quote and Socialist Meme that suggests Capitalism kills more value than it creates.

"Capital is dead labor, which, vampire-like, lives only by sucking living labor, and lives the more, the more labor it sucks." (or kills)

Beyond the Marx quote, there's a philosophical position that says buying and selling labor or commodities or products does not always create value or wealth; rather, it often destroys percentages of real value by exchanging it for money. The implication is contrary to Capitalist logic.

The Privatize Everything Ideology says, for example, that "A tree is just a log without a job." – of no inherent value if not marketed. If every tree was privately owned, it says, it could be managed like a good commodity in an open market – cut down, cut up, sold, bought, and put to good use. *BUT* the real value of a typical living tree is 10 to 1000 times greater than the few dollars the dead log will bring. Over its lifespan, measured in air quality (CO_2 absorption, Oxygen emission), water retention, wildlife habitat, soil enrichment, erosion prevention and so on, the market can never reflect the value lost by cutting it down.

Depending on the lasting value of the new thing, and how the cash profit is used, turning something into money – labor, raw material, energy, water – usually results in a net loss of actual value, on both sides, in exchange for the conversion to cash. Only if the bought item fulfills its advertised benefit, and lasts, or if the cash profit is turned directly toward a constructive investment, does that idea get tempered. That would be an indicator of a truly sustainable market system.

Remember my description of my Love-Hate Relationship with Advertising, and the idea of Advertising as a Tax, back on pages 151-3? Value is extracted, as if by a tax, by increasing the price of everything that relies on advertising for sales and consumption. The tax on the media that carry the ads (1/4 to 1/3 of all TV time is ads). The tax on our time and our minds, including programming our kids to be willing, often addicted, consumers. And ultimately the tax on the ecosystem in the form of unnecessary consumption and waste. Advertising creates fake value to sell stuff we might not otherwise want, need, or buy, while it extracts percentages of money, lowering the actual value of almost everything that is purchased.

Since the Capitalist system became dominant in the 1500s, and certainly since the dawn of the Industrial Revolution, our predecessors witnessed the greatest destruction of value – because it could be converted to money – in 4 billion years ... with the possible exception of a couple major extinction events. Since the 1970s, the destruction of value has become more extreme, due to ongoing deregulation, and because most of the value extracted and wealth "created" has been transferred from the Commons to the 1%, and remains private, hidden in off-shore accounts or held in non-productive investments. It has not been reinvested or used to correct for unpaid externalities. Do you see the connection? The real value, now destroyed, ought to be a legacy to our children. Instead it's a poisonous debt. Can we call it Dead Wealth? If that concept sticks, can we revive that wealth and put it to use creating new value or replenishing the value destroyed?

We have disrupted the precious and delicate balance of the global Ecosystem, to the point that it threatens our survival. We have also upset – almost demolished – a natural and historic balance between our numbers, our resources, our money, our comfort, a natural economy, and a long term plan. Can we now imagine disrupting our brutal and wasteful economy in order to restore both balances ... to the degree still possible? More on disruption right over there.

IMAGINE A TRULY WISE AND RESILIENT MARKET
Let's imagine, for a change, that a great and wise, but well-regulated Free Market can work for the benefit of all – people and planet – without destroying vast quantities of value, without producing vast quantities of Dead Wealth. Such a market, properly regulated and made responsible for its consequences, *MUST BE ABLE* to adjust to the sustainable demands of the living Earth, and still support a basic, working economy for working people. Especially if we can limit our numbers and our demands for excessive consumption.

Everyone in the world – whether they love Democracy and hate dictators, or praise dictators who undermine Democracies, or who never learned the difference – may face the realization that our condition demands that we think differently about the world we want to leave our children and how they will live in it. Or we, or they, will have to learn and accept it when the Earth, sooner or later, becomes the dictator of our economy and its impacts.

A SUSTAINABLE AND FAIR ECONOMIC SYSTEM MEANS:
An economy of efficiency, minimum to zero waste, fair distribution of jobs and wages, strict limits on the unnecessary extraction of great value and great wealth, from the Common Wealth, from human well-being, and from the Earth.

IF we are to survive as a species, *IF* we are to avoid killing off so many other species, *IF* we are to stop poisoning our land, air, and water, and stop forcing a Climate Catastrophe, *THEN* we have to convert to that kind of economy as rapidly as possible.

Imagine a sustainable economic model that the world can join, that creates total economic justice and funds the reparation of the Ecosystem.

DISRUPTIVE INNOVATION AKA CREATIVE DESTRUCTION
I had avoided the topic of Disruptive Innovation. Ads on the radio for Disruptive Consultants, websites promoting Disruptive Design, links to Building Leadership Brands with disruptive approaches: it just seemed like a business fad or a nasty sounding name for something conventional. But the idea would not leave me alone. I assumed it was a new idea but it is based on a 1942 theory of business called Creative Destruction, and its roots go even further back in time. Several different links and interview comments took me to Jill Lepore's article of June 23, 2014. I started reading it online before I realized it was sitting next to my TV, in The New Yorker.

Some key points of the strategy, as promoted by its advocates, are (my paraphrase): take advantage of panic; don't build on the past, throw it out and start over; don't try to be nice, be heartless; don't work within the existing system or paradigm, throw it out, disrupt it or have it disrupted by some other force. Now highlight those points, mentally or with a marker.

In her article, *The Disruption Machine, what the gospel of innovation gets wrong*, Jill Lepore gave me three insights. Two were her observations. One is my interpretation and elaboration.

First, a clear definition of what Disruptive Innovation was supposed to be about: the idea that gradual, linear changes with gradual improvements (on products or services or business plans – after all, this is a business strategy) are often the wrong things to do, because sudden radical shifts to entirely different paradigms often create the next Great Thing, even when they buck trends, contradict assumptions or destroy traditions or companies – even if they force a few people to lose their jobs or their retirement accounts. This is simply the notion of Systemic and Rapid Change, applied to individual businesses.

We could look at the 2016 argument between Hillary and Bernie in this light: gradual change that doesn't create instability vs. a political revolution.

The second insight was to learn that Disruptive practices and ideologies are right about as often as conventional economists, that is to say, not very often. They pick evidence to prove their point and ignore statistics that don't; they claim to predict successes and explain failures but can't; and they promise followers great financial gains that seldom materialize. In a prime example, one of Disruption's promoters asserts that the "theory ... continues to yield predictions that are quite accurate," ... four years after he himself predicted the Apple iPhone would be a dud.

Lepore admits that, yes, there are some notable disruptive innovations that have created great breakthroughs and large fortunes – the iPhone is clearly one example. Beyond that, the personal computer, big-box discount stores, and Toyota's decision to compete with Detroit. But without much trouble she digs up a dozen or more disruptive innovations that were complete busts or large disasters, like the *financial innovations* that led to the 2008 crash (the repeal of Glass- Steagall, mortgage-backed securities, collateralized debt, default swaps). Perhaps the most memorable conclusion is that a successful "Disruptive Innovation can reliably be seen only after the fact."

But that does not mean that it doesn't work at all, or that it is always unpredictable.

In a third insight, I take the liberty of re-interpreting her observations to fit the pattern I see. Disruptive Innovation and Creative Destruction sound a lot like Milton Friedman's Shock Doctrine, as described by Naomi Klein (mentioned back on pages 202-4). I wonder why so few progressives or environmental activists – almost none – propose fundamental shifts in the way our economy

294

doesn't work for working people or the planet.

A lot of Trump's appeal was in his promises "to shake things up in Washington," "to drain the swamp," and otherwise radically disrupt the government. His gang – now a year and a half in – have disrupted everything in sight, pretty much without a plan, a staff, expert oversight, credibility, or consistency. To the shock of aware citizens and the rest of the world. Virtually every leadership appointment was picked for his or her readiness to destroy – without creativity or innovation – the mission of their assigned department, with Pruitt's agenda for the EPA the most criminally insane. Beyond that, and Trump's nuclear threats, the worst of the damage has been directed at immigrants, the poor, the brown- and black-skinned, and our allies.

Rather than clear the swamp, his gang have turned it septic, clogged it with piss poor ideas, economic debris, and administrative sewage. No matter how long Trump and the gleefully brutal and corrupt GOP remain in power, some force is going to have to clean up the mess and repair the massive damage they have set in motion. While that will take a major political shift, and a huge effort, and a plan, and clear priorities, the nation is at least prepared to tolerate a new level of uncertainty and stress, from the top.

November 2018 will tell us a lot about how that goes.

And by the time you read this, the Democrat Party will either have accepted and empowered its Progressive wing, or will have locked itself into a more persistent split, and obsolescence sooner or later, probably sooner. Anything that upsets the failed 2-party system will be welcome.

The current conditions in the United States government, and in the world – a Systemic Failure and an urgent need for a Systemic Solution, – are right in line with what the Shock Doctrine took as fertile ground: a combination of unstable factors, political, economic, and social; an existing system that needs a radical shakeup and a new start; a mandate not to be gentle, rather to be brutal; and so on. We have economic instability, political grid-lock, social unrest, strikes and shortages, refugees from climate disasters like storms, floods, and droughts, and from civil wars, proxy wars, puppet dictators, and illegal invasions. In the Spring of 2018, Trump started the first battles in an international trade war that could cause another global recession ... or worse.

Is it possible, thinking back to page 159 or 243-4, that abso-lute power does in fact corrupt absolutely, and we are just begin-ning to recognize the pattern? Or can we imagine that somehow, Moral Sentiments would start to make an impression? (pages 184-5)?

Everywhere that Power and Wealth can be acquired through cor-ruption or violence, and where there are no systems of democrat-ic choice, quality education, reliable information, or legal justice, to keep them in check, it is almost inevitable that the power and wealth will be acquired and abused without moderation or limit, to a levels of systemic collapse. Stable society is dissolving under our feet, like an iceberg.

I continue to look with admiration and hope, to the small number of countries where that does not happen, because their regulation and decision systems have resisted corruption, like much of northern Europe, Scandinavia, Japan, and a few others.)

In the United States of America we can see, if we look, the cash flow in the lobbying business – why don't we just call it what it is, *LEGALIZED BRIBERY* – that turns a few thousands in invest-ments (payoffs to campaigns) into millions of added profits to corporations' bottom lines. Who's more corrupt? The corporate pimps or the legislative whores? I use those metaphors under-standing they may be unfair to some sex workers.

These symptoms are not an accident of bad management or administrative mistakes; it was either an inevitable accident, given the bad organizing principles, or the system was actually engineered to work this way: high health care costs and bad results, homelessness and inflated rents, a third of our adult population and half of our children living on the edge of poverty, mass shootings, for-profit prisons, and the killing of unarmed blacks by renegade racist cops; profits flowing in and corruption flowing out of Big Pharma and Big Oil and Wall Street. By now you can make your own list.

OUR TOLERANCE FOR CHANGE:
THE OVERTON WINDOW AND THE PENDULUM
In one week in September, 2017, I came across 3 pieces, in print and online, that magically intersected with each other and with this notion of Disruption.

Supreme Court Justice Ruth Bader Ginsburg quoted a "wise man" as saying (paraphrased),

The bald eagle is not the right symbol for the United States. A pendulum would be better.

The implication, I assume, is that the political pendulum in the United States swings from right to left, and has now swung way too far in the direction of state fascism, and must reverse direction. For me, that assumption has to include the possibility of a widespread paradigm shift, a leap in conscious in the US that can spread to the rest of the industrialized world.

About the same time I read about that pendulum thing, I stumbled on an article in The New Republic. It was about the Overton Window, an imaginary frame that can be wide or narrow, indicating wide or narrow tolerance for different kinds and levels of change. Sociologists studied social groups – at large in random groups, or as demographic segments – to judge how they tolerate or adapt to change, in the form of new ideas, or as new information about existing situations.

The point is to create a context for discussions about what the public finds acceptable and easy to tolerate, to controversial or radical, to unthinkable or deviant extremes: high to low tolerance for anti-social behavior, racism or sexual harassment, styles of dress or speech, or acceptance of mild or extreme pro- or anti-environment attitudes, and so on.

Another analysis, and the 3rd piece I read, was about Hallin's Spheres; it talks about tolerance in similar terms, using an image of concentric spheres. The author of the Hallin's Spheres calls the lowest tolerance for an extremely offensive idea, the "Door slam in the face" extreme. I invite you to look them up and compare them, with each other and with your personal tolerances.

The Overton Window is a simpler analog and serves the purpose. An image of a window, wide open for high tolerance, nearly closed for low tolerance.

We want to intersect this idea with RBG's Pendulum metaphor. The premise is similar for both. There are definable social norms, or pendulum swings, for what a group of people, or a national public will find:
• Obvious and not threatening, easily acceptable, within a tolerance for normal change. A wide open Overton Window, or a pendulum swinging in a narrow arc.
Or,
• Challenging, mildly disturbing, upsetting, but within a tolerance that many can adjust to, especially if the situation is already a little chaotic and the idea is accepted among peers. An Overton Window halfway open, or a pendulum swinging in a wider arc.
Or,
• Insane, disgusting, offensive to the point of provoking anger, impossible to imagine becoming an acceptable idea, fact, or possibility. An Overton Window only open a crack, for near zero tolerance, or a pendulum swinging wildly in a big arc, for extremes of change.

Let's take the idea – measuring a society's tolerance for change, high to low, on one or many topics – and apply it to the political situation the United States public faces in 2018 and beyond.

One premise is that the press and media news generally limits their topics and treatment to issues of low-to-medium levels of change, from the easy – not obvious but different, acceptable and worth mentioning – to a middle range – unusual but not so deviant or unthinkable to be upsetting or inflammatory. The implication, sad, true, and borne out by simple research, is that most commercial media will avoid – sometimes ignore altogether – stories and issues that are likely to cause extreme upset, division, or fear – the most extreme responses. Current examples, if not already obvious, would include: the ongoing release of radioactive water into the Pacific from the Fukushima meltdown, the true level of corruption in the US government, the similarities among the high number of killings of unarmed blacks by cops, the US's role in Yemen (currently the worst humanitarian disaster in the world, where, recently, the bomb that destroyed a school bus and killed dozens of children was found to have been made in the USA), the possibility of human self-annihilation in a century, the quantities of Methane that may represent the last tipping point, and so on. There appears to be a growing range of stuff that Americans, or TV news producers, or their sponsors, are just not ready to think about or accept.

It's understood that our tolerance can be compressed, to be more frightened and less open to change, or stretched, to be more open to moderate or extreme change, by a variety of factors in the public arena: politics, social trends, economic values, religious tolerance, large scale disasters, and also by changing conditions and attitudes among our peers. The parameters are comparable to the Possibility Mindset, back on pages 19-20 and 99, and are illustrated in the Millennial Divide on pages 116-121.

An odd example popped up while this was being edited. Psychologists found it was easy to get Conservatives to shift to more Liberal or Progressives views, on a variety of social and political issues, by subtly conditioning them to feel safe. The less safe they felt, the more they stuck to their Conservative views. The more safe, the more they shifted Liberal. Put that in the context of fear-based propaganda.

In the summer of 2018, these ideas point to an exciting, virtually revolutionary situation in the United States, at least in my troubled mind.

In my view, President Donald Trump and Senator Bernie Sanders both stretched the extremes of what is acceptable in the public conversation, and in the spectrum of what is possible in politics. Hillary stayed firmly rooted in the acceptable status quo, centrist norms. The 2 men often appealed to similar groups: those totally disaffected with Washington DC, the economically disadvantaged, the forgotten common man and woman ... people who wanted someone to shake up Washington, drain the Swamp, or be a Creative Disrupter. It helps to explain why many who favored Bernie in the primaries voted for Trump in the general election. It also points to the crass indifference to those voters among insider and corporate Democrats. It indicates an impulse to choose failure over compromise, and suggests, in a pinch, those Democrats would reject socialism for state fascism ... the direction Trump has us headed.

They also appealed to groups diametrically opposed to each other's values: racists vs. those tolerant of minorities and immigrants; people who respect the rights of everyone vs. those who think the rights of gays or Muslims impinge on their own rights; those who want America to become great by leading the fights for economic justice and the environment vs. those who think that means turning the clock back to the 1950s.

The point is that Trump and Sanders both stretched the Overton Window, expanded our tolerance for what presidential candidates can say and get away with. They made the pendulum swing in a much wider arc. They expanded the public consensus to include ideas, attitudes and policies that were previously – way back in 2015 for example – thought to be deviant, extreme, radical, or unthinkable. They broadened the nation's ideas of what is normal and acceptable – or they took advantage of radical and disruptive trends already happening – from tolerance for overt racist behavior in one direction, or Democratic Socialism in the other. Do you agree that we are now open to a

300

wider array of possibilities, in politics and economics, and in the
news we can tolerate, with acceptable levels of stress?

*Argument 39: We can take the combined strategies of the
Shock Doctrine, Creative Disruption, the Trump Train Wreck,
and Our Revolution, as lessons and preparation for
imagining a Green New Deal.*

The contrast ought to be clear. Bernie's ideas are radically sane:
coherent attacks on a rigged economy and a damaged Democracy; open battles against discrimination, and for getting the money and corruption out of politics; demands for higher taxes on
corporations and the super-rich, more government spending on
universal health care, lowering carbon emissions and expanding
subsidies for renewable energy systems and sustainable practices; promoting the rights of women and minorities, including
justice reform and the right to an affordable education.

**In a Sustainable, Fair Economy, Growth is Horizon-
tal. Excess Profits, Wages, and Wealth are Taxed, and
Nature makes the rest of the rules.**

Both Bernie and Trump represent a new tolerance for radical
change in the very nature of government. With the clearest and
most oppositional values imaginable.

**Will you take a chance on new leaders, bent on dis-
rupting the Outlaw Capitalist model, to reduce the
risk of self destruction?**

Bernie Sanders demonstrated that a large minority of the public,
verging on a majority of liberals, progressives, and young people, are now open to Socialist remedies to several, perhaps many
of the nation's problems, because they are so dissatisfied with an
extraction economy and a political system divided over what is
true, like science, and what matters, like suffering.

301

A backlash to the racist uprising that Trump incited will not be easy; but a multi-pronged attack will start to drive the racists back into hiding, or into changing their sick attitudes. It will include purging police departments of their secret cadres of KKKlansmen, veterans with PTSD, and White Suprematists, and ending the Code of Silence that keeps good cops from outing the bad ones.

Sooner or later, it will lead to a more public discussion of gun culture and the damage done by the US military, and their cost in lives and dollars, over the last 50 years, and the massive environmental and human abuse caused by unnecessary wars.

IS IT TOO OPTIMISTIC TO IMAGINE that our world, after Trump, will see those and other issues as agenda items for a new and expanding class of voters, as an intersection of emerging trends in a growing demand for Independent and Progressive politicians, who can either transform the Democrat Party or replace it with a new one?

The nation faces several crucial and clear options, including new ones that may be clearer now:
• The voters will be more than ready to jump to a Bernie-inspired Democratic Socialist-oriented panel of candidates, and Socialist style remedies to our biggest challenges. And/or,
• The Trump gang will be so reviled that their policies will finally bring on the actual end of the Republican Party and most of the Conservative insanity that has dominated the US over the last 35-plus years. Or,
• The country will be so terrified of both, after Trump, that they will vote for anyone who takes them back to the inert but predictable gridlock of the Obama/McConnell years. Like the next establishment Hillary. Or maybe,
• The 2-party system will collapse when the corruption of both sides is finally understood. It will provoke some political contortions, but we may be able – because we absolutely need – to come out with a more democratic, inclusive, and fair system.
302

Which is more likely, possible, or impossible? You can help decide.

One significant variable will be whether the Democrat Party can learn the lessons of 2016 and give the country the choice it has kept from them since 1944.

Two hopeful possibilities that Trump may be creating are: he may screw up the US economy and balance of trade so badly that it brings on another serious recession (Bill Maher has been promoting this idea, enraging Conservatives and Capitalists in the extreme), that will make radical remedies, like a New Deal, not only possible but essential and urgent; and that he will continue to undermine the international view of the United States, so our insulted and threatened allies will unite behind a truly Progressive administration and agenda, in a radical new path toward the international accords and agreements that the whole world needs. This idea gets expanded ahead on pages 309-10.

BIGGER PICTURE COMING INTO FOCUS
We are going to have to reverse engineer the Global Economy to a sustainable model, and we are going to have to systematically spread the reach of Real Democracy in order to do that. And we have to do it with a shared sense of The Fierce Urgency of Now, 50 years after King. We have to decide what kind of world we want to leave our children and theirs, and be prepared to use All the Means Necessary to create a world fully re-imagined.

King was right about the two shifts in power that must occur, for a truly just society to emerge and survive. Political and economic.

President Kennedy wasn't promoting a revolution in the US when he said this in 1962. But he was talking about the responsibilities of the wealthy and powerful everywhere, to demand the reforms that would preserve the fabric of their societies.

"Those who make peaceful revolution impossible will make violent revolution inevitable."

We understand that a large percentage of the wealth of the world
– half, or more – is the product of abuses of power, most significantly over the last 60 years. That money now exists as a 2-part
debt, to the health of the Earth, and to the welfare of the billion
human beings living in or near poverty. The cost of the damage
done points to its mirror image, a Systemic Solution. The debts
must be paid back, without compromise.

> *Argument 40: When we humans, as a species with a
> shared destiny, understand the fortunes and crimes, we will
> see we have everything we need to preserve the Earth
> and reclaim a viable future for every one of us: information
> about the urgency of the Ecological Crisis and knowledge
> of what must be done. We must join together and exercise
> our shared Power.*

The obviously impossible is about to be recognized as absolutely essential. The 10 or 20 national and global crises now reveal
their common roots and causes, their common corrupt values,
and common solution: the flipping of the global economic model, away from extraction and exploitation, war and waste, and
toward human rights and environmental sustainability.

> *Argument 41: There is enough excess, ill-gotten wealth in
> the world to cover the costs of repairing most of the
> damage, to humanity and the Earth, that its extraction
> caused. We only need the political will, the means, and a
> vision.*

In the simplest terms: *IF* the US can make a few decisions:
... to remove the billions in campaign and lobbying corruption,
... to go back to a strong progressive income tax,
... to enact a moderate but rising tax on wealth,
... to re-regulate banks and corporations to lesser levels of power
than the government itself, and make them pay their fair share,
... to start to cut military spending (and waste, and fraud),

... to flip coal, oil, and gas subsidies to wind, solar, and other green energy systems,

THEN, there is nothing, *NOTHING*, the US cannot afford to do.

And *IF* half or more of the other industrialized nations agree to implement the same changes, *THEN*, our human species will be well on the way to reviving our threatened civilization. Anything approaching a utopian outcome will be a century or more away. But in the context of Eco-self-annihilation, we may be able to achieve an overdue and compromised best possible case.

PART EIGHT: TOTAL GLOBAL REPARATION

FROM RECKONING TO REPAIR AND RENEWAL

The Right Wing in the United States has made the country's founding principles, and their support for democracies, seem like naive childhood fantasies, or a con job, because they are unrealistic in the toxic and paralyzed government the GOP built for their Outlaw Capitalist owners to exploit. With Democrats' help.

Republicans continue to tell us their failed ideas, from 20 and 40 years ago, will somehow *magically* work now. But the ideas that Bernie Sanders and other progressives put forward, that the public needs and wants, are ridiculed as *Magical Thinking*.

The Democrats let them get away with it because their campaigns depend on the same donors. They say, *Well those were nice ideas, and we should try to bring them back, someday.* Or they pretend they are guided by those principles now.

The limits of what can reasonably be done in the world are defined by a tiny percentage of its most unreasonable citizens, because a majority of them are opposed to change ... and justice and Democracy for that matter. The status quo has made them rich and powerful. They will not be persuaded by logic or humanity. What is thought possible has been constrained to reflect the wishes of a billionaire class, bent on holding Power and grabbing more wealth. And they will destroy anything in their way to do it – out of pure spite if nothing else – including the Earth if necessary. What the Ecosystem needs to keep us all alive has become partisan, because it will raise taxes on the rich and induce high levels of government spending. It will make the rich and powerful much less so. But that is necessary to return power to the public and stability to the Earth's climate ... to the degree that is still possible.

It is laughable – to the Right – to even suggest that humans might begin to stall global warming, *and* end the growing food and water shortages, *and* stop the refugee crisis, *and* human trafficking, *and* injustice and racism, *and* too many proxy wars to keep track of. But what is laughable to the GOP, most of the plutocrats, and the corporate Democrats, must become an urgent objective to the Progressive Left.

Looking at our failing civilization, the rest of us don't know whether to laugh in cynical irony or cry, cover our eyes, scream, or grab a pitchfork.

To think we might do all that in one lifetime, in a generation, or – imagine – to do most of it in a decade, is beyond laughable, obviously impossible, ridiculous on its face; but only to those who cannot see the risks or the opportunity. The risks: extinction of half of the life on the Earth, or more, including most or all of us, in a century or less. The opportunity: to create the best world possible, under the circumstances. It's only impossible to those with no sense of proportion or morality, no vision for a better future.

THE MORAL EQUIVALENT OF WAR

The philosopher William James (1842-1910) coined the term "the moral equivalent of war" in a 1910 essay, shortly before his death. Much more recently (2003) Chris Hedges, a war correspondent for over a decade, wrote *War is a Force That Gives Us Meaning*. They appear to take very different routes, philosophically and historically, to come to similar positions. That is, we Americans seem to be addicted to war as a necessary and ongoing practice to affirm our bravery, patriotism, nationalism, and our position of strength in the world.

James saw war as if from the armchairs of retired generals and historians. Hedges is lucky to be alive and able to sleep, given the horrors of war he witnessed first hand. They both raise the question, Are there other projects that could give us the sense of urgency and mission, that would demand the shared commitment and the sacrifices of war ... without the violence, destruction and death ... without the monumental waste of resources and lives?

James at least makes the argument I expected: a civilized people ought to be able to do two things: resolve conflicts without resorting to war, and find better projects to generate, inspire, and realize a sense of national purpose. That's the spirit in which I use the idea. It ought to guide these projects.

The US's conversion to a war economy from 1939, through '42, to '45, serves as a historical example of a massive shift in industrial output and economic power, redirected. It's a nearly perfect model of what the nation and most of the world can do, when a crisis makes it possible – because it's necessary and urgent. We must imagine a global movement with the Moral Equivalent of War that can set its sights on global ecological and humanitarian reparation, and beyond that, an end to the Mindset that drags us into continual war.

Republicans and foreign leaders, leftist economists here and authorities at the World Bank, have warned Trump that his reckless tariffs may well bring on an international recession as bad or worse than 2008. But don't be confused. In the context of the political and economic changes that must occur, that would be helpful. A few pundits in the US are openly hoping it happens. Others are suggesting that Trump may unite our allies and our opposition (Russia, China) into a total boycott that will cripple the US economy and, maybe, end the GOP reign of economic and ecological terror. A few are promoting the idea. Others wait for it to occur naturally.

In early July 2018, Trump is shocking our strongest allies by attacking them at the NATO summit, while he praises dictators like Kim and Duterte, and kisses Putin's ass. His cowardly betrayal of the US's most fundamental values, at NATO and Helsinki was ... just two more steps toward total chaos.

Either way, Trump's irrational disruptions of security treaties and trade will likely upset the US economy, and international trade practices, diplomacy, finances, and security alliances so badly that the remedies needed to correct them will have to be radical, and will provide great opportunities for a new and broad agenda of disruption and innovation that are actually creative.

Outlaw Capitalism persisted far too long as a political/economic model, while it engineered the greatest transfer of wealth and value – from people and the Earth to the 1% – in human history. For that to originate in the US, Outlaw Capitalists needed to buy the GOP and half of the Democrats, to turn the US Congress into a shell game, and Washington DC into a corrupt and septic swamp. And they needed a corporate sponsored mass media to normalize it. I think it's essential for us to admit these mistakes to ourselves and announce to the world our intent to correct them.

One way or another, a combination of forces in the US will walk past the Trump gang as they are on the way out, forced from power by indictment, impeachment, or by elections that overpower the GOP's voter suppression tactics: some old school Democrats who still have hope for the party, young Democratic Socialists running for office or marching in the streets, aging pacifists and tree huggers who have dreamt of Socialist solutions since the 1960s, Black Lives Matter, MeToo, Rev. Barber's Moral Movement and Poor People's Campaign, 350.org, Bernie's Our Revolution of course, and the growing number who see climate change and ecosystem collapse as existential threats that can and must be avoided. They will be joined by a bunch of former Republicans who can no longer deny the corruption and moral failure of the party of Family Values.

We must do more than hope. We have to make sure that happens while there is still time for it to matter.

If the ideas in this book have any traction, or even if they don't, members of a fully reformed Democrat Party, or a new and visionary People's Party will fill the gap left by the dying GOP. They will start solving our many crises, by radically

310

changing the Capitalist system that unites them. With my ideas or without them, they will have no choice but to see that the Ecological Crisis and the Gap in Income and Wealth are not only related to each other, but also to injustice, poverty, crime, discrimination, pointless wars, refugee crises, and the corruption that almost killed our Democracy.

They will be more than ready to Correct the Mis-Distribution of Wealth, by launching projects like these and others.

It will put the United States on track to regain its role as world leader, democratically, economically and ethically, supported by a well-informed and newly engaged electorate, fully prepared to reduce our consumption, our carbon footprint, and our military profile.

It has been amusing in a sick sort of way to see and hear Trump justify his many divisive plans – from a border wall and the abuse of families seeking asylum, to new threats of war, to a tax scam that is sure to backfire – by saying,

"We have to do it. We have no choice. Believe me."

Now we, the citizens of the United States, can say the same thing about a revolutionary agenda, and believe it without being told to. It is essential to our survival.

THE US MUST LEAD

The US is still the source of most of the CO_2 and other GHGs already in the atmosphere; and, sadly, the model for domination by Outlaw Capitalism.

IF the US is to regain its status as world leader, *IF* we are to reclaim our democracy, *IF* we are to guide the global economy, *THEN* we must define a new model, new objectives and strategies, and implement them first at home. Rapidly. If we are to get international buy-in – essential in the medium-term, 4 to 8 years – we have to make the model, show that it works, and use our political and economic power to spread it.

This last part of the book is offered with the assumption that ideas like these will be influential, possibly pivotal, in the necessary changes to come. You can help decide whether and how that happens.

GLOBALIZATION REDEFINED

Like the Global Eco-Crisis itself, nothing in our history or memory compares to this project, as an action plan for what we know we need to do, pragmatically and morally. We may think of it as a new definition of globalization. It will no longer represent a NeoLiberal plan, designed by and for corporations and banks to expand business and trade, in order, theoretically, to spread democracy, prosperity, consumption, and wealth – but without regard to economic injustice or environmental degradation. Instead, it will reflect a coordinated global plan to equalize economies, re-balance global wealth and poverty, and *MAINLY* to create political initiatives and funding structures to renew, preserve, and protect the Earth's ecosystem.

As with any large scale, urgent and complex project, we have to start with total, strategic commitment to the obvious first steps, and prepare to adjust tactics, methods and goals as the mission progresses and is reevaluated.

> *We can't do that until we do this. But we can't do this until that is started. So we have to imagine the complexity of the whole process.*

We can't start divesting and reinvesting, repaying the vast social and environmental debts, until we get the money and corruption out of politics. But we can't do that until we have an honest, working government. We can't begin programs of de-carbonization, ecological restoration, justice reform, or social reparation, until a different government is in place and functioning, one that will manage – and tax – the super-rich, the banks and corporations, rather than surrender to their corrupt power. But in the last 70 years, no US government has shown the willingness or capacity to do that. And we won't get the cooperation of corporations, the banks, or other nations, until we move decisively in this direction and show that it works.

You see the dilemma. There are competing starting points and premises, big obstacles to overcome, dozens of priorities needing to be balanced: the easy and difficult, the more obvious and the obscure, first, second, and third phases.

It is essential and urgent that the US and allied and like-minded governments formulate radically different methods for making large scale, collaborative decisions and acting on them. The US in particular will have to shift away from constantly reacting to short-term emergencies, self-created budget shortfalls, and election cycles, to a new, comprehensive, long-term plan, based on new organizing principles.

A reformed government will have to design and implement new interactive and integrated systems to avoid, to the degree possible, unintended consequences.

Each project must start or expand in the United States or duplicate other successful models. Each will require that we start with the easy low-hanging fruit, the obvious first and second steps, but with the medium- and long-term goals always in sight. We will have to move confidently to the more difficult middle stages (requiring international cooperation for example), and on to long-term goals; moderated by feedback and adjustments, cost/benefit analyses, constant monitoring and preparations for changes in course, as they become evident and necessary. New and innovative management techniques will be needed for a holistic and comprehensive approach, with the understanding that everything is interconnected. It means that every new decision and action will impact one central crisis at a time, and at least a few, if not all of the others.

The US Congress will be forced to find ways to cut the inherent indecision and delay in its current process, possibly and paradoxically, by using the tactics of giant corporations and the military. When the Congress is relieved of the burden of balancing every new expenditure with new budget cuts, when protecting the corporations and their profits becomes less important than the new priorities – sustainable survival and human rights – the priorities themselves will dictate the needed sequence of decisions.

In design school we learned that the most important factor in creative problem solving was defining the problem correctly and completely. We've done that. An even more rigorous and enlightened design attitude requires we sharpen our conscious foresight, to avoid mistakes and false assumptions about the objective, so they won't appear as flaws and problems later. It would implement an attempt to avoid what McLuhan warned us about: taking too much for granted, and ignoring the evidence of unintended consequences until it's too late. Most competent scientists and engineers can do those things. Politicians generally don't even understand the idea.

TOTAL GLOBAL REPARATION IS FIVE PROJECTS

The guiding premise is that we can't change or impact humanity's many crises one or a half dozen at a time. There are distinct advantages to the discovery that Capitalism, and the Toxic and Corrupt Mindsets that drove it into Outlaw territory, have pushed our country, our civilization, and the Earth's ecosystem to the brink of collapse. It gives these 5 projects a coherent and combined focus.

PROJECT ONE: Renew, Protect, Defend, and Spread Democracy: in the US first, not so much for the principles – our leaders seem to have abandoned them – but in order to proceed to Projects 2 and 3. It means that the US Democracy must separate the power of money from the entire electoral process, must educate and inform the public without compromise, offer clear and reasonable choices, remove artificial and obsolete barriers to the freedom to vote, and have every vote counted. And more.

PROJECT TWO: Convert the Economy to Principles of Economic Justice and Environmental Health. Starting in the US, reverse the flow of wealth (extracted from human well-being and the health of the Earth) from private and corporate fortunes, back into an economy based on human rights, ecological reparation and recovery. We must realize that we can correct 2 great injustices with one set of actions: limit the number and end the political power of multi-billionaires, and end global poverty.

Project 2 must define and enforce new economic priorities of maximum efficiency and sustainability, and preservation of the Commons, for minimum waste and against externalized damage, and for the human right to safe working conditions and fair wages. Once the first actions are taken, we can imagine other nations following suit. Longer term, those values will become essential principles for every public entity, corporation, investor, and bank. Tactics will include Thomas Piketty's (*Capital in the 21st Century*) idea of a Tax on Wealth. In that context, the elimination of poverty, globally, will be complicated and time consuming, but a clearly attainable goal.

PROJECT THREE: A Globalized Mandate to Repair and Reverse Ecological Damage, to the maximum degree possible. It includes the Conversion of Energy Systems from Carbon-based fuels to Solar, Wind, and other new technologies (Going Green Globally), ideally within a decade; to protect fresh water and promote viable Ag practices; and dozens of other sub-projects: to protect species and indigenous populations, to clean up the oceans and hundreds of disaster zones, like the 1300 Super Fund sites in the US, to radically limit the use and abuse of toxic chemicals; in short to Mediate and Adapt to the Global Environmental Crisis in as many ways as possible, as fast as possible.

PROJECT FOUR: Control Our Numbers. We must set international standards for getting to Net-Zero Global Population Growth, then to determine whether Negative Growth – lowering our total numbers – is also necessary.

315

PROJECT FIVE: Global Disarmament. On the premise that we will end the death grip of Outlaw Capitalism on our civilization, we will in turn remove most of the false motives for war. Over 20 years, if we have that long, or less, we must satisfy the human need and desire for a World at Peace; again, not for its own sake – as if that is not reason enough – but because it is an essential part of Project 3, environmental reclamation and preservation.

Let's expand and add some detail to the project summaries above.

PROJECT ONE: RENEW AND PROTECT DEMOCRACY
Create Lasting Universal Justice

Most members of both parties can count the lobbying dollars they brought in, take pride in the votes that money bought, and yet appear horrified at the mention of corruption. Until we force them to face it. When money and politics are separated, the voters who generally don't vote – roughly 50 percent in most elections – will be given a clear choice, and the first step toward a revitalized Democracy will be complete. The political doors will open to a long-term shift to progressive principles. Early winners in the primaries, during the summer of 2018, are inspiring, exciting, and hopeful. They have been articulate, on point, and leaning socialist – or are actual Democratic Socialists – with non-white women forming a significant segment.

In this context, it is also past time for the US to reaffirm one principle in the First Amendment, commonly stated as the separation between Church (meaning all religions) and State. We can and must hold to high moral and ethical standards, and be able to separate all religious dogmas from political ideologies.

Project One has 3 major and urgent parts, and 5 minor or less urgent objectives (some of which will happen almost automatically when the first 3 are realized):

• MONEY OUT OF POLITICS, END CORRUPTION: Yes, it will take a Congressional majority who are either free from corporate corruption of the legislative process, or are finally ready to give up their corporate campaign funding. That appears possible in 2018, likely by 2020.

Two of the first actions a new reformed Democrat/Independent/Progressive Congress will take will be to overturn the Supreme Court errors of Citizens United and McCutcheon, and the rollback of decades of voting rights legislation, or to end them by enacting new laws that cleanse the electoral system of the flow of corporate money and end voter suppression fraud. It may require a new look at the precedents for "Corporations are People," (which were never what the various courts that cited them assumed that they were). The possible impeachment or censure of one or more SCOTUS Justices must become a topic for public and legal discussion, either on the basis of a totally illegal appointment (McConnell/Gorsuch), or for lying about a respect for precedent in their Senate testimonies, prior to approval; or for political bias, somewhat harder to prove.

Assuming that we are stuck with a Conservative-biased Supreme Court, for a while at least, the Congress will have the unusual task – and, fortunately, the guts and vision – to make new laws that will stand up to SCOTUS suits in the future.

Ending corruption – in all forms and at all levels of society, commerce, and government – is a central goal in at least 4 of these 5 projects. It is an essential first step in getting the government on track. Corruption is the most direct tactic of Outlaw Capitalism in its acquisition of illegitimate Power (and a powerful link between Project One and Project Two); it relies on toxic male aggression, even anger and brutality – the driving forces behind state violence. Corruption and the abuse of power rely on a background of fear and ignorance, essential to both the motive and unconscious defense of Denial. Given the number of regimes and corporations that enforce their power with corruption, to suck more value from the common good – it's more than half of all countries, large and small – ending corruption will of

course be problematic and difficult. But, like the rest, it is absolutely essential to a livable future, and can be started in and by
the US when it begins to regain its status as a world leader.

• FIX THE ELECTORAL PROCESS: Correct for the fact that Republicans, the super-rich, big corporations, and foreign lobbyists,
have rigged the campaign and electoral systems to give them
corrupt leverage over voters. Make the liberal, leftist party stand
in firm opposition to that pattern, and commit to a Congress free
of corporate influence.

   While the first steps are taken to get the money out of
politics, other laws will either have to be written, rewritten, or
overturned, to eliminate all the racial and class biased voter
manipulations, from gerrymandering to required IDs to rigged
electronic voting systems to the criminal process of voter purg-
es. Is it too much to hope that some of the political crimes of the
Republican Revolution might be prosecuted? Older corporate
Democrats will shy away from the idea, fearful of being accused
of "political vendettas." New young Progressives will simply
see it as correcting for "justice delayed."

   The public funding of elections, including equal and free
access to media, for candidates, will certainly cost some $Mil-
lions. But to delete political ad spending from the economy,
and to reassign the time candidates spend begging for money,
together, will have the biggest impacts on revitalizing an honest
and responsive government. Higher taxes, just on the biggest
former corporate donors, for example, will cover the funding for
public elections. Shifting the legislative time commitments, back
to actual legislating, will make the first 3 larger projects feasible.

   Once the many GOP voter suppression tactics are eliminated, the US will actually be able to vote for the people and
principles that reflect our actual political majority – Center-Left/
Progressive – and the corresponding agenda.

• REFORM THE JUSTICE SYSTEM: Federal Human Rights
legislation must be revised and expanded to eliminate the

poverty-to-prison pipeline, to end the killings by cops or jailers, and the unexplained deaths of citizens in custody. We must start with a data base of every such death, which the Justice Dept. has never cared to compile. (The Guardian, based in Britain, made the best estimates in 2017; a few US NGOs are following up.) And then we must move to prosecute every perpetrator of such events as Federal Civil Rights crimes. The code of silence that keeps good cops from reporting bad ones must be seen as a conspiracy to abet felonies ... and murder.

Radical reforms must be made in bail procedures and costs, funding and training for Public Defenders, and in cuts to mandatory sentencing requirements. The US prison population must be radically reduced by freeing more minorities and poor whites who were unjustly prosecuted or convicted, and then increased, at least a little, by convicting more white collar criminals.

Merge the principles of reformed justice and a crackdown on corruption. Jail the white collar criminals and let the unjustly convicted out.

• UPDATE AND REINFORCE THE FIRST AMENDMENT: Demand more balanced and honest public media and information systems.

Once campaign ads are deducted from the revenue of the mass media monopolies, the Congress can consider a revival of the "Fairness Doctrine," that was in place before Fake Fox News became a thing. More about that in the summary, starting on the next page. It might require advertising to be separated from all news and documentary programming, while revenue from other programming is used to fund the news and documentaries. It would be no more unfair than the censorship that commercial sponsors demand. Live fact checks could be required to appear on screen during national news broadcasts. The influence of advertisers over news and opinion content, maybe even in entertainment, could be listed as corruption that is equivalent to lobbying, which will be phased our or radically regulated.

Changing the economics of advertising alone can revitalize the mass media's honesty, responsibility, and accountability.

Agreement on this priority can lead to different systems for the generation and distribution of objective information, internationally – clearly distinguished from opinion and literally fake news. To defy corporate bias and state-censored or state-authored news outlets – like Fox, Russia, China, North Korea, and several Middle Eastern states – will be a global breath of informational fresh air.

Expanded support for Freedom of Speech will also mean renewed federal spending to support quality public education, including regulations supporting the balanced and accurate teaching of science (evolution, climate change, reproduction), civics, history, and a spectrum of skills needed in the electronic information age.

• CREATE AN IMMIGRATION SYSTEM that acknowledges that most refugees from Central and South America are fleeing from the consequences of 40-plus years of US intervention, from the Drug War to puppet dictators in half a dozen countries, past and present. Put the European refugee crisis in a similar context – a byproduct of US interventions in Iraq, Afghanistan, Libya, Yemen, and Syria, combined with the failure of governments to deal with the ravages of Climate Change.

• GUN REGULATION: (This could be seen as part of justice reform, but needs its own mention.) End the blackmail power of the NRA over state and federal governments. Enact the basic gun controls that 80-plus percent of the public agrees on. Make it a crime of complicity or conspiracy *NOT* to report any person with a record of violence, especially domestic violence, who also owns guns – they will be legally required to give them up. (It's shocking and deeply disturbing to learn that 40 percent of all law enforcement officers have been charged with domestic abuse. Toxic masculinity must be separated from the application of laws, military power, and justice.)

Every gun and ammunition purchase must be registered and traceable, through the buyer and back to its seller or source, which will be held liable for sales without background checks. Those stats will will also be compiled in a national database. The Gun Show Loophole and other hard-to-trace sales will become illegal. GOP resistance to such record keeping will end.

• PREPARE FOR THE POLITICAL BATTLES IN PROJECTS 2 AND 3: Radical tax reform: Every individual high earner and every corporation and bank will start paying their fair share, as revenue producers and as limits on profit and wealth; new regulations and charters for international businesses and banks will become a required part of new regulations on international trade and finance. See details of Project Two ahead.

• USE THE PROGRESS TO REINVIGORATE international efforts to spread Democracy. In US foreign policy, aggressive exceptionalism and unilateral military actions will yield to principles of responsible global citizenship.

The concept of Global Citizen will be defined as an international good, and will become a guiding principle for trade, banking, and diplomacy, and as the public face of the new 1st and 2nd principles: ecological sustainability and human rights.

SUMMARY, PROJECT ONE

If, as liberal Democrats and Progressives allege, a majority in the US favor higher taxes on corporations and the super-rich, and want reliable social safety nets and environmental protections, Project One will slam the door on the Republican wet dream of a "permanent Conservative majority." It will open the door to a firm and lasting progressive domination of US politics.

The whiplash swings of the last 3 or 4 8-year terms, (R) Reagan, (D) Clinton, (R) Bush, and (D) Obama, and the frequent split governments – GOP presidents with Democrat Congresses and the reverse – have pin-balled the country between the same sets of Conservative and Liberal agendas, with near zero progress and several steps backward. A typical example is the US's pro-hibition on delivering information about women's health issues internationally (under the GOP), and its opposite, support for the same (by Democrats), which has changed with every switch in party dominance for 30 years or more. Sadly, agreement on a militarist foreign policy has remained consistently gruesome under both parties.

Once the US establishes the basic agenda and starting points, we will look to the international implications. It is time for international forms of government to be upgraded and up-dated to the demands of the 21st century and the Global Envi-ronmental Crisis. While the UN and international science-based organizations have given us the information on emissions, and helped manage the challenges of the Climate "debate," (and oth-er issues like international justice), we will need more of a global consensus, and more countries willing to sacrifice some of their autonomy, for a stronger international commitment to democrat-ic actions, among nations and within them, to facilitate a coordi-nated global adoption of a new set of principles and priorities.

The other countries that commit to this model, with or with-out the help of the UN, must ultimately agree on ...

A New First Human Right: the Right to Pass to the Next Generation a World in No Worse Shape than the One We Inherited.

The objectives of the first 3 Projects here (true democracy, eco-nomic justice, environmental action) can only be accomplished when national voters, and international voting states understand them as options, and can vote for candidates, parties, or prop-ositions that will advance those new priorities and mandates. Observe that the United States can use its recovered moral and ethical leadership (by relaunching its post-corruption democra-cy) and its global economic power, to persuade, seduce, or pres-sure other countries to follow suit. In turn, with commitment and a little luck, a growing contingent of nations will help these projects become global trends ... and prepare us all for revitalized and rebalanced political and economic climates, metaphorically, and the actual climate, literally and globally.

Since the 2016 election, the radical shift in political tone in the US has rapidly become a criminal coup, dumpster fire, and train wreck. Now that the tide is turning, a radical shift, moving toward a better democracy, a more fair and stable economy, and an ecosystem in recovery, will be seen as more possible, even more likely, than any time since 1944. Corporate Democrats, who can only see the future through the rear view mirror, will find themselves left in the dust.

FIGHTING THE RESISTANCE ... WITH CIVILITY? In the summer of 2018, 2 articles appeared at 2 different online news and opinion sites, authored by 2 different people. Both make the assertion that it's time (they even use the same words) "for the Democrats to Fight Dirty." One says the Republicans have long given up any pretense of an ideological argument, to engage in a "procedural war." They are forced to resort to a last ditch barrage of their winning strategy – cheating and lying to stop any liberal action, on anything, while they berate the "uncivil tone" and "underhanded tactics" of the relatively spineless Democrats. The other says that the GOP is "behaving like a party that believes it will never be held accountable." It continues its outrageous dirty tricks assuming somehow that no one in power will notice. Again, we'll see how that works out in November 2018.

This all goes back, in my mind and in my book here, to Newt Gingrich and the shift to name-calling and demonization of liberals in the 1990s. It also reminds us of the Democrats' utter failure to call them out for their vicious and divisive rhetoric and election rigging.

Many will find it hard to imagine the jarring changes that must come. But once our politics are liberated from lobbyists' bribes, voter suppression, and media propaganda, when the benefits of legal and economic justice, and of environmental protections start to make headlines and a difference in our lives, it will suddenly appear easy and obvious. The pendulum swing back may be a wild ride. But if it is propelled by a paradigm shift in the US, it can actually lead to a global mind-shift. When we are living it, we won't have to struggle to imagine it. We'll just wonder what took us so long.

As a segue from Project 1 to 2 – Reviving Democracy to Converting the Economy – lets keep in mind the political, economic, and psychological damage done by the advertising industry. The business model – of funding almost all public information with advertising revenues – has compromised the integrity of news and opinion, undermined the benefits of social networks, invaded our privacy and sold our data, made truth and honesty matters of opinion, and has now helped to hack our elections.

   IF we accept the idea that all advertising is a multi-layered *TAX*, (from pages 163 and 291) on products and services, on our economy, in our society, and on our political systems, on the health of the environment and our minds: *THEN* a tax on advertising makes perfect sense. It will revolutionize and cleanse public information generally, and renew the democratic principles the internet and the First Amendment originally promised.

PROJECT TWO: CONVERT THE GLOBAL ECONOMY
Reverse the Flow of Wealth, End Poverty, Repay Environmental Debt

The strategic goal of Project 2 is an FDR-style New Deal, *Greened* and updated to the financial and human rights crises of the present era, and, as fast as feasible, expanded to the global economy. Without endorsing her candidacy, observe that Green Party presidential candidate Jill Stein outlined a Green New Deal as part of her dual agenda of fixing the economy and advancing environmental action. In the summer of 2018, several progressive Democrats are using the same words and values.

324

Project Two has 2 large scale, urgent (and of course interconnected) parts, and 2 minor or longer term goals. Each will start as new laws, regulations, and tax schedules in the US, and will be imagined in a way that other like-minded countries can agree and participate, following one or more parts at a time. An agenda for wider international buy-in can be created as more nations join the projects, with the goal of total cooperative compliance, while respecting the differing needs and priorities of different economies and geographical/ecological regions.

The premise, established in Part 6, is that the global economy, now based on a distorted and corrupt form of Capitalism, is the root cause of the Climate Crisis and bears a lot of responsibility for the rest of humanity's most serious problems, from poverty and discrimination to war and refugees. It is based on the assertion that a large percentage of global wealth, private and corporate, is owed as a debt to remediate human exploitation and the damaged ecosystem.

Two new principles must be introduced and defined, based on the idea that taxes, from local to national, and in all nations, are the dues we pay to live in a civil and stable society – now one that makes ecological survival a top priority, in support of the New First Human Right.

• An Economic and Ecological payback reckoning is fair and decades overdue.

• Eco-progressive taxes and regulations (see a definition 3 pages ahead) are needed for every economic sector, to help subsidize sustainable practices and penalize waste, pollution, and excessive extraction of value.

The fundamental tactic of Project 2 is to reverse the flow of illegitimate wealth, away from the (fraction of) 1% that controls it, and the corrupt systems that have made it the norm, and to apply it to the many human crises caused by the extraction of that wealth, globally, with Environmental Reparation and Reclamation as the most urgent priority. Existing democracies, with mixed economies, based on fair and nearly sustainable principles, provide us with viable models, and are likely to willingly partner in our new direction. The international status of the US as an economic leader and a positive ideological model will start to rise again.

Each component of Project 2 must be imagined as starting in the US, joined by a dozen or more countries already on this path, and spreading to as much of the rest of the world as possible, by choice or through the pressures that can be applied in new international trade agreements, economic sanctions, travel restrictions, and corporate and bank regulations, rather than military threats.

Healthy economic growth will be defined in horizontal rather than vertical terms. Restrictions on banking and investment will prevent exploitation, inflated financial bubbles and crashes. Financial services and the use of innovative financial instruments will be legislatively required to protect: small businesses, local economies, green agriculture, sustainable transportation systems, and reinvestment that serves the new global priorities: ecological sustainability, human rights, and economic justice.

The UN for example might work with the US and a number of nations already on this track: to set international standards to eliminate tax avoidance everywhere, by tightening or eliminating bad laws and weak regulations; also to set international standards for income tax, toward the goal of creating a de facto Maximum Wage, in order to help fund a universal basic income ... for every adult without one.

Specifically, the off-shoring of income and fortunes, to avoid taxes, will be prevented, first in the US, with warnings and then penalties, and then seizures, as a model for new international banking regulations.

• **ANTICIPATE AND INOCULATE AGAINST RESISTANCE**
The US and partners in this project must anticipate strong and unethical resistance from large corporations and banks, from individual billionaires and multi-billionaire families, as well as

international abusers of financial and political power.

So there must be a public relations strategy incorporated into this project, with a clear timetable. Before any new laws, taxes, or regulations are discussed, publicly and specifically, laws must be passed that will prevent – in advance – unethical attempts to dodge the coming re-regulation, resist it, or hide or otherwise protect hidden and private wealth from it, that is otherwise due for ... Mis-Distribution Correction. Countries that join the US in this project must be prepared to cooperate with each other in the identification, through transparency mandates, of all excessive wealth, wherever it exists, and however it is concealed or protected.

Countries, independently or in collaboration, must be prepared to nationalize – or seize – sectors of industries, banks, brokers, and hedge funds, and any other hostile entities. Whether they are financially corrupt, rabid polluters, abusers of workers, or all three, and worse, we must be prepared in advance to quell their resistance, because controlling them, with or without their willing participation, is essential to the projects.

Such moves are nothing more or less than the national and international disruptions perpetrated earlier and over decades, like the Shock Doctrine and its variants, that led us into this Systemic Meta-Crisis.

Let's move to the 3 bigger and more urgent sub-projects:

• NEW TAX SCHEDULES FOR INDIVIDUALS
Once we in the US overturn the Conservative anti-tax obsession, and accept the notion that higher taxes fund civil society and the foundations of civilization, and when the mass media are allowed to explain how much wealth and value have actually been extracted from what human labor gave to the economy, and the value of the ecological damage done, we will be ready for a new national approach to taxation.

INDIVIDUAL EARNERS' INCOME AND WEALTH TAXES
A new US Congress will overturn the crazy, massive tax cuts

passed under Bush II and Trump, or, if necessary, replace them with entirely new progressive tax schedules.

Income taxes will be modeled on the steeply progressive income taxes of the 1940s and 50s, – which will return as the template for the IRS going forward; low earners, the unintentionally unemployed, and those in or near the poverty level will pay no income taxes, and will be eligible for the new Guaranteed Minimum Income (in the range of $500 - $1000/month); moderate earners, up to, say, $80,000/year, will be taxed on a sliding scale from 10%- 30%; high earners, from $100,000 to $10 million/year, will be taxed at progressively increasing rates from 30% to 90% at the upper limit; incomes above $10 million/year will be taxed at 100%, and will reflect the new Maximum Wage.

While the elimination of poverty, first in the US, then globally, will be aided by parts of Projects 3 and 5, the basic principle and funding are directly connected to the new tax structure.

"ECO-PROGRESSIVE" The new laws and schedules will include a new wrinkle: An *Eco-Progressive* rise or cut in income (and profit and wealth) taxes will apply to all individual earners, (and banks and corporations) based on the size of their ecological footprint – water, carbon, waste, and luxury consumption – and the Green-ness of their investments. The higher earners will get some tax breaks based, like today, on their philanthropic donations.

Ambitious entrepreneurs, sports and movie stars, TV personalities, the top scientists, musicians, and artists, will still be able to "earn" tens of millions per year, and accumulate wealth to the neighborhood of $100 million. Sums above that will be subject to ...

A TAX ON WEALTH: Like the one Thomas Piketty suggests in *Capital in the 21st Century*, of 2 percent, will be implemented and made progressive in 2 ways: it will start at 2 percent and gradually increasing to 10 percent, annual, and it will be scaled to the accounting transparency and the ecological footprint of the owners of the wealth, to the degree that can be known. (Some fortunes come almost exclusively from oil, coal, and gas, or weapons and private prisons, for example, and would be taxed at the highest rates.) Protocols, waivers, and surcharges can regulate the wealth to be allowed, based on how much is invested in the new Green economy or other human welfare sub-projects, so that government agencies, NGOs, non-profits, and other agencies for social and ecological welfare are properly funded.

Within a decade or so, there will be no billionaires or multibillionaires, no private fortunes of a hundred billion and more. To echo Eisenhower, and adjust his comment to inflation:

> *There is no reason for anyone to make more than $10 million a year, or to hold more than $100 million in wealth.*

• NEW REGULATIONS, CHARTERS, AND TAXES FOR CORPORATIONS, BANKS, STOCK AND COMMODITY MARKETS, AND TRADE

International corporations, banks, and large Wall Street brokers, that have defined the rules for banking and trade to their benefit, for so long, ignoring human rights and the environment, will have a mandate to adhere to new standards for corporate charters and access to international (and eventually all) markets.

Globalized Capitalism will no longer be permitted to control national governments and the international economy, to a level of exploitation and criminality that has become intolerable. Businesses will be required to prioritize the public good, efficiency, durability, transparency in accounting, and environmentally sustainable practices. As with individual incomes and wealth, the new and enforceable standards will require the elimination of tax evasion and the off-shoring of wealth, money laundering and corruption.

The US will lead in re-regulating international corporations and banks to adhere to new and uniform charters, allowing them to continue their basic operations and to participate in interna-

329

tional trade. Clear rules and standards will prevent the exploitation of workers and resources, penalize waste and inefficiency, and otherwise protect the environment and human rights. They will re-regulate externalities and other forms of extraction and waste, so that they pay for themselves or are zeroed out.

The priority of profits and stock valuations over the public good and the environment will be flipped.

International banks will be regulated to the degree necessary to reduce their manipulations of governments, corporate finances, or national and local economies, and to prevent their complicity in money laundering, tax avoidance, and war profiteering.

Individual nations and international democratic organizations – like the UN and its many branches – will begin to manage corporations and banks based on new principles, with the New First Human Right as the umbrella reference point.

New regulations will include strategies and methods for equalizing economies across borders, on the principles of protecting human rights and stabilizing local economies – agriculture in particular – while sharing the new tax revenues, in the US, in other nations, and then internationally, for programs to eliminate poverty, and a broad spectrum of environmental and public works projects.

There are already campaigns to get large banks to divest from fossil fuels, with some success. In this project, the US will have to lead an international effort to get the World Bank, the IMF (International Monetary Fund), the WTO (World Trade Organization), and other such entities to revise their principles to the new ones for environmental and human welfare, in all business and banking operations. See new trade regulations, 4 pages ahead.

New standards will limit profits to levels that provide adequate executive pay and creative investment, promote horizontal growth in models of circular, natural and sustainable economic principles, and otherwise support equitable practices.

330

BANK AND CORPORATE TAXES: In addition to new tax schedules for individual earners, and new regulations for large corporations and banks, a new model for corporate and bank taxes will be initiated by the US, with the intent that other nations join in requiring them.

Banks and corporations will pay minimum percentages of their profits, or percentages of their net budgets annually, with zero loopholes (the ones that used to be paid for with lobbyists' bribes). Unfair, exploitive, and unsustainable practices will effectively be regulated or taxed out of existence. Systems based on total economic justice, zero waste, and other sustainable practices will be taxed lower or subsidized for maximum growth and stability. Investors and corporations that are geared to fairness and safety for workers and to sustainable and efficiency standards, will be the only ones whose taxes may approach zero.

Like Eco-Progressive Income Taxes, the new corporate and bank tax schedules will be scaled: to the environmental footprint of each entity, including water waste and carbon emissions, efficiency, product quality, and durability; to their worker pay, its relationship to top executive pay, and to working conditions. Prohibitions on unfair labor practices, including protection for whistle-blowers, will be part of the regulations.

New national limits on rent and mortgage payments – scaled to a maximum percentage of income – will also help in two significant ways: by lowering the basic monthly budget for several million people, and dovetailing with the higher taxes on high earners ... like unregulated landlords.

Conservatives, CEOs and CFOs, and the hyper greedy in the US will initially lose their minds at the possibility of all their business profits and personal incomes being limited. But average earners will quickly be rewarded with lower income taxes (in their lower brackets), by Carbon Dividends paid out (see the next page), and by the lowered costs of many essential products and services (resulting from de- and re-regulation and new subsidies).

TAXES ON WALL STREET: A few liberal economists, and non-corporate-dependent Democrats have been arguing, since the crash of 2008, for a "micro-tax" of 1 percent or less, on Wall Street trades – stocks, bonds, futures, and other "financial instruments" (legalized gambling) – scaled progressively to 3 factors, cash value, speed of trade, and the duration of the hold, to discourage speculation among the high rollers and high-tech speed-trading giants, and to raise revenues, which are estimated to be in the multiple $ Billions in the first year. When we take the time to think about it, it will give us a clear perspective on the scale of the financial markets, and a peek at their sketchy methods. And the tax rate percentage may gradually increase, year to year.

The nature of the Federal Reserve in the US remains an opaque black box mystery to me, except to note that it is a large, private bank that is in league with other mega-banks. Some adjustments to its operations, possibly radical ones, have been promoted for decades, since its inception in the early 20th century. Thorough and transparent auditing seems like a starting point. National-ization or seizure may remain options, until its operation con-forms to the new principles. The idea of public banks is already gaining traction in the US and in some less well-developed countries.

Like several other examples in this list of 5 Projects, and many sub-projects, we are entering an area of overlap, in this case, between the Economic Conversion, here, and Project Three, spe-cifically aimed at environmental repair and preservation.

AND A CARBON TAX: We covered this at some length on pages 270-2. The Conservative proposal for a Carbon Dividend (mentioned on the same pages) has some good features (like paying some or all of the revenues back out to the public) and can be folded in to a more comprehensive plan. In practice it will take several forms and include some extended options. The first objective is to price carbon at a level equivalent to its estimated minimum environmental costs, then to make it a consistent part of global trade agreements, then to increase it until we reach net-zero carbon emissions ... globally.

Under a carbon tax, market pressures will push the industry to "leave it all in the ground," and force the market to compensate. It will be accompanied by radical cuts to all fossil fuel subsidies, and equal or greater expansion of support for alternative energy solutions in every economic sector. Imagine Going Green Globally becoming a possibility within a decade. The revenues from the carbon tax, and zeroing out fossil fuel subsidies, combined with other new revenue, will make the transition and its secondary impacts (like on family budgets) complex and difficult, but affordable and feasible with current technologies. They will radically enhance new efforts to limit emissions, to remove carbon from the air, and to stem methane leaks; such taxes will fund a speed-up of reforestation, ocean clean-up, and radically improved methods for the farming of meat (in Project 3).

AND A TAX ON WASTE AND NON-RECYCLABLES: Cities, states and some countries are moving toward limiting, taxing, or totally prohibiting single use plastic – the biggest category of landfill trash and visible and tactile (non-carbon) ocean pollution. China has stopped importing US trash, for recycling or burning, because they have more than they can handle. Sweden has implemented an amazing system to burn trash, with near zero emissions, to generate energy ... so successful they have burned all their own trash and are importing more from other countries. A simple tax on plastic and non-recyclable packaging could fund such systems in every population center within a few years ... after which the tax would become unnecessary. Lower impact and lower cost options will make everything a little less expensive.

Consumer products and food, services, energy providers, and transportation systems will be subsidized or taxed on an Eco-Progressive basis of efficiency, lower to zero waste, low energy consumption and so on.

This issue bridges Project 2, An Economic Conversion, and the Environmental programs in Project 3, so it must be seen in both contexts.

NEW TRADE REGULATIONS: Again, Trump may upset the global standards for trade and tariffs to the point that new and different regulations and agreements will be relatively easy and welcome, once the Trump gang and most of the remaining Republicans are separated from majority power. The WTO, IMF, World Bank and other organizations, created to regulate, assist, and monitor international trade and finance, and to equalize commodity and financial inequalities, especially among smaller nations, have been relatively successful. While they still struggle to get cooperation from a range of nations, most of their principles proved valid, prior to our understanding of the Global Eco-Crisis and its connections with the global gap in income and wealth. While the WTO, for example, allows variances for environmental concerns (which may admittedly be good or bad for the environment), their policies have made free trade easier, with fewer tariffs and restrictions. But it is generally agreed that their policies have increased the wealth and income gaps, not reduced them. So they will have to tweak their regulations to reverse that.

The US will have to lead a movement to get the UN, WTO, World Bank, and IMF all on the same page relative to the new set of organizing principles for international trade and finance.

At a simple and mundane level, the use of bunker fuel for most international trade transport could be regulated or taxed out of existence, as could huge variations on ship registry and the impacts on liability for spills and other environmental and social damages. Illegal over-fishing could be completely stopped in a year, as could trophy hunting and trade in biological contraband (ivory and rhino horn for example).

At another level, the WTO in particular could regulate security for intellectual property, with China for starters, and could start to correct gross inefficiencies in trade that result from huge

334

differences in labor conditions and wages; they could limit the environmental degradation that comes from uneven and unequal regulations on trade-related pollution and inefficiency.

Beyond corrections of these basic and pragmatic regulation failures, the WTO and other organizations can turn, with enough support from the bigger national economies, to enforcement of the principles of human rights and ecological rescue (Project 3) that the US will promote. Trade with individual nations – imports, exports, tariffs, and taxes – could be restricted, lightly or heavily, based on their environmental practices, from trade in endangered species, to slavery and other forms of human trafficking, to protections for indigenous populations, to limits on deforestation and water waste. Not to mention the carbon tax and trade in fossil fuels, which will need radical adjustments to meet the crucial emission reduction goals.

These new regulations will follow the model of a Carbon Tax: revenues from taxing or penalizing bad practices will help to fund good practices in the same or different regions or industrial sectors.

And now, to 2 sub-projects of lesser importance or urgency:

• RE-REGULATE THE ECONOMICS OF MASS MEDIA
This applies first to the US: the need to strengthen and expand the First Amendment to assure wider access to more reliable news and information, and to limit the predominance of advertising as the almost universal business model for funding information media.

But there are other countries where such regulations would radically change what the public can know about their governments, and their relative place among the world's economic/ political systems, with China, Russia, North Korea, and Saudi Arabia as standout examples of the needed reforms.

In the US it would be relatively simple and easy for a small portion of the new revenue from personal and corporate taxes – and most of the new taxes on advertising – to directly subsidize a broad range of non-corporate-sponsored programming. New licensing restrictions for questionable networks (guess which) will be implemented, as will tighter controls on security and content on the internet. We need, I would say desperately need, more long-form journalism in all media. Even more crucial, we need reliable and trustworthy sources that can summarize the information overload, and make sensible prioritization among important news and opinion sources, which is so terribly biased and difficult now. At the very least, new regulations, combined with a new business model and new taxes, could make a broader range of reliable information available and understandable to a much wider segment of the public, and in turn make them more engaged and responsible voters.

- **RESTORE FISCAL RESPONSIBILITY ...**
and implement broad adjustments in revenues and spending, starting in the US with cuts to military budgets. For all the GOP's ranting and raving over the years, about fiscal responsibility, the "tax and spend Democrats," and the "waste" inherent in social security and health care funding, that they want to privatize, Republicans have historically been the party of obscene overspending and randomly cutting revenues to serve the 1%.

So a progressive government can make huge strides in adjusting the overall profile of government revenues – billions in new taxes on excesses of wealth and waste – and spending – huge increases in poverty reduction and expanded environmental protections.

And the US military will be the perfect place for sensible budget cuts to start. (See Project 5.) When the corruption of lobbying is removed from the electoral/legislative systems, and every single US Congressional district no longer has to plead for the Military-Industrial Complex to bring them local operations, for the production of weapons and other military hardware, then the entire government can reorient its priorities and its spending to the real needs of people and the planet. The jobs and investment funding lost will quickly be replaced by new investments and careers in disaster prevention and recovery services, alternate energy systems and eco-restoration.

When the Pentagon cannot be audited, because their budgeting and spending are simply too huge and complex to render, and when they have *LOST* taxpayer monies to the tune of $20 Trillion or more in the last decade, and when private contractors are ripping the federal budget off, possibly to similar totals, it doesn't take much to imagine where those lost and wasted funds will go, with different priorities in place.

With an agenda like the one proposed here, the fiscal responsibility and accountability that Democrats have always brought, along with new levels of transparency in budgeting and spending, will bring a common sense approach to military spending, to the secret budgets of the intelligence services, and to the necessary funding of social services and environmental protection.

Very few citizens are aware of the fact that the total budgets for the US's 10 or more separate intelligence agencies, and the details of operations they fund, including the CIA and NSA, are unknown to 95 percent of the Congress-persons who vote for them. So, no surprise, the public hasn't a clue about their covert actions or the costs.

For starters, the Pentagon could cancel all the contracts (made by Congressional shills of the M-I Complex) for planes, submarines, and weapons, including drones, that they don't really need or want, that may or may not work anyway. It could stop the Navy from testing technologies that kill whales and dolphins. The number of serious illnesses and deaths, caused by Burn Pits, DU, and other toxic emissions and exposures can be significantly reduced in a few years, and eliminated in a decade.

See Project Five.

REPARATION and *RECKONING* have different emphases in Projects 2 and 3. Reckoning means an economic correction for the excessive extraction of wealth from human society *and* from the Earth's ecosystem. Reparation means the repayment of the extracted wealth recovered, here in Project 2 as Social/Economic

337

benefits, and, in Project 3, as Environmental Reclamation, Repair, Restoration and Renewal. So ...

SINGLE PAYER HEALTH CARE FOR ALL will be a virtually instant no-brainer in the US. Medicare for all will provide uniform quality health care for every American, at an enormous overall saving.

THE ELIMINATION OF POVERTY, homelessness, and bad working conditions. Once this is stated as a clear principle and objective, individual nations can define their needs for funding, by categories and amounts. For example, new international agencies will be created to handle an internationally shared pool of funding and resources, for access to reliable food, water, shelter, health care, education, and other social services. They will be funded by democratic and fair contributions from the new national taxes, penalties, and tariffs, and international regulatory fees, that are parts of the new trade agreements.

Remember the sums that we calculated for a theoretical Total Global Redistribution, that would pay everyone on the Earth a fair and consistent fraction of $130,000. If we imagine that kind of funding to assist only the billion of us who actually live in poverty, or worse, the revenues created by new taxes on personal/private income and wealth, and on corporate profits and wealth, will stretch almost indefinitely.

UNIVERSAL BASIC INCOME: Several cities in the US and Europe, including Stockton CA, right down the road from me, are launching trial programs for paying a Guaranteed Basic Income to all people who are unemployed, homeless, or at the brink of poverty, in the form of monthly or weekly payments, in cash or a variety of vouchers. As crazy as Conservatives will try to make this sound, it is as economically sound as Single Payer health care and higher taxes on the super-rich. It will be much more cost effective than the other services the cities have to provide to the poor and homeless. The program could easily be expanded

338

to the global un- or under-employed.

While we face resistance among the billion or so who have become used to a life of moderate security, modest to excessive consumption, and who have lived blind to their bubble and its costs, we will be able to point to success in bringing our global sisters and brothers into a shared life of modest consumption, and the ongoing mutual confidence in our shared goal of reaching our individual and shared potentialities.

COMPENSATION FOR THE IMPACTS OF DISRUPTION

A huge component of Economic Conversion is to cover a wide variety of side effects and secondary impacts. In a restructured US economy, many things will change radically over the first 5 to 10 years. Many jobs and industries will be on a sudden path toward obsolescence. Huge subsidies will be needed to help thousands of companies and millions of people adapt to relocation, new energy and transportation systems, new jobs, new housing and building regulations, and so on.

As complex as Project Two appears, it will be no more difficult than it was to skew the current system to principles of extraction and waste. The billions of dollars, approaching trillions, wasted on corrupting and manipulating the government and undermining the public good, will reappear as budgets to create economic and legal justice and the honest education of a newly informed and engaged electorate.

The urgency of enacting new organizing principles can guide these developments and make them happen much faster than the negative principles took to bring us to this economic and ecological emergency. This economic commitment is completely different from anything in our memory, except for the jobs programs and social "safety nets" that were created in FDR's New Deal, and remain as vital economic buffers.

ECONOMIC CONVERSION GOES GLOBAL

Liberated, reinvigorated, and expanded democracies will accept and enact new global standards for the elimination of corruption, for taxation and penalties, for mutual decisions on local and global priorities and shares of a massive surge in revenues, in the US first, and then for the other nations that join us. The Mis-Distribution Correction will produce $Trillions within 2 to 3 years, and $10s of Trillions within a decade. It will create new local, regional, national, and global budgets for broad programs like the ones here in Projects 2 and 3.

The less developed countries, large, flawed democracies like India, authoritarian dictatorships with hybrid economies like Russia and China, will each face different options for adoption, and will have different scales of costs and benefits, depending on their choices – to participate, to wait, or to resist.

In a partnership with other democracies with mixed economies, already on an ecological track or open to one, we will have a realistic expectation to replace short-sighted and corporate oriented NeoLiberal policies with the benefits of a Globalized Economy Converted to humane and sustainable principles.

THE ECONOMY INTERSECTS WITH ECOLOGY (FINALLY)
Project Two, here, and Project Three, coming up, are admittedly nearly impossible to imagine happening, in anyone's lifetime, let alone in a decade or two. Again, imagining it is easier when the alternate risks are aired and fully imagined, including the possibility of human extinction within 80 years.

Granted, the world sees some growing success and expanding power in the two largest and most influential hybrid Communist/Capitalist dictatorships (mainly in China, less so in Russia) hiding behind the illusion of democratic systems and choices. We see their dependence on international trade, in very different sets of markets, and with very different dynamics. We also see the rise of authoritarian – leaning toward neo-Nazi – parties and movements: stronger in Poland and Hungary, newer and a little weaker in Italy and Germany, and *WAKE UP AMERICA*, in the United States, with the direct encouragement of Trump and the corrupt and dying GOP. And the potential threats of war are not getting fewer or less destructive.

340

AND we see international trade being used more and more in two opposite ways: to promote international cooperation and efficiency – many industries have become dependent on multiple international sources for parts and materials; and to force some individual countries, or sets of allies (like China, Russia, and N. Korea) to change their policies in the face of trade restrictions, tariffs, and sanctions. Yes, Trump is trying to cancel a perfectly good, multi-nation, anti-nuclear treaty with Iran, in favor of a Bad Deal with N.Korea, also on nukes. But trade sanctions have worked with Iran, Russia, N.Korea and other nations, just as trade agreements have helped to strengthen peaceful alliances among nations (in spite of some disadvantages to workers and the environment).

The US can lead a new trend, separate from the programs in Project 3 to reduce emissions and waste. It can simply warn, then act against destructive practices like deforestation and trophy hunting, and to favor the protection of endangered species and indigenous peoples and their land and resources, all by refusing to trade or engage in finance with countries that don't comply. It will not take much more for the UN, the WTO, and the World Bank to follow suit.

The UN could implement a new and comprehensive program that monitors individual nations' campaigns against corruption, to manage the political power of banks and corporations, and to formulate new Environmental/Economic Regulations, like ending destructive agricultural practices, applied to and regulated through global trade.

There is no reason *NOT* to imagine – given the US and a few European, Scandinavian, and other countries with strong economies, strong environmental regulations, and international trade engagements – that trade advantages and sanctions can be used to persuade other countries to buy in to the US's Economic Conversion and help to spread it globally. It's clear that many nations have reluctantly followed the US model, as it devolved from NeoLiberal Globalization into Outlaw Capitalism run amok. The dissolving USSR and the economic liberalization in China seemed to adopt it willingly, only to find themselves fighting corruption, excessive pollution, and huge gaps in wealth. So, conversely, many will now follow the US in the opposite direction, purely for the fact that it makes perfect economic and environmental sense. In the medium to long term, others will conform just to remain in beneficial trade relations with the leaders.

Many nations need international trade to have stable and growing economies. To others, it's a survival requirement. The new organizing principles will come to be accepted, through persuasion, pressure, or simply because they obviously support our mutual survival. With the US leading toward the objective of a Global Green New Deal, we may well find a plurality of nations anxious and eager to join rather than be excluded.

PROJECT THREE: ENVIRONMENTAL REPARATION:
Global Reclamation, Preservation, Protection, and Renewal

SAVING THE EARTH: This is the central project with the most urgent agenda and objectives. It is the primary rationale and ultimate objective of Projects One and Two. The sole purpose of this book is to make it an acceptable paradigm for going forward, in the US and the world. It is a multi-pronged global program, to be prioritized on and tailored to the worst and biggest forms of environmental damage and waste, local, regional and global, in every economic segment.

Project 3 means a global attempt to reverse the ecological destruction that has grown as the human race has increased in numbers and consumption, especially since the Industrial Revolution, and has been accelerating exponentially since the 1970s. The main point is to start the conversation with the knowledge that something has to be done, with buy-in and cooperation from most nations, especially the ones fighting the impacts of Climate Change, and those simply struggling to provide the basics to their excessive numbers.

ONCE a plurality or majority of countries reach their decision – democratic or autocratic – to join in the Economic Conversion Project; and *ONCE* the reversal of the flow of wealth begins to produce the funding budgets necessary: *THEN*, nations and organizations will have the funding to launch massive new programs, and double down on existing ones, to reduce carbon emissions from transportation, radically reduce methane release from oil and gas wells and from the factory farming of animals for food, end deforestation and promote the planting of new forests, begin and expand programs to clean up the oceans and preserve sea life, and create new international standards for control of toxic chemicals in industry, the military, and agriculture. The protection of endangered species and indigenous peoples must be among the highest priorities.

In the US, government subsidies will accelerate the building of carbon-neutral local bus and rail, and interstate transport systems, using new green technologies, and making them affordable or free.

These moves will be new and difficult for the US and a few other high emitters and high polluters, and for countries with lax regulations on corruption. Others will expand on the policies and regulations they've had in place for decades.

While Project Three is the most important, and ultimately most complex, it can be summarized in far fewer words and pages than Projects One and Two. Simply refer to the list of a dozen or more environmental sub-crises (pages 36 to 47), and imagine new local, state, national, and international regulations on them. And then imagine the funding needed for the administrative, physical, personnel, and material costs to implement them ... being plentiful and readily accessible.

Any measurable limits on carbon emissions will take at least a decade to register. Climate or Thermal Lag will keep the atmosphere heating for at least that long, but we will finally be able to measure the decrease in GreenHouse Gas emissions, and the atmospheric totals as they stabilize. We will begin to see measurable results in some locales and in related efforts.

For example, we may well be heartened by reducing the number of extinctions – or ending them completely, also by seeing new sustainable regulations on building and agriculture implemented, and by successes in conserving water and correcting for depleted or contaminated aquifers. We will see the results of a wider application of the Cautionary Principle on new technologies, like GMOs, and old ones like toxins. We could see a 5 year moratorium, or at least strict and enforceable regulations on fishing, wherever fish stocks are depleted; in a very short time, we could end over-fishing and the waste involved in by-catch. Fishermen will be thrilled to see the selective harvest of larger and larger adult fish. And so on.

Imagine your own priorities getting enthusiastic international buy-in and adequate funding.

When the United States restores its claim to real democracy, personal liberty, and universal freedom, when it finally makes good on its promise of equal treatment and justice for all people, we won't have to make ridiculous promises to MAGA. We will simply point to the progress made on these Five Projects, and feel new and stronger partnerships with the other allies and like-minded nations that Trump has insulted and marginalized or punished with tariffs. The use of international finance and trade as persuasive methods, to induce more countries to join in this revolutionary agenda, will lead to a non-violent coalition for human rights and environmental protections like nothing in human history, like nothing we could have imagined ... until we did, and acted on the vision.

> *People who say it's impossible should not get in the way of the people doing it.*

Thorough and universal education will no longer be a luxury in the United States. Across the developing world, the elimination of poverty will rapidly be followed by universal basic education, especially for young women, which will in turn both reduce poverty and be a crucial first step in the next project.

BIG PICTURE LITTLE PICTURE: Many, many of us in the US and around the world have been struggling for decades to find more little things we can do to protect and preserve this delicate ecosystem that has given us a life and a shot at fulfillment, and to preserve an ongoing civilization for those who follow us – from obsessive recycling, to hard limits on energy consumption (remember, anyone can calculate their personal carbon footprint), to eating less meat and packaged food, to improving our home cooking skills, gardening, planting trees, and on and on.

Is anyone here old enough to remember, long before most beverages came in plastic containers, even before mass recycling efforts, that every beer and soft drink bottle was charged a 'deposit' at purchase, that was paid back when the bottles (usually with their 6-pack or box containers) were returned to the vendor for reuse? A slight increase in effort, resulting in huge decreases in trash and recycling, which at its best consumes – i.e. wastes – a lot of heat energy and water, and at worst just adds to ocean and land fill pollution.

I'd be happy to carry those bottles, and others, back to the vendor.

PROJECT FOUR: LIMITING OUR NUMBERS.
In the next decade or sooner, we may know if our global population is beginning to level off from existing pressures, or from an intuitive shared need for a limit. If we can cap our numbers at 8 billion it will be a powerful beginning.

Many environmental experts are certain we are already beyond – maybe far beyond – the Earth's carrying capacity. So if we expect a growing global middle class, with increasing demands for food, water, and energy (and refrigerators and air conditioning), then zero growth (like lowering emissions rather than ending them), will not be enough of a correction. The human family, operating democratically, all on the same page of environmental facts, will be able to calculate what is needed, and will form cooperative methods for getting there.

We will have the failed model of China's One Child policy to guide us ... away from the unforeseen consequences, like a huge gender imbalance between too many adult men seeking women partners from too few available.

As with carbon, any measurable limits on population growth will take up to a decade to register. In the meantime we can prepare to decide whether ZPG, Zero Population Growth, will be adequate, or if we will have to actually start reducing the global birth rate. The main point is to start the conversation knowing that something must be done, with some kind of buy-in from most nations, especially the ones already struggling with too many people and too few resources.

PROJECT FIVE: GLOBAL DISARMAMENT.
Like Project Four, the main point here is to open the conversation, to imagine it is possible ... because ultimately it is necessary, and because the other changes will set the stage and prepare us all for another level of global cooperation and revolutionary change. This one will take a generation, 20 years or more, to have significant impacts, without allowing or provoking the partially disarmed to attack the fully disarmed.

The US can use its overweening, exceptionalist, obscenely overblown military power, to do what all militaries ought to hold as their primary goal: to make themselves obsolete by modeling a global state of uncompromised and invulnerable, permanent peace.

Pacifists in the US have been fighting military interventions, coups, armament development and bombings, and the nuclear weapons industry above all, for decades. While their tactics are mostly symbolic, their arguments ought to register much more widely than they do.

We can start by seeing war as a form of profit-generating

346

waste that only appears unavoidable because we have been terrorized and defrauded by corrupt and toxic, mostly male leaders. They have led from their own fear, greed, and anger, using constant and sophisticated propaganda. They've been prodded – bribed – by the war industry, for 70 years, to let the M-I Complex shape the US's foreign policy and government budget, only to further distort their abusive power, and expand their profits.

War has dominated our deeply flawed civilization, more or less forever. We have now created the only threat that could equal total global war, the end of most life on Earth from pollution and over consumption. Together, that flaw and that threat keep us in our compromised state of Pre-Civilization. We must understand, as a global species, that the men who demand armies, that in turn kill millions, waste Trillions of wealth, and damage natural and human-made value everywhere, are acting on irrational fear and greed, and on their ability to infect our sons and daughters with those self-defeating motives. We must see War as the result of an irrational lust for power in the guise of National Defense and patriotism. We have to end its power to make innocent young men and women line up to die for illusions that the leaders would not risk their own well-being on, or send their children to fight for ... for a minute.

We must recognize that war is driven by the fact it is "good business," an international disgrace in a fully mature civilization, one of the biggest factors in energy and resource waste and environmental damage, and a long overdue candidate for elimination, in favor of global peace.

But now in 2018 and beyond, the argument needs not rest on the avoidable evils of war, local or civil or global, brought by ranks of soldiers or bombs or poisons or unmanned drones. The obscene and enormous, almost unmeasurable stockpile of killing machines that the M-I Complex has conned the US government into buying – ostensibly to protect us from manufactured, invented, and imagined enemies, or real ones with tiny fractions of our forces, based on stupid economic priorities, or irrational racism and religious bias – are now killing the Earth faster than

347

they could kill other humans, except at their very worst, with global nuclear holocaust.

Whether our planet's ecosystem is suddenly incinerated by nukes, or slowly choked and fried by toxic pollution and waste, our children and the cultural and biological heritage that is their birthright will be the ultimate, last and final victims of those machines.

In a global mix of quasi-democratic systems, given the choice, would we all not prefer to live at peace? ... and to share in the benefits of the redirected waste and theft of money, resources, and human life?

AGAIN, THE US HAS A DUTY TO LEAD

The US can start by stating our intention, followed by ceasing all improvements, upgrades, or innovations in the nuclear force. Followed by proposing that every US base in another country (on the premise of mutual defense) must be shared equally, in cost, personnel, energy, and equipment, by the host, or face reduction by half, or more. (The US has 38 large, fully staffed bases, and over 600 smaller bases around the world.) (The US maintained secret Black Sites, used for extraordinary rendition and detentions and other practices judged in violation of international law, of an unknown number, in more than 50 countries, in 2013.)

To further a move toward demilitarization, the US will promote UN-sponsored and -guided conflict resolution through negotiation, to precede or replace any and all violent conflicts, with trade isolation for both conflicted parties used as enforcement – not as an empty threat, but as a promised penalty.

The US will cease manufacturing, selling, exporting, purchasing, or importing weapons of all types.

And. So. On.

Such actions will give the ecosystem the biggest single advantage, among the rest of our environmental reclamation efforts, to let Nature's natural resilience help to restore its delicate balance and accelerate the reversal of damage.

The disruption? Yes the gigantic role of military hardware and fuel consumption, in the US's distorted economy, will vanish, more than half of it in a decade. But, like the economic Conversion that preceded the US's entry into WWII, and like anything with the Moral Equivalent of War, the country can make adjustments, quickly, that serve vastly different, and better objectives.

What happens in the US mid-terms of November 2018, and in the general elections of 2020 may, with luck, give us our last chance to avoid the worst case scenarios of both, ecosystem collapse and endless war.

A FOOTNOTE: UNIVERSAL PUBLIC SERVICE
With gradual demilitarization, we can expect an ongoing but much lower need for a population of military volunteers. But the unfairness of the system – especially the incongruity of low-paid soldiers being supported by high-paid (privatized) corporate contractors – needs to be corrected, for example, by returning to an older model of military support labor (by enlistees themselves) with significantly higher pay for all enlistees. Other limits on the privatization of public or government services will be a factor in 4 of these 5 Projects – cutting costs and corruption while providing new jobs.

Today, August 4, 2018, in California and across the west, and elsewhere, there are more than 50 wildfires, consuming more than a half million acres, on average less than 1/2 contained. Some states resort to calling up the National Guard, where and when authorized, to help with flood and hurricane victims. It will be a huge benefit to authorize more military units to double their training and preparedness for disaster relief and fighting fires as well. A much bigger force, fast acting and flexible, capable of stopping or limiting wildfires much more quickly, is only common sense.

Given those examples, combined with the total upset in available farm labor that Trump's immigration disaster has created, and given a new need for a large number of public service workers, in other situations of need, the US will do well to consider a new, mandatory 1 to 2 year "draft" of people between the ages of 17 and 20, to perform work in a new and broader set of public service options, like those above, and: military, farm, public health and education, the support of new infrastructure construction, and so on. Everyone will have to give a year or two of their time and labor, to the national interest, in return for financial support for college education or other post-service needs for training or for startup funding for young entrepreneurs.

THE LAST LIST
During the 4 or 5 days the last 2 pages were being written, these 6, make that 9, make that 12, make that 17 items (among several dozen) came up in my network feeds:
• Cited in HAARETZ.com: Pakistan's Deadly Paradox: It Can't Combat Climate Change, but It Has No Choice.
• Cited at FiveThirtyEight.com: What Climate Change Looks Like In 2018: "The red alert is on," ... As of 2015, global temperatures had risen about 1 degree Celsius above pre-industrial levels. "It's a race against time."
• 1 Million Women (Australia) cites Thomson Reuters Foundation: Colombia's rainforest now has the same legal rights *as a human. To help protect it from* deforestation. (Bolivia made a similar move in 2009, "recognizing the Rights of Mother Earth.") Much better than giving corporations the rights of a person.
• MarketWatch.com cites leftist economist and Nobel laureate Joseph Stiglitz: "The US needs multiple layers of regulation of the finance industry because the damage from malfunction is so much higher than the costs, ... "
• Pakistan has also embarked on a tree planting binge, with the goal of a million trees in a year, in spite of the opinion in HAARETZ above.
• EcoWatch.com reports: The Koch brothers are pouring money into grassroots state efforts to defeat public transit proposals.
350

(Of course the Kochs sponsored or faked those "grassroots ... efforts" to begin with.)

I can't stop.

• But the Koch brrothers have also turned, rather suddenly, against Donald Trump, his idiotic tariffs and his insults directed at our allies. They're telling people to vote Democrat in November.
• China is spending billions on planting a forest the size of Ireland ... while they continue to cheat on the most damaging GHGs, saying, "Everyone else does it."
• Jack Ma, Chinese multi-billionaire, co-founder of the Alibaba Group, is quoted on CNBC as saying, the US has wasted $Trillions on warfare instead of investing in infrastructure. (The key to China's rise to an economic power equivalent to the US is primarily due to its massive investments in infrastructure, in China and elsewhere, over 20 - 30 years.)

I have to stop.

• Common Dreams announces, "This is zero hour: Youth-led Marches Across the Globe Demand Immediate and Ambitious Climate Action."
• Republican Congressman Jim Leach proposes a 28th Amendment to the US Constitution, enforcing the end of "corporations are people," thereby "dismantling corporate hegemony ..."
• Climate Reality and TheYearsProject.com tell us that India is leading in a $1 Trillion project, called the International Solar Alliance, that will triple the total solar energy generation in the world by 2030 (barely more than a decade). It's concentrated in the tropics, the area with the most sun and the biggest need for sustainable economic development.

I can't stop.

PART EIGHT: TOTAL GLOBAL REPARATION

• The bomb that killed dozens of children, on a school bus in Yemen, was made by Lockheed Martin, USA.
• An editor of the Conservative Daily Caller, after a brief encounter with Alexandria Ocasio-Cortez, had to rescue herself from falling into the trap of believing that "education for your kids," or "healthcare," or "a living wage," ought to be rights that we all have. Whew! Lucky for her. I guess.
• Brian L Kahn posts an item from the Heartland Institute's America First Energy Conference. Referring to Alexandria Ocasio-Cortez, "The Louisiana AG kicked off his talk noting 'what's concerning is her message is resonating.'" (The Heartland Institute, in my view, is one of the worst environmental gaslighters, simultaneously denying the impacts of Climate Change, and promoting nuclear energy as the way to escape them. !! ??)
• Good news from CommonDreams.org: (July 21, 22, 23, 2018) This is Zero Hour: Youth-Led Marches Across the Globe Demand Immediate and Ambitious Climate Action.
• Bad news from CommonDreams.org: (Sunday July 22, 2018) Terrified by Progressive Enthusiasm Sweeping the Nation, Corporate Democrats Have Begun Planning a 'Counterrevolution.' (both pieces by Jake Johnson)

PESSIMISTIC?
The order of those last 2 items creates a positive/negative tension, but leaves a sort of pessimistic tone. Am I optimistic or pessimistic? Ought we encourage pessimism, in the context of a nearly hopeless challenge? ... or optimism, in the possibility of an almost unimaginable shift in political and economic power, globally?

What odds, what chance would I give the US – public and/or government – of leading to prevent ecosystem collapse? Given the course we are on, doing little or nothing, blinded by Denial and mental inertia, less than 5 percent. 1 chance in 20, at best.

However, I can imagine a widespread and dramatic paradigm shift in the US, even triggering a Mind-Shift in most of the

352

world. Having staked my life on creative thinking, learning, and creative action, I might go as high as 50 percent. Break even. Pessimism and optimism, survival and extinction, on a knife edge. In a race against time.

RADICAL?

I realize I've used the word *radical* more than 30 times in this book, and I thoroughly enjoyed quoting Martin Luther King's use of it. A number of agents and publishers rejected this book in its earlier form because it was "too broad" or "too radical."

And it has not felt the least bit awkward to write about *ethics* and *morality,* in several contexts.

So it is bracing, refreshing, and hugely inspiring to see brave young political candidates stand up, non-white, non-corporate women in particular, and to hear them assert,

It is not radical to take a moral position, or to demand a moral political agenda in the United States Congress.